W9-BTR-973

Houghton Mifflin Science
DISCOVERYWORKS

Welcome

to Houghton Mifflin **Science DiscoveryWorks** – a science program that engages students in active investigations of scientific concepts. **Science DiscoveryWorks** reflects our belief that the best science education for students is one that gradually introduces them to the knowledge, methods, skills, and attitudes of scientists, while simultaneously recognizing and respecting the educational and developmental needs of all students.

HOUGHTON MIFFLIN

Boston • Atlanta • Dallas • Denver • Geneva, Illinois • Palo Alto • Princeton

Grade 5 Unified Teaching Guide   ISBN 0-382-41669-4   ISBN 0-382-31984-2

Modular Teaching Guides
Unit A: Plants   ISBN 0-382-41670-8   ISBN 0-382-33476-0
Unit B: The Solar System and Beyond   ISBN 0-382-41671-6   ISBN 0-382-33477-9
Unit C: Energy, Work, and Machines   ISBN 0-382-41672-4   ISBN 0-382-33478-7
Unit D: Populations and Ecosystems   ISBN 0-382-41673-2   ISBN 0-382-33479-5
Unit E: The Solid Earth   ISBN 0-382-41674-0   ISBN 0-382-33480-9
Unit F: Light and Sound   ISBN 0-382-41675-9   ISBN 0-382-33481-7
Unit G: Movement and Control   ISBN 0-382-41676-7   ISBN 0-382-33482-5

9 10 11 12 W 03 02 01 00 99

About the Program

THE AUTHORS
Coming from Diverse Backgrounds, Meeting on Common Ground

Mr. William Badders

Science Resource Teacher, Cleveland Public Schools, Cleveland, OH

A 1992 Presidential Awards Winner, Mr. Badders teaches science to students in grades K through 6. He is a member of the Working Group on Science Assessment Standards, a subcommittee of the National Research Council's National Committee on Science Education Standards and Assessment. He specializes in the biological and physical sciences.

Dr. Victoria Fu

Professor of Child Development, Virginia Polytechnic Institute and State University, Blacksburg, VA

Dr. Fu has over twenty years of experience in teaching child development. She has been involved, on the national level, in developing guidelines for appropriate practices, curriculum, and assessment in early childhood programs. She is currently researching and writing papers on how young children construct knowledge.

Dr. Lowell Bethel

Professor of Science Education, The University of Texas at Austin, Austin, TX

Dr. Bethel recently served as Program Director for Teacher Enhancement at the National Science Foundation. He specializes in the biological and physical sciences, urban and multicultural education, constructivism, and the development of learning and teaching models.

Mr. Donald Peck

Director, The Center for Elementary Science, Fairleigh Dickinson University, Madison, NJ

Mr. Peck's extensive experience in science education includes conducting over 500 hands-on science workshops for elementary school teachers. He specializes in the physical and earth sciences.

Dr. Carolyn Sumners

Director of Astronomy & Physics, Houston Museum of Natural Science, Houston, TX

Dr. Sumners directs the museum's Burke Baker Planetarium, the Challenger Learning Center, and the rooftop Brown Observatory and astronomy lab. Her experience includes extensive involvement in the creation and dissemination of science materials and the design and operation of the nation's first Challenger Learning Center. She has a strong background in physics and astronomy.

Ms. Catherine Valentino

Senior Vice President for Curriculum Development, Voyager Expanded Learning, West Kingston, RI

Ms. Valentino has experience as a classroom teacher, as a curriculum coordinator, and as a director of elementary and secondary education. In her current position, she is specializing in developing materials for after-school programs. She has a background in the biological sciences, particularly in the science of the human body.

CONSULTING AUTHOR

Mr. R. Mike Mullane

Astronaut, retired
Albuquerque, NM

As one of the first mission specialist astronauts, Mr. Mullane logged 356 hours aboard the space shuttles. Now retired from NASA, Mr. Mullane works to bring the experience of spaceflight to "Earthbound" students and adults. He has a strong background in engineering and in the physical sciences.

We believe . . .

As individuals we come from a variety of backgrounds, but, as educators, we meet on common ground. We share a vision of effective science education for all children. Our vision is based on these principles.

Our Principles

- Students learn science concepts most effectively when they explore concrete examples of these concepts. We provide students with many opportunities to construct their own knowledge of science through hands-on activities that are pertinent to the concerns of their daily lives.

- In a world that is growing increasingly dependent on the contributions of science, scientific literacy is an important educational goal for all students. To enable you to help your students achieve this goal, we provide resources that help you respond to the needs of individual students and to the cultural diversity of students.

- Science education is enhanced when based upon reliable educational standards that guide student attainment, curriculum content, and teaching practices. *Science DiscoveryWorks* is based on the *Benchmarks for Science Literacy* prepared by Project 2061, a long-term educational reform project of the American Association for the Advancement of Science, and the *National Science Education Standards* prepared by the National Research Council.

- Students should learn about the big ideas or common themes of science as identified by Project 2061. Four common themes—systems, models, constancy and change, and scale—are used throughout *Science DiscoveryWorks*.

The Authors

CONSULTANTS & REVIEWERS

Teacher Reviewers

Lisa Acy
Louis Agassiz Elementary Sch.
Cleveland, OH

Judith Ball
Coordinator for
Math/Science/Health
School District U46
Elgin, IL

Karen R. Bishop
Ferron Elementary School
Ferron, UT

Jean Blackshear
Fred A. Toomer Elementary Sch.
Atlanta, GA

Bonnie Bohrer
Brookview Elementary School
Brook Park, OH

Robert L. Burtch
1990 Presidential Award Winner
Batavia Middle School
Batavia, IL

Martha Christine
Calypso Elementary School
Bethlehem, PA

Mary Eve Corrigan
The Columbus Academy
Gahanna, OH

John S. Detrick
Emeritus Dept. Chair of
Mathematics and Holder of the
McElroy Chair of Mathematics
The Columbus Academy
Gahanna, OH

Robert C. Dixon
National Center to Improve the
Tools of Educators (NCITE)
University of Oregon, College
of Education
Eugene, OR

Denise Pitts-Downing
James Elverson Middle School
Philadelphia, PA

Michaeline A. Dudas
Science and Math Instructional
Support/Consultant
Northbrook, IL

William Dudrow
The Columbus Academy
Gahanna, OH

Barbara Elliott
1990 Presidential Award Winner
Ray E. Kilmer Elementary School
Colorado Springs, CO

Fred Fabry
Retired teacher of Geology
and Biology
Deerfield High School
Deerfield, IL

Rhea Foster
Anderson Park Elementary Sch.
Atlanta, GA

Linda Froschauer
1993 Presidential Award Winner
Weston Middle School
Weston, CT

Joanne Gallagher
Tamarac Middle School
Melrose, NY

Marlene Gregor
Elem. Science Consultant
Bloomington, IL

William L. Handy, Jr.
Parkland School District
Orefield, PA

Beverly Hanrahan
Franconia Elementary School
Souderton, PA

Renee Harris
Northwestern Lehigh Mid. Sch.
New Tripoli, PA

Rhonda Hicks
James Elverson Middle School
Philadelphia, PA

**Sr. Marie Patrice
Hoare, S.L.**
Loretto Middle School
El Paso, TX

**Lester Y. Ichinose,
Ph.D.**
Evanston, IL

Mace A. Ishida, Ph.D.
Diversity and Ed. Consultant
Blacklick, OH

Kristine D. Jackson
Belleville, IL

Pearline A. James
W. F. Slaton Elementary School
Atlanta, GA

Evette Jones
Grover Cleveland Elementary
Philadelphia, PA

Charlene Kalinski
L. L. Hotchkiss Elementary Sch.
Dallas, TX

**Sr. Sharon Kassing,
S.L.**
St. Pius Catholic School
Kirkwood, MO

John Kibler
InterAmerica Intercultural
Training Institute
Des Plaines, IL

Sharon Lempner
R. G. Jones School
Cleveland, OH

Barbara Leonard
1992 Presidential Award Winner
Heritage Elementary School
Pueblo, CO

Gus Liss
Young Elementary School
Burlington Township, NJ

Jo Ann Liss
Intervale School
Parsippany, NJ

Marlenn Maicki
1990 Presidential Award Winner
Detroit Country Day School
Bloomfield Hills, MI

Lynn Malok
Spring Garden Elementary Sch.
Bethlehem, PA

Barbara Mecker
Rockwood South Middle Sch.
St. Louis, MO

Leonardo Melton
Fred A. Toomer Elementary Sch.
Atlanta, GA

Bonnie Meyer
Tremont Elementary School
Cleveland, OH

Dr. Suzanne Moore
L. L. Hotchkiss Elementary Sch.
Dallas, TX

Kathy Morton
Christ the King School
Atlanta, GA

**Dr. Ngoc-Diep T.
Nguyen**
Director, Bilingual and
Multicultural Program
Schaumburg, IL

Michael O'Shea
R. G. Jones School
Cleveland, OH

Wendy Peterson
Harvey Rice Elementary School
Cleveland, OH

Alexandra Pond
Science Coordinator
North Shore School
Chicago, IL

Erika Silverman
Public School 41
Bronx, NY

Christine Spinner
Parma, OH

Jean Ann Strillacci
Kennedy Elementary School
Succasunna, NJ

Laura Swanson
WATTS Intermediate School
Burlington City, NJ

Arthur F. Tobia
Public School 41
Bronx, NY

Nancy Vibeto
1993 Presidential Award Winner
Jim Hill Middle School
Minot, ND

Sandra Wilson
McKinley Elementary School
Abington, PA

Bonita Wylie
Excelsior Middle School
Shorewood, MN

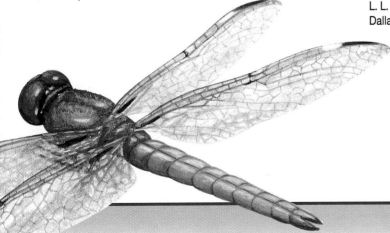

THE SCOPE OF THE PROGRAM
An Overview of Concepts and Themes

	KINDERGARTEN	GRADE 1	GRADE 2
Life Science 	**UNIT A Characteristics of Living Things** Classification of objects as living or nonliving; basic needs and stages of growth of living things **Themes:** *Systems, Constancy and Change*	**UNIT A Kinds of Living Things** The similarities and differences between plants and animals; classifying plants and animals according to one characteristic **Theme:** *Systems*	**UNIT A Interactions of Living Things** The needs of living things; plant and animal adaptations to various habitats; the effect of living things, including people, and natural forces on environments **Themes:** *Constancy and Change, Models* 
Physical Science 	**UNIT B Exploring With the Senses** Using the senses to observe the physical characteristics of objects; grouping objects by their physical characteristics **Theme:** *Systems* **UNIT D Pushes and Pulls** Different ways things move; pushes and pulls; surfaces; directional motion **Themes:** *Systems, Models*	**UNIT C Magnets** The properties of magnets; magnetic force; magnetic fields; temporary magnets; magnets and compasses **Themes:** *Systems, Scale* 	**UNIT B Light and Color** Characteristics of light, such as light sources, how light affects vision, and the way light travels; how shadows are formed and changed; the spectrum and color mixing **Theme:** *Systems* **UNIT D Solids, Liquids, and Gases** Properties of solids, liquids, and gases; the changing of materials from one state to another **Theme:** *Constancy and Change*
Earth Science 	**UNIT C Looking at the Sky** Daytime sky and the Sun; differences between the daytime and nighttime sky; the Moon and the stars **Themes:** *Constancy and Change, Scale*	**UNIT B Weather and Seasons** Factors that affect the weather; seasonal weather changes; how people, plants, and animals respond to weather conditions **Theme:** *Constancy and Change* **UNIT D Earth's Land and Water** Properties of soil and rocks; how water and soil mix; how water flows; recycling through composting **Themes:** *Systems, Models*	**UNIT C Earth Through Time** Characteristics of different dinosaurs; how fossil imprints and fossil remains provide clues about Earth's history **Themes:** *Models, Scale, Constancy and Change* 
The Human Body 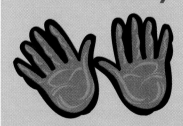	**UNIT E Body Parts** Identification of internal and external body parts; the functions and importance of individual body parts, including the hands, bones, muscles, heart, stomach, and brain **Themes:** *Systems, Models*	**UNIT E Keeping Fit and Healthy** The importance of good nutrition, exercise, sleep, and proper hygiene; the food pyramid and a healthful diet **Themes:** *Systems, Constancy and Change*	**UNIT E What Makes Me Sick** How germs cause illness; how illnesses spread; prevention of illnesses and injuries; how to stay healthy **Themes:** *Systems, Scale*

"*The science that all students are expected to learn is defined so that students have sufficient time to develop a deep understanding of essential scientific ideas rather than superficial acquaintance with many isolated facts.*"

National Science Education Standards

GRADE 3

UNIT A Life Cycles
Stages in the life cycles of animals and plants; changes in animals and plants as they mature; ways that animals and plants survive
Theme: *Models*

UNIT E Roles of Living Things
The needs of living things in relation to their environments; how living things adapt to their environments, change them, and respond to them
Theme: *Constancy and Change*

UNIT C Forms of Energy
The forms of energy and their effect on matter; how heat energy moves, changes matter, and is measured; the benefits and drawbacks of different energy sources
Theme: *Systems*

UNIT B Sun, Moon, and Earth
The physical features of the Sun and Moon; the rotation and revolution of Earth and the Moon; Earth's seasonal changes; eclipses
Theme: *Scale*

UNIT D Earth's Water
Characteristics of Earth's water, including sources of fresh water and the water cycle; water distribution, pollution, and conservation
Theme: *Systems*

UNIT F What's for Lunch?
Nutrients and the types and amounts of food in a healthful diet; sanitary food storage and preparation; care of teeth and gums; digestion
Theme: *Systems*

GRADE 4

Unit C Animals
Basic needs of animals; adaptations that help animals meet their needs; classification of living things; characteristics of different animal groups
Theme: *Systems*

UNIT B Properties of Matter
Physical properties; states; effects of heat loss or gain and of physical and chemical changes
Theme: *Scale*

UNIT D Magnetism and Electricity
Properties of magnets; forms of electrical energy; electric circuits; sources of electric current; how electric current is changed into useful energy
Theme: *Models*

UNIT A Earth's Land Resources
How moving water, wind, and ice shape the land; natural resources and conservation efforts; consequences of producing and disposing of trash
Theme: *Constancy and Change*

UNIT E Weather and Climate
Earth's atmosphere; effects of changes in the air on weather; weather patterns and predictions; seasonal weather changes and climate
Theme: *Constancy and Change*

UNIT F The Body's Delivery Systems
Organs and functions of the respiratory, circulatory, and excretory systems; health measures that prevent or fight disease; harmful effects of nicotine, alcohol, and other drugs
Theme: *Systems*

GRADE 5

UNIT A Plants
Parts of flowering plants; plant cells; plant processes; classifying plants; structural adaptations
Theme: *Systems*

UNIT D Populations and Ecosystems
Dynamic interactions of living and nonliving things in an ecosystem; how energy and matter flow through an ecosystem; biomes; biodiversity
Theme: *Systems*

UNIT C Energy, Work, and Machines
Properties of energy, including its forms, ability to change form, and effects; friction; simple machines
Theme: *Systems*

UNIT F Light and Sound
Properties of light; lenses and their uses; color; properties of sound; the sense of hearing; controlling, recording, and transmitting sound
Theme: *Models*

UNIT B The Solar System and Beyond
The night sky; how astronomers learn about space; the solar system; stars and galaxies; survival in space
Theme: *Scale*

UNIT E The Solid Earth
Properties and uses of minerals and rocks; the rock cycle; Earth's structure; fossils as clues to the age of rocks; the formation of mountains; faults
Theme: *Constancy and Change*

UNIT G Movement and Control
Organs and functions of the skeletal and muscular systems; avoiding bone and muscle injuries; organs and functions of the nervous system; harmful effects of tobacco, alcohol, and other drugs
Theme: *Systems*

GRADE 6

UNIT A Cells and Microbes
Structure and life processes of cells, including mitosis; protists and fungi; bacteria and viruses
Theme: *Models*

UNIT D Continuity of Life
Asexual reproduction; sexual reproduction, including meiosis; inherited and acquired traits; evolution, including evidence for evolution and evolutionary processes
Themes: *Constancy and Change*

UNIT C The Nature of Matter
Physical/chemical properties; elements, compounds, mixtures; physical and chemical changes; acids and bases; atomic structure
Theme: *Scale*

UNIT F Forces and Motion
Characteristics of motion; gravity; measuring changes in motion; friction; action/reaction forces; how forces affect the motion of objects
Theme: *Scale*

UNIT B The Changing Earth
Theory of plate tectonics; the movement of continents; the formation of mountains; earthquakes and volcanoes
Theme: *Models*

UNIT E Oceanography
Contents and properties of ocean water; features and exploration of the ocean floor; currents, waves, and tides; resources from the ocean; ocean pollution
Theme: *Systems*

UNIT G Growing Up Healthy
Human reproduction; the endocrine system and the human life cycle; defenses of the immune system; illness and immune system disorders; reducing health risk factors
Theme: *Systems*

The major concepts for a unit are listed on the first page of that unit in this Teaching Guide.

Houghton Mifflin Science
How DiscoveryWorks
in Grades 3-6

The Teaching Guide and Activities and Resources in the Student Edition, together with the supporting Equipment Kits, present strong science content in an exciting and innovative format. Additional materials, including CD-ROM technology, support and expand the concepts in each investigation.

Trade Book Library

Trade Books in each grade-level library provide in-depth science content, biographies of famous scientists, and science-related fiction. Trade Books can be used to introduce each unit and reinforce investigation concepts.

Teaching Guide

The *Teaching Guide* is a road-map for moving through the activities and resources.

Science Notebook

The *Science Notebook* includes space for students to record their observations and conclusions as they work through Activities, Investigate Further Extensions, and Unit Project Links. Used as the basis for a Portfolio, students can use the notebook to generate ideas about concepts and reassess their learning.

Educational Technology

SCIENCE PROCESSOR: An Interactive CD-ROM contains investigations that can be used in place of or as extensions of print materials. Tools such as Grapher and Spreadsheet allow for easy data interpretation. VIDEOTAPES and VIDEODISCS complement specific units.

Assessment
Portfolio and performance based assessment opportunities are embedded throughout the investigations.

A wide range of resources provide additional opportunities for teaching and learning through different modalities.

Choose from these resources:

Investigate Further Cards

Equipment Kits

Color Transparency Packages

Teacher Resource Book

• Home-School Connections
• Activity Support Masters
• Unit Project Support Masters

Standardized Tests

Student Edition

Available in textbook and modular formats, the *Student Edition* includes:

Activities - provide students with opportunities for hands-on explorations

Resources - present science content in several engaging formats

Assessment Guide

This guide offers a wealth of assessment choices including objective tests, performance tests, and strategies for compiling and assessing portfolios. The guide contains:

• Checklists for Observation and Interview
• Investigation Reviews
• Chapter Tests
• Unit Written and Performance Tests

3-6 Components

Student Editions

• **Grade Level Book**
• **Module Books for each unit**

Teaching Guide

Science Notebook

Science Notebook, Teacher Edition

Assessment Guide

Standardized Tests

Teacher Resource Book

• **Home-School Connections**
• **Activity Support Masters**
• **Unit Project Support Masters**

Color Transparency Package

Trade Books

• **Grade Level Libraries**
• **Individual Copies**

Technology Packages

• **Science Processor: An Interactive CD-ROM**
• **Problem-Solving Videodiscs**
• **Books on Tape**
• **Best of the Net CD-ROM**

Professional Handbook

Equipment Kits

• **Grade Level Kits**
• **Module Kits**
• **Consumable Kits**

A Learning Model for

Houghton Mifflin Science
DISCOVERYWORKS

Flexibility is an important feature of the **Science DiscoveryWorks** *program. Although the Teaching Guide suggests ways in which you can use the program components to organize and guide each lesson, you can adapt these suggestions or develop your own teaching strategies. The model shown here is one way of teaching a unit.*

Get Ready to Investigate!
Using the Unit Opener

Use the **unit opener** to engage students' interest in the topic to be studied. Using the four column headings, have students speculate about what they might discover as they explore the unit.

- Trade Book: Point out the trade book selections, and suggest that students select one they are interested in exploring.
- Unit Project: Introduce the idea of the unit project. Have students record their initial impressions about the project topic in their *Science Notebooks*.

Teaching Each Chapter

Setting the Stage:
Using the Chapter Opener

- Do a warm-up activity (suggested in the *Teaching Guide*) that relates to the chapter concept.

- Use the photo and introductory copy to begin a discussion of the chapter topics.

- Have students record their initial thoughts on the chapter topic in their *Science Notebooks*.

- Note the availability of Home-School Connections (found in the *Teacher Resource Book*) and Technology opportunities for use at appropriate times in the chapter.

Investigate

Investigations form the heart of the **Science DiscoveryWorks** program. Investigations are made up of two types of student pages—Activities and Resources.

Activate Prior Knowledge

Use the suggested baseline assessment in the *Teaching Guide* to determine what students already know. Then revisit these assessments at the end of each Investigation to allow students to look back at what they've learned.

Provide Hands-on Experiences with Activities

Doing hands-on activities first provides students with concrete experiences that make subsequent readings more meaningful. These experiences will help form the basis of conceptual development.

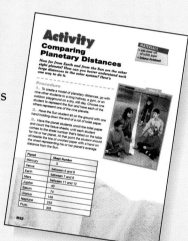

- Choose one or more Activities for each Investigation. Have students record their observations, data, and responses in their *Science Notebooks*.

- Go beyond the basic Activity using suggestions found in Investigate Further boxes.

- Have students use the *Science Processor CD-ROM* to make spreadsheets and graphs and to record their observations using Painter and Writer tools.

Develop Depth of Understanding with Resources

Resources are content-rich articles that provide students with information that helps them synthesize the inferences they made while carrying out hands-on activities.

- As extensions, use the Science in Literature selections on the student pages, or the Integrating the Curriculum and the Investigate Further suggestions in the *Teaching Guide*.

- Continue developing the unit project by using the Unit Project Links and the associated *Science Notebook* pages.

Close the Investigation

- Bring the Investigation to a close by having students write the answers to the *Think It Write It* questions in their *Science Notebooks*.

- Supplement the Investigation assessment with the Investigation Review found in the *Assessment Guide*.

Reflect and Evaluate

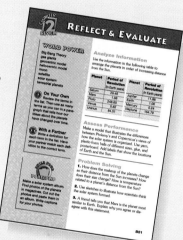

- Use the chapter review found on the Reflect and Evaluate page to help students link concepts developed in each investigation. Have students reflect on their understandings by writing in their *Science Notebooks*.

- A formal assessment of chapter concepts is available on the Chapter Test in the *Assessment Guide*.

Investigate Further!
Unit Wrap-up

After completing the chapters, re-emphasize the big idea of the unit using one or more suggestions from Investigate Further!

- For students who have completed the unit project, a Big Event for wrapping up the project is suggested.

- Ideas for further research and experiments related to unit topics are also suggested.

- As a final assessment, use the Unit Test and/or the Unit Performance Test found in the *Assessment Guide*.

The Role of
SCIENTIFIC THINKING

> *The scientific way of thinking is neither mysterious nor exclusive. The skills involved can be learned by everyone, and once acquired they can serve a lifetime, regardless of one's occupation and personal circumstances.*
>
> *Benchmarks for Science Literacy*

Developing scientific thinking in students is an important part of science education. To learn how to think scientifically, students need frequent opportunities to develop the science process skills, critical thinking skills, and scientific reasoning skills that support scientific inquiry.

In *Science DiscoveryWorks*, students develop process skills as they actively investigate concepts and evaluate the results of their investigations. They develop critical thinking skills and scientific reasoning skills as they respond to thought-provoking questions that conclude every activity and lesson or investigation. In the *Teaching Guide*, questions that promote scientific reasoning skills are identified by this symbol.

The common themes or big ideas that run through science, as well as many other disciplines, are another important aspect of scientific thinking. Common themes are identified for every unit of *Science DiscoveryWorks*, and the connections between the themes and the concepts within a unit are explained in the *Teaching Guide*.

Science Process Skills

Skill	Description
Observing	Determining the properties of an object or event by using the senses
Classifying	Grouping objects or events according to their properties
Measuring/Using Numbers	Skills include: • describing quantitatively using appropriate units of measurement • estimating • recording quantitative data • space or time relationships
Communicating	Using written and spoken words, graphs, tables, diagrams, and other information presentations, including those that are technology based
Inferring	Drawing a conclusion about a specific event based on observations and data; may include cause-and-effect relationships
Predicting	Anticipating consequences of a new or changed situation using past experiences and observation
Collecting, Recording, and Interpreting Data	Manipulating data, either collected by self or by others, in order to make meaningful information and then finding patterns in that information that lead to making inferences, predictions, and hypotheses
Identifying and Controlling Variables	Identifying the variables in a situation; selecting variables to be manipulated and held constant
Defining Operationally	Defining terms within the context of one's own experiences; stating a definition in terms of "what you do" and "what you observe"
Making Hypotheses	Proposing an explanation based on observations
Experimenting	Investigating, manipulating materials, and testing hypotheses to determine a result
Making and Using Models	Representing the "real world" using a physical or mental model in order to understand the larger process or phenomenon

Critical Thinking Skills

Skill	Description
Analyzing	Studying something to identify constituent elements or relationships among elements
Synthesizing	Using deductive reasoning to pull together key elements
Evaluating	Reviewing and responding critically to materials, procedures, or ideas, and judging them by purposes, standards, or other criteria
Applying	Using ideas, processes, or skills in new situations
Generating Ideas	Expressing thoughts that reveal originality, speculation, imagination, a personal perspective, flexibility in thinking, invention, or creativity
Expressing Ideas	Presenting ideas clearly and in logical order, while using language that is appropriate for the audience and occasion
Solving Problems	Using critical thinking skills to find solutions to a problem

Scientific Reasoning Skills

Scientific Reasoning Skill	Description
Longing to Know and Understand	The desire to probe, find information, and seek explanations
Questioning of Scientific Assumptions	The tendency to hold open for further verification presented assumptions, encounters, and ideas
Search for Data and Its Meaning	The propensity to collect information and to analyze it in context
Demand for Verification	The inclination to repeat and replicate findings and studies
Respect for Logic	The inclination to move from assumptions to testing and data collection to conclusions
Consideration of Premises	The tendency to put into context the reason for a particular point of view
Consideration of Consequences	The tendency to put into perspective the results of a particular point of view
Respect for Historical Contributions	The inclination to understand and learn from earlier ideas, studies, and events.

Common Themes*

Theme	Description
Systems	A system is a collection of things that influence one another and appear to be a unified whole. Examples of systems include body systems, the system created as matter and energy interact, and interactions of living and non-living components of ecosystems.
Scale	Ideas concerning the differences in magnitude of variables, such as size, distance, weight, and temperature, including the idea that the properties of something change at different rates as scale changes. Examples of scale include the study of parts of a system, the effects of changing variables in equations, and comparisons of size and distance within systems.
Constancy and Change	The ways in which anything in nature remains the same or changes, as well as the rate at which change occurs. Examples include predator-prey relationships, the idea of conservation of matter and energy, and the continuous cycling of matter and energy in nature.
Models	A model is a physical, mathematical, or conceptual likeness of a thing or process that helps to explain how it works. Models are used to think about processes that happen too slowly, too quickly, or on too large or small a scale to be directly observed. Examples include models of atoms and computer simulations.

*Adapted from _Benchmarks for Science Literacy_ (Oxford University Press, 1993).

ASSESSMENT TOOLS

> "Concepts are learned best when they are encountered in a variety of contexts and expressed in a variety of ways, for that ensures that there are more opportunities for them to become imbedded in a student's knowledge system.
>
> *Science for All Americans*

The key to evaluating the success of any science program lies in assessment methods that help you and your students measure progress toward instructional goals.

A varied assessment program can

- help you determine which students need more help and where classroom instruction needs to be expanded.

- help you judge how well students understand, communicate, and apply what they have learned.
- provide students with strategies for monitoring their own progress and ways to demonstrate their talents and abilities.

Science DiscoveryWorks provides the following comprehensive assessment package.

The *Science DiscoveryWorks* Assessment Package

Learner Objectives	Assessments Available in *Science DiscoveryWorks*	Sources in *Science DiscoveryWorks*
Mastery of content	Observation	TG, AG
	Written Reviews and Tests	SE, TG, AG
	Portfolios	SE, TG, AG
Development of process skills and critical thinking skills	Observation	TG, AG
	Performance Assessment	SE, TG, AG
	Portfolios	SE, TG, AG
	Student Self-Assessment	AG
Development of scientific reasoning skills	Observation	TG, AG
Evaluation of individual or group progress	Portfolios	SE, TG, AG
	Student Self-Assessment	AG
	Group Self-Assessment	AG
Effectiveness of instruction	Written Reviews and Tests	SE, TG, AG
	Portfolios	SE, TG, AG
	Performance Assessment	SE, TG, AG

KEY: SE-*Student Edition*; TG-*Teaching Guide*; AG-*Assessment Guide*

PERFORMANCE ASSESSMENT

Purpose: Performance Assessment helps you evaluate the skills and concepts developed through hands-on activities. In the *Assessment Guide:*

- **Performance Assessment** pages present a formal task for each unit that demonstrates students' ability to apply process skills.
- **Administering the Assessment** provides teacher instructions.
- **Performance Assessment Scoring Rubric** provides a way to evaluate student performance in relation to stated goals.

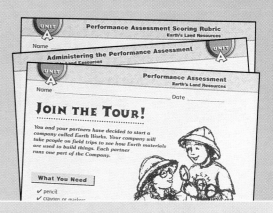

OBSERVATION AND INTERVIEW

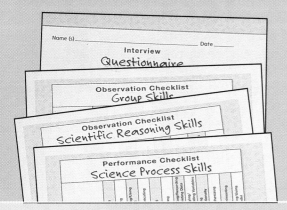

Purpose: Observation and Interview allow you to document the day-to-day development of student understanding using the following checklists in the *Assessment Guide:*

- **Observation Checklist: Group Skills**
- **Interview Questionnaire**
- **Observation Checklist: Scientific Reasoning Skills**
- **Performance Checklist: Science Process Skills**

SELF-ASSESSMENT

Purpose: Self-assessment helps students analyze their own performance. In the *Assessment Guide:*

- **Self-Assessment: Student Checklist** helps students evaluate their own performance by rating themselves on set criteria.
- **Self-Assessment: Group Checklist** helps students analyze their group skills.

PORTFOLIO ASSESSMENT

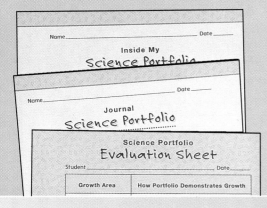

Purpose: Portfolio assessment provides a way of demonstrating a student's growth and progress over time. In the *Assessment Guide:*

- **Inside My Science Portfolio** provides criteria for students to use in selecting work for their portfolios.
- **Journal: Science Portfolio** provides students the opportunity to reflect on and write about their individual portfolio selections.
- **Science Portfolio Evaluation Sheet** provides a method for you to record *how* included materials demonstrate growth.

WRITTEN REVIEWS AND TESTS

Purpose: Written reviews and tests measure students' understanding and retention of concepts at the end of investigations, chapters, and units. In the *Assessment Guide:*

- **Investigation Reviews** focus on material covered in each investigation.
- **Chapter Tests** evaluate students' understanding of chapter concepts and vocabulary.
- **Unit Tests** measure students' understanding and retention of concepts developed over an entire unit.

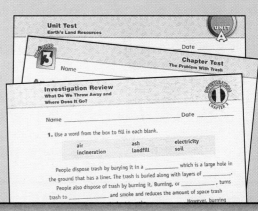

TECHNOLOGY RESOURCES
Extending Our Reach

Science DiscoveryWorks offers a wide variety of technology resources that provide alternative ways of presenting and developing science concepts. These resources also provide students with opportunities to use technological tools and to develop understanding of how technology contributes to advances in science.

The *Teaching Guide* for each unit of **Science DiscoveryWorks** offers strategies for using the technology resources in lessons or investigations. Suggestions include using technology to introduce a concept, as a stimulus for group discussion, as the basis for an activity or project, and to reinforce a concept.

Technology Resources for Grades K–2

Audiotapes and Compact Discs

The audiotapes and CDs feature a variety of delightful songs that relate to many of the lesson concepts. Students reinforce important concepts as they sing along or pantomime the actions in the songs. One audiotape or CD is available for each grade.

Videotapes

Videotapes present unit concepts in fresh and visually appealing ways; they are both entertaining and educational. Titles include: *Arthur's Eyes, What Good Are Rocks?,* and *Keep the Lights Burning, Abbie.* One videotape is available for each unit; grade level libraries are available.

Technology Resources for Grades 3–6

Science Processor, an Interactive CD-ROM

The CD-ROM Interactive software provides an interactive, child-centered learning approach. The CD-ROM provides Investigations that replace or enhance Investigations in the student book, a Science Workshop in which students can explore and create in an open environment, and a customized encyclopedia. On-screen tools include a Spreadsheet, a Grapher, a Writer, a Painter, a Calculator, and a Timer.

Problem-Solving Videodiscs

The videodiscs use exciting full-motion video, animated diagrams, graphics, and still images to create a captivating learning environment for your students. Each grade-level videodisc contains problems keyed to specific units.

Videotapes

Videotapes that enhance or extend science concepts are suggested on the Using the Power of Technology pages that precede each unit. The videotapes are available from many sources; look for the * to determine which can be ordered from Silver Burdett Ginn.

SCIENCE & LITERATURE
Partners in Learning

In **Science DiscoveryWorks**, literature is used to enhance students' understanding of science concepts. **Science DiscoveryWorks** offers collections of grade-level fiction and non-fiction books that engage students in friendly encounters with the science concepts in each unit of study.

The literary elements of the trade books — imaginative stories, interesting facts, delightful characters, appealing illustrations — have the effect of personalizing science concepts for students. They help connect students' everyday lives to science and heighten their sense of wonder about the natural world.

Trade Books for Grades K–2

A total of ten trade books, two per unit, is available for each grade. The *Teaching Guides* contain suggestions for integrating the trade books into *every* lesson. Suggestions include using the trade books to:

- introduce a unit or a lesson concept;

- make a baseline assessment of students' understanding;

- deepen understanding of concepts explored in activities or through the Poster Book;

- stimulate group discussions;

- guide students' independent explorations in the Science Center; and

- prompt student writing about science.

The *Teaching Guide* also lists other trade books for teachers and for children.

Trade Book Libraries for Grades 3–6

A Trade Book Library, containing a book for each unit, is available for each grade. Highlighted in the Science in Literature features throughout the student editions, the unit trade books provide real-world connections through fictional stories, biographies, and informational genres. The student edition also suggests additional books of interest for each unit that can be used to supplement the Trade Book Library.

CURRICULUM INTEGRATION
Forming Real Connections

In the **Science DiscoveryWorks** program meaningful connections are made between science and other areas of the curriculum. Science becomes more important to students when they become aware of how fundamental it is to every aspect of their lives. Examples of the types of connections made between science and other areas of the curriculum are shown in the model below.

THE SCIENCES

- Exploring how the areas of Life, Earth, and Physical science are related

LITERATURE

- Using science concepts to explain natural events that occur in a story
- Predicting future events in a story by applying knowledge of science concepts
- Using literature to compare the technology and technological practices of the past and the present

MATH

- Using computational and estimation skills in science activities
- Using different units of measurement and measurement tools
- Collecting scientific data and displaying it in graphs

LANGUAGE ARTS

- Writing and illustrating stories and poems
- Exploring the properties of objects that play an important role in a story
- Building vocabulary through an exploration of science terms and related words

CONNECTING SCIENCE TO

CULTURAL CONNECTIONS

- Exploring the natural environments of distant places and the ways in which people have adapted to them
- Exploring the plants and animals of distant places through the literature of other cultures
- Studying the ways in which people from diverse backgrounds have contributed to science

SOCIAL STUDIES

- Studying the ways in which scientific ideas develop over time
- Exploring the influence of social forces on science
- Exploring how geography and natural resources affect the development of science ideas and practices

TECHNOLOGY & SOCIETY

- Exploring the benefits, risks, and limitations of technology
- Relating science concepts to the use of tools and inventions
- Exploring the relationship between science and technology
- Studying the impact of science on society

THE ARTS

- Using music and dance to express science concepts
- Drawing pictures of natural objects and events

SAFETY
An Essential Element

In order for students to develop respect for safety, they need to understand exactly what is meant by safe and unsafe behavior and what the rationale is behind safety rules. Through your teaching as well as your example, students can develop the "safe science" attitudes and skills that are essential both in school and at home.

General Safety Guidelines

- Post an easy-to-read list of safety rules in a prominent place in the classroom. Review it with students on a regular basis.

- Become familiar with the safety procedures that are necessary for each activity before introducing it to your students.

- Discuss specific safety precautions with students before beginning every hands-on science activity.

- Always act as an exemplary model of safe behavior.

- Have students wear protective aprons, goggles, and gloves whenever these items will prevent injury.

- Keep safety equipment, such as fire blankets and fire extinguishers, readily accessible and know how to use it.

- Prepare students for emergencies by having them practice leaving the classroom quickly and safely.

- Show students how to obtain help in an emergency by using the telephone, an intercom, or other available means of communication.

- Never leave students unattended while they are involved in science activities.

- Provide ample space for science activities that require students to move about and handle materials.

- Keep your classroom and all science materials in proper condition. Check their condition regularly.

- Tell students to report all injuries to you immediately.

For more detailed information on safety, you may wish to order the NSTA publication *Safety in the Elementary Science Classroom* (1993). Write or call the National Science Teachers Association, NSTA Publication Sales, 1840 Wilson Boulevard, Arlington, VA 22201-3000; telephone: (703) 243-7100 or (800) 722-6782.

MATERIALS LIST

Following is a complete list of materials needed for all activities included in the Grade 5 student book. Quantities are for a class of 30 students working in groups of 5. Quantities are also listed for those materials included in the Grade Level Deluxe Kit. **Additional kit options are available. Contact your sales representative for details.**

Consumable Materials

Materials	Class Quantity Needed	Grade Level Deluxe Kit Quantity	Activity Page
alum	500 g	500 g	E22
aluminum foil	1 roll	1 roll	A42, B58
apples	6		E66
bags, brown paper	6	1 pkg (6)	A32
bags, plastic (sealable, large)	15	75	A76
bags, plastic (sealable, small)	30	18	A58, B20, B78, C24, D32
balloons, small	12	6 pkg (36)	C6
batteries, AA	12	12	B58, C8
batteries, D-cell	36	18	B58, F20, F30, F44
bone specimens	6		G6
bromothymol blue (BTB)	1 bottle	6 bottles	D33
cardboard	6 sheets	6 sheets (30 cm × 30 cm)	B8
cardboard tubes (paper towel)	12	6 sets (12)	B18, F36
cardboard, large piece	6	6	F20
carrot tops	6		A58
cellophane: blue, green, red	1 roll, each color	1 sheet, each color	F44, F46
charcoal (activated)	1 lb	1 lb	D46
clay (4 different colors)	6 lb	6 lb	C14, C46, E72, E80, E82, F36
copper sulfate squares	6		A64
corn kernels (seeds, corn)	1 pkg	1 pkg	A32, A56
cornstarch	1 lb	1 lb	A32
cups, paper	42	102	B76, C46, D8, D32, F61
egg cartons, cardboard	6		E6, E36
fertilizer pellets	1 pkg	1 pkg	A64
film canisters, black plastic (35-mm) (cans, film)	6	1 pkg (8)	B6
flowers, cut	6		A6
folders, manila	6		F30
food coloring (4 colors)	4 bottles	5 bottles	A8, A22, E74
geranium cuttings (or other common houseplant)	6		A58
gloves, plastic disposable	66 pairs	1 pkg (50 pairs)	D6, E22, G6
glue	6 bottles		B8, E36, E74
index cards	50		G34
iodine solution	1 bottle	1 bottle (100 mL)	A30, A32
leaves (broad-leaved, needle-leaved, succulent)	6 of each type		A84, E72
leaves (with petioles)	12		A42
lens paper	6 sheets	1 pkg (50)	F30
lettuce	1 leaf		A32
markers, black (pens)	6	6	D15, E6, E36, G34, G48
milk cartons (1 pt)	6		E74
oil, corn	36 oz	3 bottles (36 oz)	A32, F21
onions	6		A22, A58
owl pellets	6	6	D14
paper, blotting	3 sheets	1 pkg (3 sheets)	A8, A48
paper, construction (black)	61 sheets		D28, F76
paper, drawing (at least 32 cm × 32 cm)	30 sheets		B55
paper, graph	60 sheets		D56
paper, tracing	6 sheets	1 pkg (40)	B6
paper, unlined	12 sheets		C41, D8
paper clips, jumbo	12	1 box	C38, C46, F61
paper fasteners	36	1 pkg (100)	B8, G7
paraffin (wax, paraffin)	12 blocks	2 lb	B58
peanuts (edible)	6		A32
pencils, colored	6 sets		A64, B30, B54, B55, B88, C41, D8, D28
pencils, grease	6	2 pkg (6)	A48
pencils, round	33		C46, C56
petroleum jelly	1 jar	1 jar	A42
plants, bean (with 4 or 5 leaves)	6		D32

Materials	Class Quantity Needed	Grade Level Deluxe Kit Quantity	Activity Page
plants, broad-leaved, needle-leaved, and cactus	6 of each type		D46
plants, *Elodea* (coupon)	12 cuttings	2 coupons (24 sprigs)	A40, D33
plants, potted (such as geraniums)	6		A6
plastic wrap	1 roll	1 roll	A8
pollinating kit (dried honeybees; toothpicks)	6 dried honeybees; 1 box	8 dried honeybees; 1 box	A64
postcards, blank	30		B88
posterboard	42 sheets		G56, G7, G48
potato	1		A32
radishes	2		A32
salt	1 lb	1 lb	E10
sand	11 lb	12 lb	D46, E56, E74
sandpaper, coarse	6 sheets	6 sheets	C26
seeds, grass	1 pkg	1 pkg	D46
seeds, lima bean	1 pkg	1 pkg (1 lb)	A48, A56
seeds, pea	1 pkg	1 pkg	A30
seeds, radish	2 pkg	2 pkg	A8, D8
seeds, Wisconsin Fast Plants™ (*Brassica rapa*)	2 pkg	1 pkg	A64
soil	6 lb	5 bags (20 qt)	A30, A58, A64, D46
sticks, wooden (craft sticks)	6	1 pkg (12)	E74
string or twine (Venetian blind cord)	2 rolls	2 rolls	B55, B76, C26, C38, C48, D6, D28, F55, F61
tape, electrical	1 roll	1 roll	C8
tape, masking	1 roll		C16
tape, transparent	4 rolls		A42, A76, B6, B18, B78, C41, C46, D28, F36, G7, G48
thread, nylon	1 spool	6 spools	E22
toilet paper, 400-sheet rolls	3 rolls		B32
tongue depressors	6	1 pkg (6)	B20
toothpicks	2 boxes	2 boxes	A22, A56, A58, D6, D14
twigs	6		E72
twist ties	18	2 pkg (12)	A40
vials with lids	12	12	E56
wax paper	1 roll	1 roll	B18, E66
yarn, colored (pieces 10-cm long)	1 skein	1 skein	F55

Nonconsumable Materials

Materials	Class Quantity Needed	Grade Level Deluxe Kit Quantity	Activity Page
aquarium tubing	18 m	18 m	C16
audiocassettes, blank	6	1	F88, F89
balls, rubber (small)	6	6	C14, E82
BBs (or small marbles)	6	1 pkg (100)	C16
beakers (250 mL)	18	6	D33
blindfolds	6		F82
boards (3 different lengths)	18	6 of each length (18)	C26, C38, C40, C56
bottles, small-necked plastic (identical)	18		F64
bottles, spray (spray mister)	1	1	D46
bowls, shallow	6		E22
boxes, cardboard (small)	6	6	F65
boxes, shoe, cardboard w/lid	6	6	F77
cans, aluminum (empty)	15		F60
carts, small (with wheels) (toy trucks)	6	6	C40
clips, spring	6		G16
clock, wind-up	1	1	F77
compasses, drawing	6	6	C56
container, plastic, with lid	6		A64
copper wire, insulated	1 roll	1 roll (100 ft)	C8, F7
copper wire, uninsulated	6 lengths	6 lengths	E8
cups, plastic	78	3 pkg (75)	A30, A42, A48, A58, F60
dishes, shallow (dishes, petri)	6	1 pkg (6)	A8, A30, A58
dowels, wooden (small—10 cm long)	6	6	F65
droppers	12	plastic (6); glass (6)	A30, A32, D33
filters, green and red (color paddles)	6 of each	6	B54
flashlights (standard)	18	12	B58, F20, F30, F44
flashlights (penlight)	6	6	B58
garden trowels (shovels, garden)	6	6	D6
glass plates (8-cm square panes)	6	6	E8, E38
globe	1		D56
gloves, gardening	6 pairs	6 pairs	D46

Item			
goggles	30	6	as needed
hand lenses (magnifiers)	6	6	A6, A8, A56, A84, B20, D6, D14, D15, E10, E36, E38, E50, G6
jars with lids, glass (500 mL)	6	6	E22
jars, plastic (16 oz)	6	12	D46, F21
knives, plastic	6	1 pkg (6)	A6, A56, E66, E80, E82
lamp with cool-white fluorescent bulb	1		A64
lamps with clear glass bulbs (light bulb, 40W)	6	6	B54
lenses, concave	6	6	F30
lenses, convex	6	12	B18, F30
lenses, convex (A–15 cm focal length)	6	6	F36
lenses, convex (B–5 cm focal length)	6	6	F36
light bulbs A (TrueValue Krypton Bulb, K-2)	6	6	F7
light bulbs B (Ray-O-Vac Bulb, K3-2)	6	6	F7
light bulbs, small (flashlight)	6	2 pkg (12)	C8
light bulb holders (bulb sockets)	6	12	C8, F7
magnets, bar	6	3 sets (6)	B20, F88, F89
materials, sound-absorbing (cotton balls, bubble wrap, plastic-foam peanuts)	variety	cotton balls (300); bubble wrap, 2 sheets; plastic foam peanuts, 1/2 cu ft	F77
measuring cups	6	6	A58
metersticks	6	6	C14, C24, D6, F76, F77, G27
microscope slides and coverslips	1 pkg	1 pkg (72)	A22, B20
microscopes	6	6	A22, B20
mineral sets	6	6	E6, E8
mirrors, concave	6	6	F20
mirrors, convex	6	6	F20
mirrors, plane	6	6	F20
model, human skeleton	1	1	G7
nails, steel	6		E8
objects, small (such as buttons)	12	1 pkg (30)	B30
objects, small and heavy (weights)	assortment	1-lb weights (6)	C24, C40, C48
objects, small, of different colors	assortment		F46
pans, aluminum roasting	6	6	B20
planters (flower pots)	6	30	A64
pulleys, single	6	6	C48
pushpins	60	1 pkg (100)	B6, D28
rock sets	6	6	E36, E38, E50, E56
rubber bands (assorted sizes)	as needed	5 pkg	B58, C6, C26, C38, D32, F44, F54, F65
rulers, metric, wooden	6	6	A6, A32, A64, A84, B18, B30, B55, B58, C26, C38, C40, C41, C46, C48, C56, D8, D26, D46, D56, E22, E80, F21, F30, F36, F54
scissors	6		A40, A42, A48, B6, B8, B18, B58, B76, C41, C56, D26, D28, E22, F36, G7, G48
screwdrivers (Phillips)	6	6	C56
screws, wood, flat, (Phillips,) 1 in.	6	35	C41, C56
seashells	6	1 pkg (6)	E56, E72
sound makers (bells, whistles, rattles, clickers)	6 of each	bells (6); clickers (6)	F82
spectroscopes	6	6	B54
spoons, plastic	6	1 pkg (6)	E22, E74
spring scales	6	6	C24, C40, C48
springs, plastic coil (spring toys)	6	6	F14, F55
stakes, wooden (dowels)	24	4 pkg (24)	D6
sticks, wooden (thin)	6		E88
tape measures, metric (tapes, metric)	6	6	B58, G14
tape recorder	1		F89
test tubes, large	12	6	A40, D33
thumbtacks	24	1 pkg (100)	C26
tiles, ceramic, white and unglazed (streak plates)	6	6	E6
timers (stopwatches)	6	6	A32, A40, D33, G16, G34
trays, plastic	6	6	D6
tweezers (forceps)	6	6	A22, D14
washers, metal	6	1 pkg (6)	B76
wood, blocks of	12	12	C26

UNIT F
Light and Sound

Overview Light and Sound investigates the nature and properties of waves and how waves transfer light and sound energy. Through the activities and resources, students discover the nature of light and sound, and the ways light and sound interact with matter. Students also explore reflection and refraction of light and how color is produced.

Theme The use of models allows students to reproduce aspects of the real world on a scale that can be manipulated. Students use physical models of waves to help them understand how light and sound travel through and interact with matter. Students will realize that models are imperfect though useful representations of the world.

THE BIG IDEA

Light and sound are forms of energy that travel in waves and can be described by their speed, wavelength, frequency, and amplitude.

Tracing Major Concepts

Light, a form of electromagnetic radiation, travels in waves and can be reflected and refracted.

Subconcepts

- Visible light is a form of energy known as electromagnetic radiation, which includes ultraviolet rays, infrared rays, X-rays, microwaves, and radio waves.

- Light travels as waves, which can be compared by measuring their wavelengths and frequencies.

- Light reflects off mirrors in predictable ways; it changes direction as it passes from one medium to another in a process called refraction.

Lenses, which change the direction of light, have many uses; the color of objects depends on how they absorb and reflect light.

Subconcepts

- Lenses are used to change the direction of light, and are used in cameras and to correct vision.

- In telescopes, lenses and sometimes mirrors enlarge and clarify the appearance of distant objects; in microscopes, lenses enlarge and clarify tiny objects or thin slices of larger objects.

- The color of an object depends on the colors of light absorbed and the colors of light reflected.

Sound, a form of energy that travels in waves, can be described by its wavelength, frequency, amplitude, speed, and pitch.

Subconcepts

- Sound, which is produced by vibrations, is a form of energy that travels through matter as a wave; sounds can be characterized by the wave's wavelength, frequency, and amplitude.

- Sound travels more quickly through solids than through liquids and more quickly through liquids than through gases; sound also travels more quickly through matter as the temperature of the matter is raised.

- Pitch, the highness or lowness of a sound, depends on the frequency of the sound waves.

Controlling sounds can protect the ear and auditory nerve; various inventions have changed how sound is recorded.

Subconcepts

- The intensity of sound can be controlled by using various materials and devices.

- Sounds are transmitted through the ear structures to the auditory nerve, where nerve impulses are produced and transmitted to the brain.

- Various electronic devices are used to amplify, record, and transmit sound.

CONTENTS

Standards & Benchmarks CORRELATIONS

The National Science Education Standards and Project 2061 Benchmarks* are the framework around which *Silver Burdett Ginn Science DiscoveryWorks* is built.

- Energy is a property of many substances and is associated with heat, light, electricity, mechanical motion, sound, nuclei, and the nature of a chemical. Energy is transferred in many ways. (p. 155) *Entire Unit*

- Light interacts with matter by transmission (including refraction), absorption, or scattering (including reflection). To see an object, light from that object—emitted by or scattered from it—must enter the eye. (p. 155) *Ch. 1, Inv. 3; Ch. 2*

- Electrical circuits provide a means of transferring electrical energy when heat, light, sound, and chemical changes are produced. (p. 155) *Ch. 1, Inv. 1*

- The sun is a major source of energy for changes on the earth's surface. The sun loses energy by emitting light. A tiny fraction of that light reaches the earth, transferring energy from the sun to the earth. The sun's energy arrives as light with a range of wavelengths, consisting of visible light, infrared, and ultraviolet radiation. (p. 155) *Ch. 1, Inv. 1 and 2; Ch. 2, Inv. 2 and 3*

- Many different people in different cultures have made and continue to make contributions to science and technology. (p. 166) *Ch. 1, Inv. 1*

- Throughout all of history, people everywhere have invented and used tools. Most tools of today are different from those of the past but many are modifications of very ancient tools. (p. 45) *Ch. 2, Inv. 1 and 2; Ch. 3, Inv. 3; Ch. 4*

- Technology enables scientists and others to observe things that are too small or too far away to be seen without them and to study the motion of objects that are moving very rapidly or are hardly moving at all. (p. 45) *Ch. 2, Inv. 1 and 2; Ch. 4, Inv. 3*

- Measuring instruments can be used to gather accurate information for making scientific comparisons of objects and events and for designing and constructing things that will work properly. (p. 45) *Ch. 2, Inv. 2*

- Technology extends the ability of people to change the world: to cut, shape, or put together materials; to move things from one place to another; and to reach farther with their hands, voices, senses, and minds. The changes may be for survival needs such as food, shelter, and defense, for communication and transportation, or to gain knowledge and express ideas. (p. 45) *Ch. 4, Inv. 2 and 3*

- There is no perfect design. Designs that are best in one respect (safety or ease of use, for example) may be inferior in other ways (cost or appearance). Usually some feature must be sacrificed to get others. How such trade-offs are received depends upon which features are emphasized and which are down-played. (p. 49) *Ch. 4, Inv. 1*

- Even a good design may fail. Sometimes steps can be taken ahead of time to reduce the likelihood of failure, but it cannot be entirely eliminated. (p. 50) *Ch. 4, Inv. 3*

- Technology has been part of life on the earth since the advent of the human species. Like language, ritual, commerce, and the arts, technology is an intrinsic part of human culture, and it both shapes society and is shaped by it. The technology available to people greatly influences what their lives are like. (p. 54) *Ch. 4, Inv. 2 and 3*

- Scientific laws, engineering principles, properties of materials, and construction techniques must be taken into account in designing engineering solutions to problems. Other factors, such as cost, safety, appearance, environmental impact, and what will happen if the solution fails also must be considered. (p. 55) *Ch. 4, Inv. 3*

- Things that give off light often also give off heat. Heat is produced by mechanical and electrical machines, and any time one thing rubs against something else. (p. 84) *Ch. 1, Inv. 1*

- People have always tried to communicate with one another. Signed and spoken language was one of the first inventions. Early forms of recording messages used marking on materials such as wood or stone. (p. 197) *Ch. 4, Inv. 2 and 3*

- Communication involves coding and decoding information. In any language, both the sender and the receiver have to know the same code, which means that secret codes can be used to keep communication private. (p. 197) *Ch. 1, Inv. 2; Ch. 4, Inv. 2 and 3*

- People have invented devices, such as paper and ink, engraved plastic disks, and magnetic tapes, for recording information. These devices enable great amounts of information to be stored and retrieved—and be sent to one or many other people or places. (p. 198) *Ch. 4, Inv. 3*

- Communication technologies make it possible to send and receive information more and more reliably, quickly, and cheaply over long distances. (p. 198) *Ch. 4, Inv. 3*

*Standards are based on *National Science Education Standards* (© 1996) published by the National Research Council. Benchmarks are based on *Benchmarks for Science Literacy* (© 1993) published by the American Association for the Advancement of Science.

Curriculum INTEGRATION

S cience as a discipline does not exist in isolation. An integrated approach to the teaching of science will help students understand how science connects to other school subjects as well as to technology, to diverse cultures, and to literature. The location in the unit of activities that connect to other disciplines is indicated in the chart.

THE SCIENCES

- Life Science, page F8
- Life Science, page F32
- Earth Science, page F57
- Life Science, page F80
- Life Science, page F85
- Life Science, page F86

LITERATURE

- E-M Spectrum, page F10
- Radio Waves, page F18
- Bending Light, page F25
- A Biography, page F38
- Illustrate, page F69
- Science in Literature features, pages F25, F42, F58, F80

MATH

- Graphing, page F12
- Speed of Light, page F24
- Graphing, page F33
- Large Numbers, page F40
- Sound Speed, page F62
- Decibel Scale, page F78

LANGUAGE ARTS

- Writing Sci-Fi, page F16
- Word Origins, page F39
- Writing Stories, page F47
- "Sounds" Like, page F56
- Sign Language, page F84
- Commercials, page F91

CONNECTING SCIENCE TO

CULTURAL CONNECTIONS

- Write a Story, page F17
- Solar Cookers, page F22
- Global Medicine, page F42
- Making Paint, page F49
- Ancient Music, page F66
- Music Notes, page F68
- Comparing Music, page F92

SOCIAL STUDIES

- Global TV, page F93

TECHNOLOGY & SOCIETY

- Doing Research, page F11
- Mirrors, page F23
- Space Travel, page F41
- Synthesizers, page F71
- Decibel Chart, page F79
- Recording, page F90

THE ARTS

- Lighting a Play, page F48
- Drawing Sounds, page F58

The Electromagnetic Spectrum

by Dr. Janet M. Sisterson

Dr. Janet Sisterson is a research associate at the Cyclotron Laboratory, Harvard University, Cambridge, Massachusetts.

WAVE CHARACTERISTICS

The electromagnetic (E-M) spectrum describes the electromagnetic radiation that surrounds us. This energy results from variations in electric and magnetic fields and takes the form of waves. Humans can see only a tiny part of the spectrum, the region referred to as *visible light*.

Electromagnetic waves have a regular shape and can be described by wavelength, frequency, and energy. These three characteristics are related: As the frequency increases, the wavelength decreases, and the energy increases.

Scientists don't know if the electromagnetic spectrum has a beginning or end, but they do know that the range of wavelengths already detected is huge—from fractions of a nanometer to hundreds of kilometers. Electromagnetic radiation may be grouped by wavelength.

ULTRAVIOLET AND SHORTER

Visible light is only a tiny part of the E-M spectrum; its wavelengths extend from about 350 to 750 nanometers (nm). Since our eyes are sensitive to only this small range of wavelengths, we can see only a limited range of colors.

The ultraviolet region, at about 10 to 350 nm, lies just beyond the visible light we see as violet. We feel the effects of these shorter, more energetic waves whenever we get a suntan. Many in-

sects can see these rays. Just beyond the ultraviolet range, at even shorter wavelengths, lies the X-ray region, which is used for medical diagnoses. At still shorter wavelengths are the very energetic gamma rays. Gamma rays are produced in nuclear interactions both on Earth and in space.

INFRARED AND LONGER

On the other end of the visible light region, at longer wavelengths than visible red light, is the infrared region (wavelengths of 750 nm and longer). Humans sense infrared radiation as heat. The microwave region has longer wavelengths (about 1 mm to about 30 cm) than those of infrared waves. We use these waves for communication, radar, and to cook food.

At even longer wavelengths—about 10 cm to several kilometers—are the radio waves. AM radio uses waves of the longest wavelengths; FM radio and television pick up waves with shorter wavelengths. Radio telescopes detect these waves from other sources in the universe.

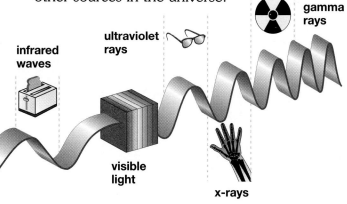

gamma rays

ultraviolet rays

infrared waves

visible light

x-rays

microwaves

radio waves   television waves

Take your students to a farm or to a zoo. Have students observe the eyes of different animals, noticing especially the different shapes of the pupils and how the pupils change in different light intensities.

Sr. Marie Patrice Hoare
El Paso, Texas

In addition to observing light passing through a polarizing filter, my students use thin layers of mica and several other rocks to see if they will act as a natural polarizing filter. Then we try passing light through plastics, liquids, and other substances. After students are comfortable with these activities, we look at laser light passing through the same substances and make comparisions.

Ann Linder
Owasso, Oklahoma

To illustrate the Doppler effect—the apparent change in the pitch of a sound as you move toward or away from the source of the sound—tie a key alarm to the end of a 5-foot rope. (Caution: Be sure the alarm is tied on securely and have students stand at a distance.) Swing the rope in a circular motion. Tell students to listen for the change in pitch as the alarm moves toward and away from them. Vary the activity by lengthening the rope and by having students swing the rope themselves. Ask students to describe differences they hear under the different circumstances.

Robert Neuner Jr.
Richmond, Virginia

Experiences that *Silver Burdett Ginn Science DiscoveryWorks* provides are aimed at developing a wide range of science processes and skills. These tools provide a basis for a lifetime of participation in society as a whole. As described in *Science for All Americans* by F. James Rutherford and Andrew Ahlgren (Oxford University Press, 1990), the skills developed through scientific inquiry foster habits of mind that relate directly to a person's outlook on knowledge and learning and ways of thinking and acting.

Process Skills provide a framework in which ideas can be conceptualized, tested, and evaluated. The processes listed here are developed through a wide range of hands-on experiences.

Process Skills

Activities	Page	Observing	Classifying	Measuring/Using Numbers	Communicating	Inferring	Predicting	Collecting, Recording, and Interpreting Data	Identifying and Controlling Variables	Defining Operationally	Making Hypotheses	Experimenting	Making and Using Models
Seeing the Light	F6	•	•		•		•						
All Aglow	F7	•				•	•				•		
Light Waves	F14	•				•	•			•			•
How Mirrors Affect Light	F20	•			•	•	•						
The Bending Pencil	F21	•				•	•						
Becoming Focused	F30	•			•			•	•				
Telescopic View	F36	•			•								•
Circles of Light	F44	•				•	•						
Filtered Light	F46	•				•	•				•		
Rubber-Band Banjo	F54	•					•				•	•	
Waves and Sound	F55	•			•	•							•
Ear to the Wall	F60	•			•		•				•		•
A String Phone	F61	•			•		•				•		•
Highs and Lows	F64	•			•		•				•		•
Changing Pitch	F65	•			•		•			•			•
Directing Sound	F76				•		•					•	
Muffling Sound	F77			•		•	•	•				•	•
Identifying Sounds	F82				•	•		•					
Magnetic Sounds	F88	•			•		•						
Tape-Recording	F89	•					•	•			•		

Critical Thinking Processes are embedded in the questioning strategies throughout the program. The chart below summarizes the processes assessed in the Think It/Write It sections that end each investigation.

Critical Thinking Skills

Process	Description	F13	F19	F26	F35	F43	F50	F59	F63	F72	F81	F87	F94
Analyzing	Studying something to identify constituent elements or relationships among elements		•		•	•	•	•	•	•			
Synthesizing	Using deductive reasoning to pull together key elements	•	•	•		•		•		•	•	•	
Evaluating	Reviewing and responding critically to materials, procedures, or ideas and judging them by purposes, standards, or other criteria	•											
Applying	Using ideas, processes, or skills in new situations			•			•	•	•	•	•	•	
Generating Ideas	Expressing thoughts that reveal originality, speculation, imagination, a personal perspective, flexibility in thinking, invention, or creativity	•			•								•
Expressing Ideas	Presenting ideas clearly and in logical order, while using language that is appropriate for the audience and occasion								•		•	•	•
Solving Problems	Using critical thinking processes to find solutions to a problem	•		•		•	•						

Through the development and reinforcement of science processes and critical thinking processes, the following **Scientific Reasoning Skills** are developed. This symbol 🔲 identifies questions within the teaching material that highlight Scientific Reasoning Skills.

Scientific Reasoning Skills

Reasoning Skill	Description
Longing to Know and Understand	The desire to probe, find information, and seek explanations
Questioning of Scientific Assumptions	The tendency to hold open for further verification of presented assumptions, encounters, and ideas
Search for Data and Its Meaning	The propensity to collect information and to analyze it in context
Demand for Verification	The inclination to repeat and replicate findings and studies
Respect for Logic	The inclination to move from assumptions to testing and data collection to conclusions
Consideration of Premises	The tendency to put into context the reason for a particular point of view
Consideration of Consequences	The tendency to put into perspective the results of a particular point of view
Respect for Historical Contributions	The inclination to understand and learn from the contributions of earlier ideas, studies, events, and so on

Ongoing Assessment

Daily observations and a variety of ongoing assessment activities can provide comprehensive appraisal of student growth. *Silver Burdett Ginn Science DiscoveryWorks* **provides several methods to help you monitor student growth.**

Performance Assessment

Observation checklists provide concrete descriptions of student behaviors. Performance assessments allow students to demonstrate their ability to use the tools of science and science processes in hands-on activities, at the end of each investigation and chapter, and in a culminating unit performance task.

Portfolio Assessment

Portfolios of student work can be used to holistically assess student understanding and progress. The *Assessment Guide* provides support materials for developing portfolios and in using them to evaluate growth in science.

Written Reviews and Tests

Think It/Write It sections at the end of each investigation foster critical thinking and provide a snapshot of student understanding. Written tests provide additional tools for assessing how well students understand, integrate, and apply key concepts. Opportunities for periodic review are included in Analyze and Conclude at the end of each activity, in Reflect and Evaluate at the end of each chapter, and in Chapter Tests and Unit Tests in the *Assessment Guide.*

Unit Performance Assessment

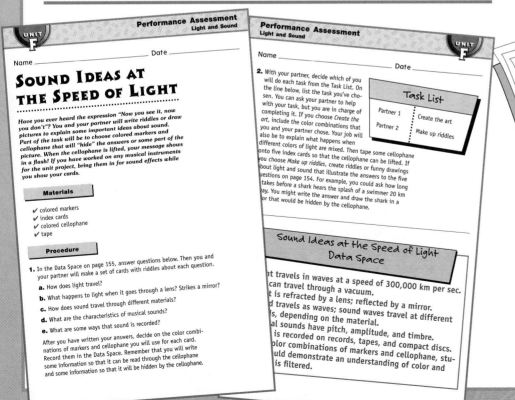

PORTFOLIO ASSESSMENT

Choose among the following products students can put in their Portfolios.

- data from activities
- data from Video, Videodisc, or CD-ROM projects
- data from outside research
- integrated curriculum projects
- projects from Investigate Further activities
- results from Think It-Write It activities

Ongoing Assessment Opportunities

	Performance	Portfolio	Written Reviews and Tests
Chapter 1			F27, AG 137–138
Investigation 1	TG F13		F13, AG 134
Investigation 2	TG F19		F19, AG 135
Investigation 3		TG F26	F26, AG 136
Chapter 2			F51, AG 142–143
Investigation 1		TG F35	F35, AG 139
Investigation 2		TG F43	F43, AG 140
Investigation 3	TG F50		F50, AG 141
Chapter 3			F73, AG 147–148
Investigation 1	TG F59		F59, AG 144
Investigation 2		TG F63	F63, AG 145
Investigation 3		TG F72	F72, AG 146
Chapter 4			F95, AG 152–153
Investigation 1		TG F81	F81, AG 149
Investigation 2		TG F87	F87, AG 150
Investigation 3	TG F94		F94, AG 151
Unit Close	AG 154–155		AG 158–161

Key: TG = Teacher Guide   AG = Assessment Guide   All other pages are from the Student Edition.

Unit Tests

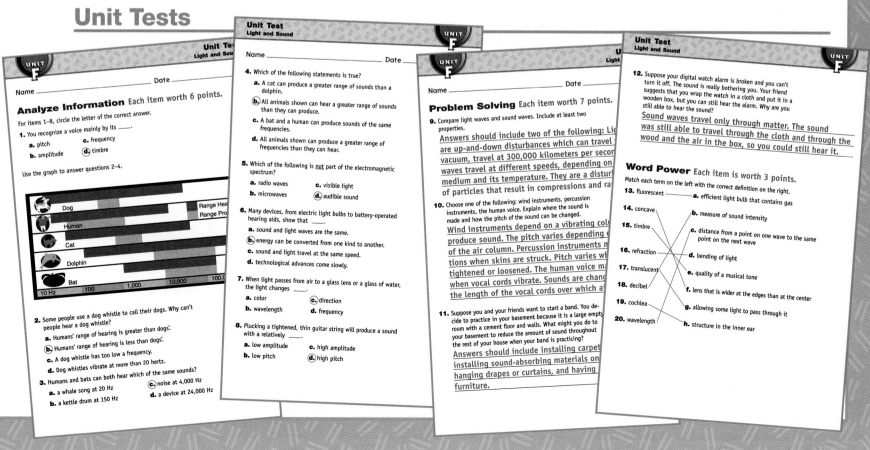

Using Light and Sound to Present a Show

Students apply what they have learned about light and sound to produce a puppet-show reenactment of a folk tale, using student-made instruments for sound effects and cellophane-covered flashlights for lighting effects.

Getting Ready

Group Size
4 to 6 students

Have each group choose different folk tales to reenact.

Materials

For Research

• Books of folk tales

• "How-to" books about making musical instruments, such as *My First Music Book* (Dorling Kindersley)

For Models and Presentations

• Flashlights, opaque and translucent materials, white paper

• Red, green, and blue cellophane, scissors, rubber bands, tagboard, wooden sticks or dowels, tape, markers, paints, fabrics

• Materials for making instruments will vary. Invite students to bring in the following from home: containers (soda cans and bottles, small tins, and so on), gravel, uncooked beans, small bells, rubber bands, boxes of varying sizes, metal washers, cylindrical cardboard boxes, dental floss, thick cord, plastic pipe, empty paper towel rolls, and so on.

• Cassette recorder, audiotape

Other Materials

• Unit Project Masters F1–F9, TRB pp. 99–107.

• *Science Notebook* pp. 288, 301, 326, 339

Plan Ahead

Choose a location in the classroom where the puppet show can be performed. Begin collecting materials for making instruments.

Building the Project
Through Project Links

Chapter 1, p. F15 Students use flashlights focused on various opaque and translucent objects to explore shadow properties. Have students turn objects in different ways to explore how different shadows can be made from one object. Encourage students to predict which objects can be used to create certain 2-dimensional shadows resembling familiar objects.

Chapter 2, p. F31 Students use flashlights covered with red, green, and blue cellophane to explore how different lighting effects create different visual and emotional effects. Students construct puppets and act out a situation, using lighting effects to create an emotion or mood. Puppets can be made by cutting out figures from tagboard and then taping them to wooden sticks or dowels. Unit Project Master F1, (TRB p. 99) includes instructions for making puppets.
Assessing Student Progress: Students should be able to explain why they chose the lighting effects they did.

Chapter 3, p. F67 Students choose a folk tale to reenact. Tales may be traditional, told from another point of view (as in *The Stinky Cheese Man*), or they may be modified in some

- **Invent Your Own Music.** Collect numerous things that can be banged, scraped, rubbed together, plucked, shaken, or blown into to make agreeable noises. Explore the sounds these things can make. Using these "instruments," compose some music. With classmates, form an orchestra. Practice your composition and then record it.

- **Make a Guide to Music in the Air Around You.** Go on a walk and pay close attention to the various sounds you hear. Identify the sounds and their locations. Publish a guide to sound in your environment that will help people identify sounds and their sources.

other way. Have students write a script for the tale (use Unit Project Master F2, TRB p. 100), and plan sound and lighting effects. Students will then make instruments to provide sound effects for the tale as well as for the individual characters (use Unit Project Masters F3–F7, TRB pp. 101–105). Using puppets, sound-effects devices, instruments, and cellophane-covered flashlights, have students begin staging and rehearsing the tale.

Assessing Student Progress: Evaluate each group's cooperative effort in writing the script, planning sound and lighting effects, assembling puppets, and making instruments.

Project Link **Chapter 4, p. F83** Students record a soundtrack for their folk tale. A narrator or several narrators read the script, and the sound-effects students accompany the narrators. The soundtrack can be made available to a class of younger children as a follow-up to a performance.

Assessing Student Progress: Evaluate whether or not each group's soundtrack is appropriate for the tale they chose.

Wrapping Up the Project

After students have rehearsed the show, invite a class of younger children to see the performance. After the performance, take the younger children on a backstage tour to show them the instruments that were used, and how students created the lighting effects. Provide the class with a copy of the audiotape. Use Unit Project Scoring Rubric Master F9 (TRB p. 107) to evaluate students' projects.

PEOPLE TO CONTACT

In Person

- Contact a sound engineer to talk about the role of an audio technician and the equipment used in the recording studio.

By Mail

- **American Lighting Association,** 435 N. Michigan Avenue, Suite 1717, Chicago, IL 60611

- **National Sound & Communications Association,** 10400 Roberts Road, Palos Hills, IL 60465

By Computer

- Connect to the *SilverShare Bulletin Board* to exchange data and the results of your investigations with other *Silver Burdett Ginn Science DiscoveryWorks* users. Watch for our Internet address, coming soon!

PLACES TO VISIT

- **Recording studios** are a source of information on how high-quality sound is reproduced.

- **Theaters or auditoriums** often have sound and lighting equipment to enhance performances.

- **Business districts** reveal how lighting is used to create displays and provide for added safety.

CD-ROM
Interactive

Using the
POWER OF TECHNOLOGY

Light and Sound

Overview   In these CD-ROM activities, students investigate the nature of light and sound. They observe and label the features of light and sound waves and alter aspects of the waves to see how light and sound change. Students mix colors of light, noting the effect of combining primary colors. Students learn about the frequencies of sound that different animals can hear. They find out how the length of guitar strings is related to pitch. Finally, students explore functions of parts of the ear and learn how hearing deficits can be helped. This CD-ROM unit consists of five parts: a unit opening and four investigations.

Using the CD-ROM

Unit Opening Meet the Waves! *(Beginning the Unit)*

Students learn that sound and light are produced by waves and observe some basic features of a wave. In an amphitheater they click sources of sound and light to observe similarities and differences. Students then compare a labeled diagram of a wave to a picture of an ocean wave.

Investigation 1 Making Waves *(Enhances or replaces Chapter 1, Inv. 1, 2)*

What is the nature of light?

In Making Waves, students explore the nature of light. They label a diagram of a typical wave. Students then explore amplitude to discover how altering the amplitude of a wave changes the light that is produced. Finally, students explore the relationship between color and wavelength.

Investigation 2 Mixing Colors *(Enhances or replaces Chapter 2, Inv. 3)*

What is the relationship between light and color?

Students explore how the primary colors can be combined to produce secondary colors. They predict which colors will be produced when certain colors of light are combined and then check their predictions by combining colored light on-screen. They then describe the lighting effects they might create for a concert. Finally, students watch a video to see how a lighting director recreates the color of sunlight at dawn.

Investigation 3 Sound of Music *(Enhances or replaces Chapter 3, Inv. 1 and 3)*

What are the characteristics of sound?

Students explore the characteristics of a moving diagram of a sound wave. After watching a video on the hearing ranges of different animals, students record the frequencies animals can hear. Students investigate how changing the length of a guitar string affects its sound. Finally, they design an experiment to test the relationship between the thickness of a guitar string and its frequency.

Investigation 4 Ears to You *(Enhances or replaces Chapter 4, Inv. 2)*

How does the ear function?

Students observe a diagram of the ear, label its parts, and investigate the function of each part. They learn how each part of the ear is well-suited to its function. Students find out how injury to the eardrum may lead to hearing loss. Finally, they watch a video about a hearing-impaired girl whose use of a hearing aid enables her to participate fully in school activities.

CD-ROM Interactive

The CD-ROM includes Data Packs and Tools that can be used to enhance Light and Sound.

Using the Data Packs

The Data Packs listed below can be accessed for information that relates to this unit. Suggest that students use the information in these packs as they write research reports that extend unit concepts.

Electromagnetic Spectrum   **Energy**
Sound, Light, and Waves

Using the Tools

On-screen tools can help students report results of activities, produce reports, or organize data.

Spreadsheet   Students can use this tool to chart their observations of lenses in Chapter 2 activities.

Writer   Students can list light sources and their observations of a light circuit, the light wave model, and the effects of mirrors on light in Chapter 1 activities. They can also describe what they see through their telescope and their predictions and observations of filtered light in Chapter 2 activities. This tool will be useful for recording results of the sound activities in Chapters 3 and 4 and observations of the coiled spring activity in Chapter 3.

Painter   Students draw their observations of the pencil in water in Chapter 1. They can also draw and label bottles to show their observations of pitch in Chapter 3.

OTHER TECHNOLOGY RESOURCES

Science DiscoveryWorks
Videodisc Problem

Sounds Right to Me   Students use sound wave, intensity, and pitch information to discover what makes the difference in sound when the source is moving toward them and when it is moving away. Use in conjunction with Chapters 3 and 4.

Video

Physical Science: Light, Color and the Visible Spectrum   Students learn about how color is produced through reflection, refraction, diffraction, and scattering. They see how color can affect the way we see objects and observe how red, green, and blue colors are used to produce images. Use with Chapter 2. (Coronet Film & Video: 1-800-321-3106. ISBN 0-3880-7698-4)

Light and Sound

GET READY TO INVESTIGATE!

Overview

In this unit, students will be learning about the properties of light and how light and color are related. They will also learn about the properties of sound—how people hear and how sound is transmitted and recorded.

Warming Up

As students look at pages F2–F3, stimulate discussion with these questions:

- **What do you see in the photograph in the first column? What do you know about how sound is transmitted and recorded?**

- **What is the student in the second column doing? How can experimenting with telescopes and hypothesizing help us to make new discoveries?**

- Point out the book cover to students. Invite them to read the summaries. The book pictured is in the Trade Book Library. **What role might radio waves play in affecting how radios work?**

- **What are the students in the last photograph doing? Have you ever taped your singing or speaking voice?** As you work through this unit, think about how you can apply what you learn in staging a puppet show.

 Have students use *Science Notebook* p. 277.

GET READY TO

OBSERVE & QUESTION

How is sound transmitted and recorded?

Today, sounds—and images—are transmitted in an instant to all parts of the world. Find out how this instantaneous transmission of music, voices, and images affects you.

EXPERIMENT & HYPOTHESIZE

How are lenses used in telescopes and microscopes?

Telescopes were first invented in the early 1600's. Build your own telescope much like the ones built hundreds of years ago.

F2

Home-School Connection

The Opening Letter at the beginning of the unit introduces family members to the topics of light and sound. Distribute the Opening Letter (TRB p. 27) at the start of the unit.

Opening Letter

Dear Family,

Light and sound are forms of energy that everybody uses in one way or another. Think about all the different ways you rely on light and sound. For the next few weeks, our science class will be investigating the properties of these forms of energy. We will explore how people use light and sound for work and enjoyment.

There are many ways in which you can reinforce your student's understanding of this subject. With your student, make a list of the different kinds of light found in the home, such as fluorescent lights, incandescent lights, natural light, candlelight, and fire light. Talk about noise levels in your home and what you do to keep out unwanted sounds. Look for news stories about new devices to help hearing impaired and visually impaired people.

For this unit, we will also be using the materials listed below. Can you donate any of these items? If so, we'd appreciate receiving your donated items by _____.

- *coiled spring toy*
- *flashlight*
- *paper cups*
- *cardboard tubes*
- *rubber bands*
- *shoe box*
- *mirrors*

Finally, we can always use help in the classroom. Do you or other family members have any special interest or expertise in the study of sound or light? Would you be available to help with activities? If so, please fill out the form below and have your student return it to class.

Thank you for your help!

Opening Letter
Light and Sound

Your name _____ Student's name _____

Home phone _____ Work phone _____

INVESTIGATE!

RESEARCH & ANALYZE

As you investigate, find out more from these books.

- **Tuning In: The Sounds of the Radio** by Eve and Albert Stwertka, Illustrated by Mena Dolobrowsky (Julian Messner, 1992). How can music and information travel invisibly from a radio station to your house? Find out what radio waves are and how radios work.

- **Extremely Weird Micro Monsters** by Sarah Lovett (John Muir Publications, 1993). Discover how powerful microscopes can take pictures that make incredibly small creatures look gigantic!

- **That's a Wrap: How Movies Are Made** by Ned Dowd, Photography by Henry Horenstein (Silver Burdett Press, 1993). How are stunts and special effects recorded? How does sound make a film exciting? Find out how movies are made by reading this book.

WORK TOGETHER & SHARE IDEAS

How can you put together a sound and light show?

Working together, you'll have a chance to apply what you have learned. You and your class will stage a puppet show. You'll write, rehearse, and perform your own narration. Then you'll mix lights of different colors to achieve special effects. Finally you'll build models of musical instruments from around the world and provide the music for your show.

F3

Additional Student Resources

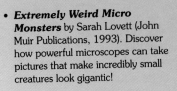

Light by Robert Gardner (Julian Messner, 1991). A wealth of hands-on investigations with clearly stated background; excellent for students looking for science project ideas. **(Text Correlation: Chapter 1)**

Optics: Light for a New Age by Jeff Hecht (Scribner's Young Reader, 1988). An in-depth explanation of the working of the human eye, optical instruments, cameras, television, fiber optics, and more.
(Text Correlation: Chapter 2)

Sounds Interesting: The Science of Acoustics by David Darling (Dillon Press, 1991). A pairing of experiments and explanatory text to teach children about vibrations, pitch, the human ear, music, and the speed of sound.
(Text Correlation: Chapter 4)

BOOKS AND ARTICLES FOR TEACHERS

Experimenting With Light by Robert Gardner (Watts, 1991). A collection of simple experiments that demonstrate theories of light waves, diffraction, reflection, and the effects of lenses.

Experimenting With Sound by Robert Gardner (Watts, 1991). An exploration of the properties of sound through experiments and activities that may be done as classroom demonstrations or recommended as extension activities.

How Science Works by Judith Hann (Reader's Digest Association, 1991). A guide to the process of science through projects and activities focusing largely on physics and chemistry. There is a separate chapter on light and sound. Good source for background and extension ideas.

Light by David Burnie (Dorling Kindersley, 1992). A guide to the origins, principles, and history of light that incorporates bold-colored pictures and a succinct paragraph per idea. An excellent resource to use for background information or for the classroom reference shelf.

Mirrors: Finding Out About the Properties of Light by Bernie Zubrowski (Morrow Junior Books, 1992). A collection of activities that explore how mirrors work and how they demonstrate the properties of light.

Sound: More Than What You Hear by Christopher F. Lampton (Enslow, 1992). An explanation of sound and a discussion of such topics as human hearing, sound recording, ultrasound, and sonar.

Sound Science by Etta Kaner (Addison-Wesley, 1991). Utilizes common, readily available materials as resources for activities. Packed with varied information and projects.

CHAPTER 1

PROPERTIES OF LIGHT

Subconcepts	Activities	Materials
Investigation 1 What Is Light, and Where Does It Come From?		

Visible light is a form of energy known as electromagnetic radiation, which also includes ultraviolet rays, infrared rays, X-rays, microwaves, and radio waves.
 	
Suggested Pacing: 2–3 class periods
Standards
  pp. 155, 166
Benchmarks
  p. 84
	Seeing the Light, p. F6
	Science Processes: observe; classify; infer; collect, record, and interpret data
	
	All Aglow, p. F7
	Science Processes: observe; predict; collect, record, and interpret data; make hypotheses
		Science Notebook p. 281
		
		light bulb *A** (True Value Krypton bulb K-2, or its equivalent), light bulb holders*, batteries* (size D), insulated copper wire*, light bulb *B** (Ray-O-Vac Krypton bulb K3-2, or its equivalent), tape, *Science Notebook* pp. 282–283

Investigation 2 How Does Light Travel?		

Light travels in the form of waves; light waves can be compared by measuring their wavelengths and frequencies.
 	
Suggested Pacing: 2–3 class periods
Standards
  p. 155
Benchmarks
  p. 197
	Light Waves, p. F14
	Science Processes: observe; predict; collect, record, and interpret data; define operationally; make and use models
		goggles*, large plastic spring toy*, *Science Notebook* pp. 286–287

Investigation 3 How Does Light Behave?		
Light reflects off various kinds of mirrors in predictable ways; it changes direction as it passes from one medium to another in a process called refraction. *Suggested Pacing: 3–4 class periods* **Standards** p. 155	**How Mirrors Affect Light,** p. F20 *Science Processes:* observe; communicate; predict; collect, record, and interpret data **The Bending Pencil,** p. F21 *Science Processes:* observe; predict; collect, record, and interpret data	flashlight*, plane mirror*, large piece of cardboard, concave mirror*, convex mirror*, *Science Notebook* pp. 290–291 metric ruler*, unbreakable jar*, water, paper towel, vegetable oil*, *Science Notebook* p. 292

Overview

In this chapter students investigate the wave nature of light, learn how light travels and its speed of travel, and explore how light interacts with matter.

Chapter Concept

Light, a form of electromagnetic radiation, travels in waves and can be reflected and refracted.

Advance Preparation	Curriculum Connection	Assessment
Seeing the Light None **All Aglow** Remove the insulation from the ends of the copper wire ahead of time.	Integrating the Sciences TG p. F8 Literature TG p. F10 Science, Technology, & Society TG p. F11 Math TG p. F12	**Chapter 1 Baseline Assessment:** *Science Notebook* pp. 279–280 **Investigation 1 Baseline Assessment:** TG p. F6 **Investigation 1 Review:** AG p. 134 **Think It/Write It,** p. F13; *Science Notebook* p. 285 **Following Up on Baseline Assessment:** TG p. F13 **Performance:** TG p. F13
Light Waves None	Language Arts TG p. F16 Cultural Connection TG p. F17 Literature TG p. F18	**Investigation 2 Baseline Assessment:** TG p. F14 **Investigation 2 Review:** AG p. 135 **Think It/Write It,** p. F19; *Science Notebook* p. 289 **Following Up on Baseline Assessment:** TG p. F19 **Performance:** TG p. F19
How Mirrors Affect Light None **The Bending Pencil** None	Cultural Connection TG p. F22 Science, Technology, & Society TG p. F23 Math TG p. F24 Literature TG p. F25	**Investigation 3 Baseline Assessment:** TG p. F20 **Investigation 3 Review:** AG p. 136 **Think It/Write It,** p. F26; *Science Notebook* p. 294 **Following Up on Baseline Assessment:** TG p. F26 **Performance:** TG p. F26 **Chapter 1 Summative Assessment:** Reflect and Evaluate, p. F27 Chapter 1 Review/Test: AG pp. 137–138 *Science Notebook* pp. 295–296

TG= Teaching Guide   TRB= Teacher Resource Book   AG= Assessment Guide   *Materials in the Deluxe Equipment Kit

Chapter Overview

Chapter Concept Light, a form of electro-magnetic radiation, travels in waves and can be reflected and refracted.

Theme: Models

Physical models can help students to conceptualize the wave nature of light and understand its behavior.

Common Misconceptions

Students may think that light propagates instantaneously. The speed of light is finite, a fact that has important implications in the study of nature.

Options for
Setting the Stage

Warm-Up Activity

 Darken the classroom and have a slide projector shine light on a chalkboard 1 m away. Trace around the lighted area and ask students to note the brightness. Move the projector back a meter and repeat the activity. Ask students to compare the size and brightness of the illuminated areas. Explain that they have observed a property of light and will learn more in this chapter.

Use *Science Notebook* pp. 279–280.

Discussion Starter:
Lighten Up

Use the photo and text to start a discussion about light.

- **Why can you see the children's outfits in the dark?** Parts of them glow when black light is shone on them.

- **Where have you seen things that glow when black light shines on them?** Responses might include posters, costumes, or even rocks.

- **Career:** Theatrical Lighting Designer
A lighting designer analyzes a stage production for lighting needs and by designing suitable effects helps establish the mood of the production.

PROPERTIES OF LIGHT

Black lamps don't seem to give off much light. But shine them on surfaces covered with a certain kind of paint and see what happens! What is light, anyway? How can light be black?

Lighten Up

 **R**ichard Green is founder of Wildfire Incorporated, a company in Los Angeles that creates lighting effects for music videos, television commercials, theme parks, and movies. Richard is a lighting specialist, someone who designs and produces just the right lighting for shows and other events.

One popular lighting technique involves making objects fluoresce, or glow. Richard covers objects with fluorescent paint and then shines a black light on them. The objects seem to glow! He says that people experience fluorescent objects in different ways. For some it is like stepping into an animated cartoon world of bright, crazy colors. For others the color and light seem to appear from nowhere.

F4

Home-School Connection

 In the Explore at Home activity "Sun Prints" students use light to create an art project. Distribute the activity (TRB, p. 28) when the students have completed the chapter. Discuss what might happen to the color of a sofa near a window.

Explore at Home

Name _____ Date _____

SUN PRINTS

What kinds of artificial light do you have in your home? How many different kinds of light are there? Our science class has been studying light. We have learned about light's properties, how it travels, and how it bends. We have also learned that light is a form of energy. You can demonstrate that light is energy while you make Sun prints.

Materials

✔ several leaves (real, artificial, or cut from paper)
✔ 1 sheet of construction paper (dark color works best)
✔ a few small rocks

tion paper in direct sunlight for two hours. Remove the leaves.

Results

What happened to the areas covered by the leaves? Can you guess why? The energy from the Sun faded or bleached the uncovered areas. How might the Sun's light affect other materials? Does this effect suggest that people need to pay attention to the Sun's energy when they are directly exposed to sunlight?

Procedure

Arrange the leaves on the construction paper. Use some small rocks on the leaves to hold them in place. Place the construc-

◀ These people seem to glow because of fluorescent paint and black lights.

F5

Technology Alert

CD-ROM

Meet The Waves!, and **Making Waves** Enhance or replace investigations 1, 2, and 3

In **Meet The Waves!** students observe, describe, and classify different types of sources of light and sound. They learn that sound and light travel as waves and study the basic features of a wave.

In **Making Waves** students learn that light is a form of energy that travels in waves. They also label the parts of a wave. They explore the effect amplitude has on intensity and differences in the wavelengths of different colored lights.

Chapter Road Map

What Is Light, and Where Does It Come From?

Activities	Resources
✳ Seeing the Light	✳ Lighting the Way
All Aglow	Light Through the Ages

How Does Light Travel?

Activities	Resources
✳ Light Waves	✳ Light as a Wave
Lasers	

How Does Light Behave?

Activities	Resources
How Mirrors Affect Light	✳ Bouncing Light
✳ The Bending Pencil	Bending Light

✳ **Pressed for Time?**

As you work through the upcoming investigations, focus on the activities and resources identified by the clock.

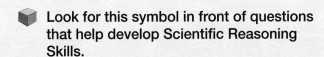 Look for this symbol in front of questions that help develop Scientific Reasoning Skills.

WHAT IS LIGHT, AND WHERE DOES IT COME FROM?

Planner

Subconcept Visible light is a form of energy known as electromagnetic radiation, which also includes ultraviolet rays, infrared rays, X-rays, microwaves, and radio waves.

Objectives

• **Observe**, **describe**, and **classify** different types of light sources.

• **Observe**, **predict**, and **record** what happens in a simple electric circuit.

Pacing 2 – 3 class periods

Science Terms energy, electromagnetic radiation, visible light

Activate Prior Knowledge

Baseline Assessment Ask: **Why is light important to us?** List students' responses for Following Up.

WHAT IS LIGHT AND WHERE DOES IT COME FROM?

Have you ever been home when the electric power went out? A power failure can make you stop and think about something you take for granted—light! In this investigation you'll find out about light you can see and its relatives you can't see.

Activity

Seeing the Light

MATERIALS
• *Science Notebook*

There are lights all around you. Try a "scavenger hunt" to find some of them.

Procedure

Work with a group of other students to investigate light sources in various places. Look for all possible light sources. List the locations and the light sources in your *Science Notebook*. **Record** the kind of energy you think is being used to produce the light.

Rank the light sources from brightest to dimmest, using 1 for the brightest. Note whether any heat was given off from each light source.

Analyze and Conclude

1. What were the light sources your group found?

2. For each source, what kind of energy change produces the light? What can you **infer** about the connection between light and heat?

F6

Activity Seeing the Light

Preview *Students hunt for light sources and should discover that most sources are electrical or chemical. The Sun is a natural source of light energy.*

1. Get Ready

Time 30 minutes

Grouping groups of 4–6

 Collaborative Strategy One group member might record data while others locate and observe the light sources.

Safety Review safety precautions with students.

2. Guide the Procedure

• Have groups look around school to light sources.

 Have students record their data and answer questions on *Science Notebook* p. 281.

 Have students use the CD-ROM Spreadsheet to organize data.

3. Assess Performance

Process Skills Checklist
• Did they **classify** the kind of energy used to produce the light?
• Could they **infer** what kinds of energy changes occurred?

Analyze and Conclude
1. Incandescent and fluorescent lamps, Sun, flashlights
2. Light bulbs: electrical energy to light; flashlights: chemical energy to electrical energy, then to light energy; candles, burning wood: chemical energy to light energy. Heat and light are closely related because things that give off light also give off some heat. Students are not likely to identify nuclear energy as the source of the Sun's light.

Activity
All Aglow

A simple electric circuit contains one battery, a light bulb, and a couple of connecting wires. What changes can you see in the light as you experiment with the different parts of the circuit?

MATERIALS
- light bulb *A*
- 3 batteries (size D)
- insulated copper wire
- light bulb holder
- light bulb *B*
- tape
- *Science Notebook*

Procedure

1. Insert light bulb *A* into a light bulb holder. Connect one battery to light bulb *A*, using copper wire. Use tape to hold the wire in place.

2. **Observe** what happens when you complete the electric circuit. Carefully note if the bulbs are warm. **Record** your observations in your *Science Notebook*.

3. **Predict** what will happen if you add a second battery to the circuit. **Record** your prediction. Then add the second battery and **record** the results.

4. Add a third battery to the circuit and again **record** your observations.

5. Replace light bulb *A* with light bulb *B*. Repeat steps 1–4. **Record** the results.

Step 1

Analyze and Conclude

1. In step 3, how did your prediction match what happened?

2. What happened when you added more batteries to the circuit? **Suggest a hypothesis** to explain what you observed.

3. What change occurred when you replaced bulb *A* with bulb *B*? Why did this change occur?

4. What do you think is flowing from the battery to the bulb through the copper wire?

5. What causes the bulbs to glow? Were the bulbs warm?

6. What evidence do you have that light is energy?

F7

Responding to Individual Needs

Students Acquiring English Students can draw a diagram of the circuits they built and label the parts of the circuit in their native languages and in English.

Activity All Aglow

Preview *Students focus on a simple circuit and should notice that the bulb's brightness increases with the addition of each battery.*

Advance Preparation *See p. F4b.*

1. Get Ready

Time about 30 minutes

Grouping groups of 4–6

Safety Remind students not to short-circuit the batteries. If a battery is short-circuited, it may overheat and rupture.

2. Guide the Procedure

- Test batteries before students do the activity.

 Have students record their data and answer questions on *Science Notebook* pp. 282–283. You may wish to assemble the circuits with the additional equipment shown on p. 282.

You may wish to have students use the CD-ROM Spreadsheet to organize and display their data.

3. Assess Performance

Process Skills Checklist
- Could they **predict** bulb brightness when another battery was added to the circuit?
- Did students accurately **record data** about how the brightness of the bulbs changed?
- Could they suggest a reasonable **hypothesis** for what happened when more batteries were added?

Analyze and Conclude
1. Predictions may vary, but all observations should indicate that the bulb gets brighter.
2. The bulb became brighter. More energy is provided when another battery is added.
3. As with bulb A, bulb B got brighter as more batteries were added to the circuit. However, bulb B did not light as brightly as bulb A—bulb B is not converting as much electrical energy to light energy.
4. Electrical energy
5. Electrical energy is converted to light and heat in the filament.
6. The more electrical energy in the circuit, the more light is produced.

Lighting the Way

Preview *Students focus on light as a form of energy and as a part of the electromagnetic spectrum.*

1. Get Ready

Science Terms
energy, electromagnetic radiation, visible light

Background

- Electromagnetic (E-M) radiation is energy in the form of waves emitted from excited electric charges. The electromagnetic spectrum ranges from very low-energy, low-frequency, long wavelengths to very high energy, high-frequency, short wavelengths. Radio waves are on the low-energy end of the spectrum, while gamma rays are on the high-energy end.

- High-energy electromagnetic waves have very short wavelengths. These waves can pass through plant and animals cells. The high-energy of these waves is harmful to living cells.

Discussion Starter

- **Why do you think light is considered a form of energy?** Encourage discussion on how light can be produced from other forms of energy.

Lighting the Way

Imagine that it is summertime and you are lying on a sandy beach. Through your sunglasses you can see the light of the Sun. You can feel the heat of the Sun on your bare skin. The Sun's rays provide Earth with light and heat, which are both forms of energy. You may recall that **energy** is the ability to do work or cause a change in matter.

The Sun, a star, supplies nearly all of Earth's natural light energy. From Earth you can see other stars during the night, but the amount of light from those stars is very small compared to the amount received from the Sun. Moonlight, the light Earth receives from the Moon, is really sunlight that has bounced off the Moon's surface.

Energy From the Sun

The Sun gives off huge amounts of energy that travel to Earth through the vacuum of space. The energy given off by the Sun is called **electromagnetic radiation** (ē lek trō mag net′ik rā dē ā′shən). There are many kinds of electromagnetic (E-M) radiation; some kinds you can see, and others you can't see. **Visible light** is the type of E-M radiation that you can see.

Most types of E-M radiation are invisible. For example, infrared radiation and ultraviolet radiation are two types of invisible E-M radiation. Infrared radiation from the Sun is what causes you to feel warm when you

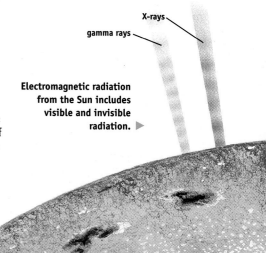

X-rays

gamma rays

Electromagnetic radiation from the Sun includes visible and invisible radiation. ▶

F8

Investigate Further

Integrating the Sciences

LIFE SCIENCE

What to Do Have students research the harmful effects of ultraviolet light and make a poster illustrating their findings.

What's the Result? **What are some of the harmful effects of ultraviolet light?** Ultraviolet light can cause sunburn and skin cancer in people. It can also damage the retina of the eye and cause reduced vision or blindness.

stand in sunlight. Heat lamps also produce infrared radiation.

Ultraviolet radiation, or UV light, is sometimes called black light because an ultraviolet lamp looks dark to us when it is on. But some materials glow, or give off visible light, when UV light shines on them. That painful sunburn you get from lying too long on the beach is caused by ultraviolet radiation.

Electromagnetic radiation can cause changes in matter. For example, sunlight heats water in the oceans. Light can also be used to heat water in solar collectors. Have you ever seen a solar calculator? When light shines on the calculator's solar cells, electricity to run the calculator is produced. In each case, light is changed to other forms of energy.

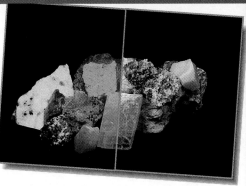

▲ Certain minerals glow under ultraviolet (UV) light (*left*). The same minerals are shown under normal light (*right*).

Light starts many chemical reactions. One of the most important reactions started by light is photosynthesis, the food-making process of plants. During photosynthesis, plant cells convert carbon dioxide and water to oxygen and sugar. In this reaction, light energy is stored as chemical energy.

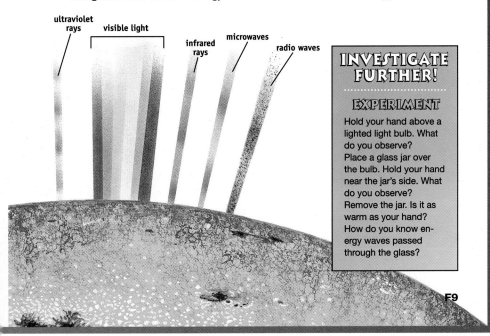

ultraviolet rays   visible light   infrared rays   microwaves   radio waves

INVESTIGATE FURTHER!

EXPERIMENT

Hold your hand above a lighted light bulb. What do you observe? Place a glass jar over the bulb. Hold your hand near the jar's side. What do you observe? Remove the jar. Is it as warm as your hand? How do you know energy waves passed through the glass?

F9

Experiment

When the lamp is turned on, your hand starts to get hot. The light also passes through the glass jar. Heat energy can be felt near the side of the jar, although the jar remains relatively cool. Remind students to record their observations in their *Science Notebooks* on p. 284.

Choose from the following strategies to facilitate discussion.

Making Inferences

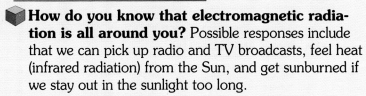

How do you know that electromagnetic radiation is all around you? Possible responses include that we can pick up radio and TV broadcasts, feel heat (infrared radiation) from the Sun, and get sunburned if we stay out in the sunlight too long.

Responding to Individual Needs

Gifted and Talented Activity Students could use reference books on photography to find out how infrared rays are used to take pictures in total darkness. Students can share their findings with classmates.

Connecting to the Activities

* *All Aglow, p. F7*
  Think back to All Aglow. **Where did the electrical energy come from that was used to light the bulbs?** From batteries **Where else could it come from?** From a power plant

Making Comparisons

* **What do you think radio waves and X-rays have in common?** Possible answers include that they are both E-M radiation and that they have energy.

Have students research the kinds of waves in the electromagnetic spectrum using the Electromagnetic Spectrum Data Pack on the CD-ROM. You may wish to have students use the Activity Support Master "Compare–Contrast Diagram" (TRB p. 68) to compare kinds of radiation in the electromagnetic spectrum.

🐾 Responding to Individual Needs

Students Acquiring English Have students make drawings of things that use or emit light and write one or two sentences as a caption for each drawing. Students should be encouraged to use invented spelling and constructions in order to get their ideas on paper.

Thinking Critically

🔲 **What are some other cool light sources besides the "light sticks" or fluorescent lights?** Possible answers include lightning bugs, glow worms, and certain fish.

Making Comparisons

🔲 **Why are fluorescent lamps better to use than incandescent bulbs?** They do a more efficient job of changing electrical energy into light energy, and they don't get as hot. Incandescent bulbs produce a lot of heat, which is wasted energy. You may wish to have students use the Activity Support Master "Compare-Contrast Diagram (TRB p. 68) to compare sources of visible light.

Making Light

How many light sources can you think of other than the Sun? Light bulbs are the most common sources of artificial light. But fire was the first source of light that humans were able to control.

A campfire is a chemical reaction that gives off light. When a substance burns, the energy stored in it is given off as heat and light. The matter being burned is not used up. Instead, it is changed to other substances.

Most of the chemical reactions that give off light also produce heat. With a campfire, you may be more interested in the heat than in the light. If you light a candle, on the other hand, you're interested in the light that is released. If you burn a candle, less than 1 percent of the stored energy in the candle is changed to light. The rest is changed to heat.

Have you ever carried a "light stick"? People often take these along on camp-

▲ A campfire is a chemical reaction in which light and heat are given off.

ing trips for emergency lights. The plastic tubes contain two sets of chemicals. When you bend the light stick, you break a small tube inside it. When the inner tube breaks, chemicals mix. A reaction occurs that gives off light. This reaction does not make much heat, so the tube does not get hot.

In an incandescent light bulb, there is a very thin wire, called a filament, that carries electricity. The wire gets very

A light stick before its chemical reaction (*left*); breaking the tube releases chemicals that mix, causing a chemical reaction (*center*); the glowing light stick (*right*)

F10

Integrating the Curriculum

Science & Literature

What to Do Small groups of students could look at and read pp. 40–45 in *Eyewitness Science: Light* by David Burnie (Dorling Kindersley) to find out how scientists proved that invisible parts of electromagnetic radiation exist. Ask them to find out how infrared and ultraviolet rays were discovered, where they fit into the E-M spectrum, and how they affect other objects.

What's the Result? Groups could make an illustrated chart of the electromagnetic spectrum and then share their chart with the class.

Sources of light: fluorescent light bulbs (*left*); lightning bolt (*center*); sparks given off during welding (*right*)

hot when the electricity goes through it. This makes the wire glow. But only about 2 percent of the electrical energy is changed into light.

Your classroom probably is lighted by fluorescent (floo res'ənt) lamps. These electric lights don't contain a filament. Instead, they contain a gas that gives off ultraviolet light when electricity flows through it. Remember that you can't see ultraviolet light. To make visible light, the fluorescent tube is lined with chemicals that glow when ultraviolet light strikes them. Ultraviolet lights do a much better job of changing electrical energy into light energy than do incandescent lights. About 30 percent of the electrical energy is changed into light. As a result fluorescent bulbs don't get as hot as incandescent bulbs do.

One familiar source of light doesn't last very long, but it can be very bright. What is it? Lightning! Lightning is a very bright electrical spark. Perhaps you've seen a lightning flash light up the night sky so that it's as bright as day. What are other examples of light coming from sparks? ■

▲ Incandescent light bulb with glowing filament

F11

Investigate Further

What to Do Have students use reference books to find out the purpose of lightning rods on buildings in rural areas. They should also find out why they are not often seen in cities. **What's the Result?** 🔲 **What are lightning rods?** They are metal poles attached to the tops of buildings. They attract lightning and direct its electricity through a wire or cable safely into the ground. **Why are lightning rods used?** To protect buildings from damage by lightning; lightning that strikes buildings can cause fires. **Why aren't lightning rods often used in cities?** Because there is so much metal used in the buildings, and the buildings are so close together.

Making Inferences

• **What kind of energy change occurs in lightning?** Electrical energy is changed to light and heat.

Making Comparisons

🔲 **Besides lightning, what other ways can light be produced from sparks?** Responses might include a spark produced by static electricity when you walk across a rug and touch a doorknob; sparks produced when metal chain is dragged along the highway from a truck; or sparks produced by striking two pieces of stone together.

3. Assess Understanding

Students can work in groups of three or four. Invite each group to construct a chart of sources of light and the kinds of energy changes that take place to produce light in each case. You may wish to have students use the Activity Support Master "Word Web" (TRB p. 70) to organize and review the elements of the electromagnetic spectrum.

Light Through the Ages

Preview *Students focus on how light has been produced artificially through various inventions.*

1. Get Ready

Background

- When gas lighting became widespread in towns and cities, gaslights were simply jets of burning gas. Later, their brightness was increased by using a mantle, a fine net of chemically-treated fabric fitted over the head of the gas jet.

Discussion Starter

 How would our lives be different if our only sources of light were the Sun and fire? We would have to read by candlelight or lantern, cars wouldn't be able to travel after dark, and streets would be dark at night.

2. Guide the Discussion

Choose from the following strategies to facilitate discussion.

Connecting to the Activities

- ***Seeing the Light, p. F6***
  Think back to Seeing the Light. **What light sources on your list were used many years ago?** Candles, perhaps kerosene lamps

Making Inferences

 In the 19th century, many whales were hunted almost to extinction. Why was this? Their oil was needed for lamps.

3. Assess Understanding

Students can work in small groups to decide the three most important developments in the history of light shown in the time line. Have a student from each group present the group's ideas and reasoning.

Light
Through the Ages

 For thousands of years the only sources of light humans had were the Sun and fire. Progress in producing artificial light occurred very slowly over long periods of time. Finally, in the mid-1700s, real strides were made. In recent years the advances in light technology have been fantastic! Follow the time line to see the changes that have occurred in light through the ages.

Sumerians used oil-burning lamps. Candles and oil lamps are used to light homes for many centuries.

3000–2500 B.C.

18,000 B.C.
People learn to make torches out of pieces of wood tipped with flammable tree resin.

A.D. 1786
First attempts to provide inside gas lighting in Germany and England

Whale blubber oil is used in oil lamps
1800–1900

Kerosene replaces whale oil in house lamps.
1850

EARLY 1800s
Gaslights are used in cities. The gas was carried to buildings by a series of pipes. As cities grew, gas lighting became common in homes and apartments. At twilight, lamplighters went around the city, lighting gas-fueled street lamps.

F12

Integrating the Curriculum

Science & Math

GRAPHING

What to Do Different types of lighting can provide different amounts of light per unit of energy. Incandescent lamps provide about 20 lumens (amount of light) per watt (amount of energy). A fluorescent light provides about 70 lumens per watt, mercury vapor lamps provide 50 lumens per watt, metal halide lamps provide 90 lumens per watt, and high-pressure sodium lamps provide 110 lumens per watt. Students can prepare a bar graph or pictogram comparing the efficiencies of different kinds of lights.
What's the Result? **Which type of lamp is most efficient?** High-pressure sodium lamps **If your community were installing new street lights, what kind should be chosen?** High-pressure sodium lamps might be a good choice.

Lewis Howard Latimer, an African American inventor, invented an improved, long burning carbon filament. **1881**

Fluorescent light bulbs are invented. **1927**

2000

1980
The halogen light, an incandescent lamp that burns more brightly than standard lamps, is invented.

1911
Tungsten filament is invented.

1879
Thomas Edison (American) and Joseph Swan (British) invent an improved light bulb. Both Edison and Swan had been experimenting with light bulbs. At the same time, both came up with the same idea. On October 21, 1879, using a carbon filament made from a burned thread, Edison made a light bulb that lasted for 13.5 hours before the filament burned out.

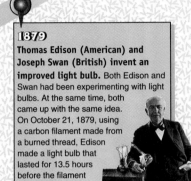

Building a Better Light Bulb

Since 1980, advances in lighting technology have taken place. Most recently, scientists have invented different kinds of lighting that are brighter or use less energy.

One of these energy-efficient light sources is the compact fluorescent bulb. It uses 75 percent less energy than an incandescent light bulb and can last for about 10,000 hours! In the years ahead, engineers will be working to create lighting that is brighter, lasts longer, and saves more energy. ∎

— **INVESTIGATION 1** —

THINK IT WRITE IT

1. Describe two different ways that you can produce light energy.

2. Imagine that you are an engineer who is designing an improved light bulb. Describe the characteristics that your improved light bulb would have.

F13

Assessment

Performance
Debate Student teams could debate the pros and cons of using fluorescent bulbs. They should research statistics and other data to support their positions.

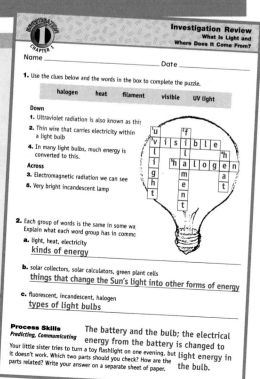

Investigation Review
What Is Light and Where Does It Come From?

Name _____ Date _____

1. Use the clues below and the words in the box to complete the puzzle.

| halogen | heat | filament | visible | UV light |

Down
1. Ultraviolet radiation is also known as this
2. Thin wire that carries electricity within a light bulb
4. In many light bulbs, much energy is converted to this.

Across
3. Electromagnetic radiation we can see
5. Very bright incandescent lamp

2. Each group of words is the same in some way. Explain what each word group has in common.
a. light, heat, electricity
    kinds of energy
b. solar collectors, solar calculators, green plant cells
    things that change the Sun's light into other forms of energy
c. fluorescent, incandescent, halogen
    types of light bulbs

Process Skills
Predicting, Communicating
Your little sister tries to turn a toy flashlight on one evening, but it doesn't work. Which two parts should you check? How are the parts related? Write your answer on a separate sheet of paper.
The battery and the bulb; the electrical energy from the battery is changed to light energy in the bulb.

Critical Thinking Skills
Synthesizing, Evaluating, Generating Ideas, Solving Problems

1. Possible answers include: changing electrical energy into light energy by using a filament that glows; changing electrical energy into light energy by producing ultraviolet rays that can cause chemicals inside a fluorescent tube to give off visible light; chemical changes that occur during burning; or other chemical reactions, such as that in the light stick.

2. Possible responses include that it would produce less heat, last longer, use less energy to produce more light, and cost less to operate.

Challenge Students can provide further evidence that light is a form of energy by identifying examples of light being converted to other forms of energy (e.g., solar calculator—light to electrical to light; light to heat in matter).

Following Up
Baseline Assessment Return to the class list of reasons why light is important to people. Ask whether students would like to add to the list or revise any of their responses and, if so, how.

Reteaching Students might enjoy making up riddles about light sources and/or parts of the electromagnetic spectrum. Encourage students to read their riddles to the class. The person who correctly answers the riddle reads the next riddle to the class.

 Use *Science Notebook* p. 285.

◀ **Investigation Review**
Use Investigation Review p. 134 in the *Assessment Guide.*

How Does Light Travel?

Planner

Subconcept Light travels in the form of waves; light waves can be compared by measuring their wavelengths and frequencies.

Objectives
- **Observe, predict,** and **record** data about how light travels.
- **Investigate** waves and lasers.

Pacing 2 – 3 class periods

Science Terms wave, vacuum, wavelength, frequency, hertz

Activate Prior Knowledge

Baseline Assessment Ask: **What evidence is there that waves carry energy?** Small groups work together and write answers on paper for use in Following Up.

Activity Light Waves

Preview *Students focus on the wave model of light by making waves in a coil spring.*

1. Get Ready

Time about 30 minutes

Grouping groups of 4–6

Collaborative Strategy One group member should record observations while others manipulate the coil spring.

Materials Hints Coils should not be stretched too far; the coils could break or become warped.

Safety Review safety precautions with students.

How Does Light Travel?

Have you ever been in a sports stadium when one section starts a "wave"? Think about how the motion travels from one part of the stadium to another. The traveling of light is a little like this human wave.

Activity
Light Waves

Light is a form of energy that travels in waves. Can you imagine what a light wave looks like? This activity will show you a model of the way a light wave travels.

MATERIALS
- goggles
- large plastic coil spring
- *Science Notebook*

SAFETY
Wear goggles.

Procedure

1. Work with a partner. Stretch a plastic coil spring between yourself and your partner. Be careful that you don't overstretch and damage the coils.

2. While your partner holds one end of the coil spring still, make one quick motion to the side and back to the center position. **Observe** the wave you created. **Record** your observations in your *Science Notebook*.

3. Repeat step 2 several times and **record** your observations.

Step 1

F14

Responding to Individual Needs

Students Acquiring English For the first question in Analyze and Conclude, students can make drawings of the two ways the coil spring can move and write a sentence about each drawing.

---

4. Predict what will happen if you move the coil spring up and down. **Record** your prediction. Then try moving the coil spring up and down. **Record** how the wave moves this time. **Make a** sketch of the wave.

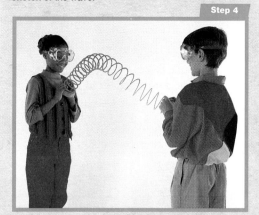

Step 4

Analyze and Conclude

1. Write a statement describing two ways the coil spring moves.

2. What evidence is there that the wave carries energy as it travels along the coil?

UNIT PROJECT LINK

You can use your investigations of light and sound to help you plan a puppet show. Start by making a catalog of the different shadows you can create with common objects. Choose objects with interesting shapes. Look around your classroom or your home for the objects.

Darken the room. Shine a flashlight at the objects from different angles to produce different shapes. Try moving the flashlight far away from the objects and then near them to see what happens. Choose one object. On a sheet of white paper, trace the different shadows you can make from that object. Remove all the objects. Then see if anyone can guess the object that made the shadows.

F15

2. Guide the Procedure

- For best results, perform the side-to-side motion with the spring lying on the floor. Then have students suspend the spring while they stand for the up-and-down motion.

 Have students record their data and the answers to questions on *Science Notebook* pp. 286–287.

 You may wish to have students use the CD-ROM Spreadsheet to organize and display their data and the Painter to draw diagrams of their observations.

3. Assess Performance

Process Skills Checklist

- Did students follow directions for **using the model** of wave motion?
- How carefully did students **observe** and **record** data about the wave motion?
- Did students make reasonable **predictions** about what would happen if the coil spring was moved up and down?

Analyze and Conclude

1. The coil spring moves from side to side or up and down, forming a series of waves.

2. There is successive movement all along the coil spring even though it was set in motion only at one end. Finally, it causes the partner's hand to move at the far end of the coil.

Investigate Further

Unit Project Link

If students choose an asymmetrical object, they will be able to make a greater variety of shadows from the object. Remind them that they can turn the object sideways and upside down to create different shadow shapes. Encourage students to record their observations in their *Science Notebooks* on p. 288. To give students assistance in making rod puppets for their puppet show, have them use Unit Project Master F1 (TRB p. 99.)

Lasers

Preview *Students learn how a laser works and how laser light is different from ordinary light.*

1. Get Ready

Background

- Laser is an acronym for *Light Amplification by Stimulated Emission of Radiation.* Lasers consist of three basic parts—a power supply, a solid or liquid medium to generate the laser light, and a set of mirrors placed at the ends of the medium to amplify the beam.

Discussion Starter

- **Where have you seen laser light?** Scanners in stores, in CD players, at concerts, in hospitals

2. Guide the Discussion

Choose from the following strategies to facilitate discussion.

Thinking Critically

Why is laser surgery less dangerous than regular surgery? Smaller wounds, less blood loss, less muscle damage.

Connecting to the Activities

- *Light Waves, pp. F14 – F15*
  Think back to Light Waves. How is laser light like ordinary light? Laser light travels in waves and carries energy.

Responding to Individual Needs

Gifted and Talented Activity Groups could research a laser light-emitting substance, make a drawing of their laser light, and list its purposes for display.

3. Assess Understanding

Small groups could draw a picture of ordinary light waves and laser light waves moving out from a source and then discuss similarities and differences.

Lasers

How It Works

What do supermarket checkouts, CD players, and rock concerts have in common? Lasers! Laser beams are used in the scanners that make barcode readers and CD players work. Laser beams are also used in concert light displays. How does a laser work? What makes laser light different from ordinary light?

All light beams travel in a straight line, but ordinary light beams spread out as they travel. Ordinary light beams aren't as bright after they spread out. Laser beams, however, don't spread out, allowing them to travel a long distance without getting dim.

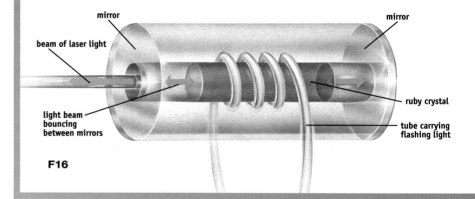
▲ **Laser lights at rock concert**

One use for lasers is in communications. Lasers are used to send signals along telephone and television cables. The cables are made of optical fibers, which are long, thin strands of glass. Even if the fibers are bent, the light bounces off the sides of the fiber wall and follows the bending pathway.

Today, laser beams and optical fibers are used in medicine. For example, laser light can help repair a detached retina in the eye. It can cut and seal blood vessels or destroy skin cancers. Optical fibers and lasers make microsurgery possible. Doctors can use optical fibers to work through a small incision in the body. ■

PARTS OF A LASER This laser contains a ruby crystal surrounded by a coil of light. As the light flashes, energy builds up in the crystal. When enough energy has built up, an intense beam of laser light is released.

mirror

mirror

beam of laser light

light beam bouncing between mirrors

ruby crystal

tube carrying flashing light

F16

Integrating the Curriculum

Science & Language Arts

WRITING SCI-FI

What to Do In the 1958 science fiction film *Colossus of New York*, a monster with the brain of a dead scientist emitted deadly light rays from his eyes. In the *Star Wars* films, light beams were also used as weapons. Students could write a short science-fiction story that includes the use of lasers or laserlike devices.

What's the Result? Students could read their stories to the class. Class members could vote on which stories they liked best.

Multi-Age Classroom Students can work in pairs or small groups to do this activity. Before they begin, students can brainstorm ideas for the story and that aspect they might want to illustrate. As they work, some students can be writers and others can be illustrators.

Light as a Wave

A **wave** is a disturbance that moves away from its starting point. As a wave moves, it transfers energy. Think about what happens if you drop a stone into a pond. As the stone hits the water, it creates waves that travel out across the pond from that spot. As they reach the shore, the waves may move sand and pebbles.

Light also travels as a wave. Light waves are different from water waves in an important way. Without water, there would be no water waves. But light waves don't need water or air or any kind of matter to carry them. Light waves can travel through a vacuum. A **vacuum** is a space that is empty of any matter. Light

▲ Waves travel outward from a pebble tossed into water.

waves from the Sun travel through space without being carried by matter.

The Shape of a Wave

You can see light, but you can't see light waves. Still, scientists know that light waves do many of the same things that other kinds of waves do. So scientists use the wave model to explain how light behaves. To use and understand the wave model of light, you need to know the parts of a wave. Refer to the drawing below as you read the following description.

Measuring Light Waves

The lengths of light waves can be

▼ Parts of a wave

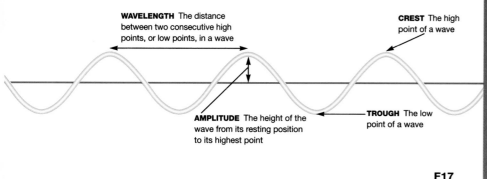

WAVELENGTH The distance between two consecutive high points, or low points, in a wave

CREST The high point of a wave

AMPLITUDE The height of the wave from its resting position to its highest point

TROUGH The low point of a wave

F17

Investigate Further

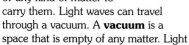

Cultural Connection

WRITE A STORY

What to Do Explain that ancient peoples had no clear idea why the Sun produced light, but they thought they could guard against its light going out by worshipping the Sun as a god. The Sun god, Aton, was an important god to the ancient Egyptians. The Incas of South America worshipped the Sun and believed their rulers were the Sun's living descendants. Many cultures have stories or legends about the Sun and what produces its light. Have small groups of students imagine that they know nothing about why the Sun produces light. Have each group write a legend to explain the light of the Sun.

What's the Result? Group members could act out the legend.

Light as a Wave

Preview *Students focus on the properties of light waves.*

1. Get Ready

Science Terms
wave, vacuum, wavelength, frequency, hertz

Background

- Light energy travels as waves. Visible light is a small part of the larger electromagnetic spectrum. Quantum theory explains the transference of light and other forms of E-M radiation as having dual characteristics of both particles, called photons, and waves.

Discussion Starter

- **Where have you seen water waves?** Possible answers include in an ocean, lake, pool, or bathtub.
- **What did you notice about all of the waves in water?** The water moved up and down and the waves moved away from their energy source.

2. Guide the Discussion

Choose from the following strategies to facilitate discussion.

Making Comparisons

- **How are light waves like water waves?** They both travel as waves and move out from a source. **How are they different?** Water waves have to have water to travel through, but light waves don't need any kind of matter to travel through. They can travel through a vacuum. You may wish to have students use the Activity Support Master "Compare–Contrast Diagram" (TRB p.68) to compare light waves and water waves.

Thinking Critically

■ **Why wouldn't life be possible on Earth if light waves traveled the same as water waves?** If light waves couldn't travel through a vacuum, light would never reach Earth from the Sun. Without sunlight, life wouldn't be possible.

Connecting to the Activities

• *Light Waves, pp. F14–F15*
Think back to Light Waves. **Where were the crests of the waves in your model?** The crests were the places where the spring moved furthest from its resting position.

Responding to Individual Needs

Visual/Spatial Activity Students could make a color drawing of the different colors of light that make up visible light and label each color with its range of wavelengths.

Thinking About the Data

• **How do the wavelengths of radio waves and visible light compare? How do their frequencies compare?** Radio waves have wavelengths longer than those of visible light, but they have lower frequencies.

■ **How are frequency and wavelength related?** From the diagram, students should conclude that as frequency increases, wavelength decreases, or as frequency decreases, wavelength increases.

3. Assess Understanding

Students can work in groups of four or six. Invite each group to make waves, using a 1 meter length of string or yarn. Challenge the groups to make two complete waves, then three, four, and so on, up to ten. They can measure the wavelength for each set of waves and describe what happened as the number of waves increased. (Wavelength decreased.)

Have students research light waves using the Sound, Light, and Waves Data Pack on the CD-ROM.

To illustrate electromagnetic waves, use **Transparency 28,** "The Electromagnetic Spectrum."

---

measured. **Wavelength** is the distance from one crest of the wave to the next crest. Of course, you can't place a ruler next to a light wave because you can't see it. But the wavelength of light has been measured in the laboratory. Scientists have found that each color of light has a different range of wavelengths. The wavelengths of visible light are shown in the table. Because light wavelengths are so short, they are measured in a tiny unit called a nanometer (nm). One nanometer equals one billionth of a meter.

Wave Frequency

The number of waves produced each second is the **frequency** of a wave. Wave frequency is measured in a unit called the **hertz** (Hz). If ten waves are produced each second, the frequency of the wave is 10 Hz. The frequency of light waves is measured in a unit called a megahertz (MHz). One megahertz is equal to 1 million hertz.

Speed of Light

Although each color of light has a different range of wavelengths and frequencies, all light waves travel at the same speed. The speed of light is 300,000 km/s (186,000 mi/s).

The electromagnetic spectrum ▼

Wavelengths of Light	
Color of Light	**Wavelength (nm)**
Violet	350–400
Indigo	400–450
Blue	450–500
Green	500–550
Yellow	550–600
Orange	600–650
Red	650–700

Imagine light traveling through an optical fiber wrapped around the equator. Light travels so quickly that it could travel around the world 7.5 times in one second! Light traveling from the Sun, which is 150 million km (about 93

F18   radio waves   television waves   microwaves

Investigate Further

Using the Trade Book

RADIO WAVES **What to Do** Students can read pp. 9–17 of *Tuning In: The Sounds of the Radio* by Eve and Albert Stwertka. They can then work in small groups to do the "Try this…" activities on pp. 14, 16, and 17 in the book. Once they have examined the AM and FM dials on the radio, they can turn on a radio and slowly turn the dial. They can count the number of AM and FM stations the radio receives. Each student could list the location on the radio dial of his or her favorite station. **What's the Result?** **How many AM stations did you find on the radio? How many FM stations?** The number of stations received in an area will vary from location to location. In large metropolitan areas, there are usually many more stations on the air than in rural areas.

million mi) away, takes 500 seconds, or 8.3 minutes, to reach Earth.

The speed of light depends on the material through which it moves. The value 300,000 km/s is the speed of light traveling in a vacuum.

The Electromagnetic Spectrum

As you know, light is only one kind of electromagnetic radiation. E-M radiation also includes gamma rays, microwaves, infrared waves, X-rays, radio waves, and other kinds of waves.

From the drawing below, you can see that radio waves have the longest wavelengths and gamma rays have the shortest wavelengths. How do the wavelengths of visible light compare to those of radio waves? to microwaves?

The energy of electromagnetic radiation is related to wavelength—the shorter the wavelength, the more energy carried by the wave. How does UV light compare with visible light in terms of energy?

Although the wavelengths, frequencies, and energy levels of electromagnetic waves vary, E-M waves have two things in common: (1) When traveling through space, they all travel at the same speed, and (2) they all can travel through a vacuum. ■

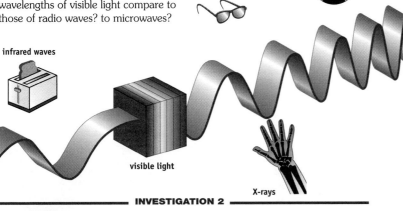

gamma rays

ultraviolet rays

infrared waves

visible light

X-rays

────── INVESTIGATION 2 ──────

1. Ultraviolet light has a higher frequency than any color of visible light. How would you expect its wavelength to compare to those of visible light?

2. Describe visible light in terms of (a) its speed in a vacuum, (b) how the colors of light differ, and (c) the form in which it travels.

THINK IT WRITE IT

F19

Assessment

Performance

Demonstrate Using the coil spring, students can demonstrate the characteristics of a wave that they can control.

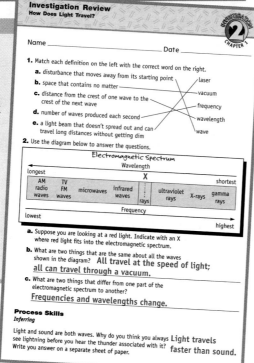

Investigation Review
How Does Light Travel?

Name _____ Date _____

1. Match each definition on the left with the correct word on the right.

a. disturbance that moves away from its starting point — laser
b. space that contains no matter — vacuum
c. distance from the crest of one wave to the crest of the next wave — frequency
d. number of waves produced each second — wavelength
e. a light beam that doesn't spread out and can travel long distances without getting dim — wave

2. Use the diagram below to answer the questions.

Electromagnetic Spectrum
Wavelength
longest   X   shortest
| AM radio waves | TV FM waves | microwaves | infrared waves | rays | ultraviolet rays | X-rays | gamma rays |
Frequency
lowest   highest

a. Suppose you are looking at a red light. Indicate with an X where red light fits into the electromagnetic spectrum.
b. What are two things that are the same about all the waves shown in the diagram? **All travel at the speed of light; all can travel through a vacuum.**
c. What are two things that differ from one part of the electromagnetic spectrum to another? **Frequencies and wavelengths change.**

Process Skills
Inferring

Light and sound are both waves. Why do you think you always see lightning before you hear the thunder associated with it? Write your answer on a separate sheet of paper. **Light travels faster than sound.**

Critical Thinking Skills
Analyzing, Synthesizing

THINK IT WRITE IT **1.** The wavelength of ultraviolet light is shorter than the wavelengths of visible light.

2. Light (a) travels at 300,000 km/s; (b) the colors differ in wavelength; (c) travels in waves

Challenge Suggest that students find out more about electromagnetic radiation and list two more uses for each type of radiation.

Following Up

Baseline Assessment Return to the answers generated by the small groups. Let each group review their answers to the questions. Ask each group if they would like to change any of their responses and, if so, how.

Reteaching Tie a long rope to a doorknob and move the free end of the rope with quick flicks of your wrist. Ask students to identify changes you make in the frequency, wavelength, and amplitude of your wave. Then untie the rope and lay it on the floor. Ask one student to arrange it in the shape of a wave and identify the crest, trough, and wavelength. Then ask another student to change the wave in some way and again identify the crest, trough, and wavelength.

Use *Science Notebook* p. 289.

◀ **Investigation Review**
Use Investigation Review p. 135 in the *Assessment Guide*.

How Does Light Behave?

Planner

Subconcept Light reflects off various kinds of mirrors in predictable ways; it changes direction as it passes from one medium to another in a process called refraction.

Objectives

- **Observe**, **describe**, and **predict** the reflection and refraction of light.
- **Investigate** how reflection and refraction are used

Pacing 3–4 class periods

Science Terms reflection, plane mirror, concave mirror, convex mirror, refraction

Activate Prior Knowledge

Baseline Assessment Ask: **How do you know that light can bounce off surfaces?** Let students write answers and save them for Following Up.

How Does Light Behave?

Have you ever used mirrors to look around a corner or over a wall? If so, you know that some kinds of matter can change the direction that light travels. In this investigation you'll find out under what conditions light bounces and bends.

Activity

How Mirrors Affect Light

In this activity you'll see how three different kinds of mirrors change the direction that light travels.

MATERIALS
- flashlight
- plane mirror (flat)
- large piece of cardboard
- concave mirror (curves inward)
- convex mirror (curves outward)
- *Science Notebook*

Procedure

Darken the room. Turn a flashlight on and point it at an angle toward a plane mirror. Hold a large piece of cardboard at the edge of the mirror, as shown. **Record** your observations in your *Science Notebook*.

Repeat the above procedure, but this time use the concave mirror. **Observe** and **record** your results. **Predict** what will happen with the convex mirror. Try it. **Observe** what happens and **record** your results.

Analyze and Conclude

Describe the effect of each mirror on the light beam. What uses can you think of for each mirror?

F20

Activity How Mirrors Affect Light

Preview *Students focus on how visible light interacts with mirrors.*

1. Get Ready

Time about 30 minutes

Grouping groups of 4–6

Safety Remind students to be careful moving in a dark room. Caution them about handling glass mirrors.

2. Guide the Procedure

- Use a penlight or place a disc with a hole punched in the middle in front of the flashlight.

 Have students record their observations on *Science Notebook* pp. 290–291.

Have students use the CD-ROM Spreadsheet to organize and display their data.

3. Assess Performance

Process Skills Checklist
- Did students make careful **observations?**
- Did they accurately **record data?**
- Were their **predictions** reasonable?

Analyze and Conclude

The light beam is reflected off the surface of each mirror. A plane mirror image is the same as the object; such a mirror is used in bathrooms and clothing stores. Concave mirrors magnify and are used in makeup mirrors, car headlights, and flashlights. Convex mirrors offer a wider field of vision and are used in rear-view mirrors on cars.

Activity
The Bending Pencil

Sometimes things aren't quite what they appear to be. That's the idea behind many of the tricks that magicians perform. With some water and oil, you can "break" a pencil in two. To do the trick, you have to learn how to bend light.

Step 2

Procedure

1. Place a pencil in a plastic jar. **Observe** the jar and pencil from the side. In your *Science Notebook,* **draw** the jar and pencil. Label the drawing *Step 1.*

2. Keep the pencil in the jar. Then fill the jar almost to the top with water. **Observe** the jar and pencil from the side and from above. In your *Science Notebook* **draw** pictures of what you observe from the side and from above. Use a dotted line to show where you think the pencil in the water *actually* is. Label the drawings *Step 2.*

3. Remove the pencil from the jar. Pour out the water. Use a paper towel to dry the inside of the jar. Now, fill the jar almost to the top with vegetable oil. **Predict** how the pencil will look from the side and from the top. **Record** your prediction. Then place the pencil back in the jar. **Observe** and **draw** as you did in step 2. **Label** the drawings *Step 3.*

Analyze and Conclude

1. What is the difference between the way the pencil looked in step 1 and step 2? What evidence is there that light changes direction as it leaves the water?

2. Describe the difference between the appearance of the ruler in water and its appearance in vegetable oil. Give a reason for any difference.

INVESTIGATE FURTHER!

EXPERIMENT

Predict what would happen if you used other liquids in this activity. Try several liquids and compare the results.

F21

Investigate Further

Experiment

Students should observe that the other liquids also refract light. (The degree of refraction by the liquid varies with the index of refraction.) Remind them to write observations and predictions in their *Science Notebooks* on p. 293.

Activity The Bending Pencil

Preview *Students focus on the refraction of light and should observe that both the water and the oil refract light.*

1. Get Ready

Time about 30 minutes

Grouping groups of 4–6

 Collaborative Strategy One member of the group could record data and make drawings of observations while other members manipulate the materials.

Materials Hints Oil can be reused. Pour it back into its container and use again when needed.

Safety Review safety precautions with students. Clean up water or oil spills promptly to prevent falls.

2. Guide the Procedure

- For best results, students should stand so that they can see the top as well as the side of the jar.

- Liquids used in Investigate Further should be monitored. Many cleaning liquids are caustic.

 Have students record their data and answer questions on *Science Notebook* p. 292.

You may wish to have students use the CD-ROM Spreadsheet and Painter to organize and display their data.

3. Assess Performance

Process Skills Checklist

- Did students make accurate **observations** of how light is bent by different media?

- Did they accurately **record data** about their observations?

- Were their **predictions** about how the pencil and jar would look reasonable?

Analyze and Conclude

1. In step 1 the pencil looked normal, but in step 2 the pencil looked broken. The water refracted the light, causing the part of the pencil in the water to appear to be at a different position than it actually was.

2. Possible answer: The part of the pencil in oil looked displaced from its actual position even more so than when in water. Oil refracted light differently than did the water.

Bouncing Light

Preview *Students focus on the behavior of light waves as light strikes a surface.*

1. Get Ready

Science Terms reflection, plane mirror, concave mirror, convex mirror

Background

- As long ago as 300 B.C., the Greek mathematician Euclid investigated and understood how the reflection of light takes place. It was not until the 1100s, however, that the Arab scientist Alhazen put together the law that explains exactly what happens to a ray of light when it strikes a surface and reflects. His law is known as the law of reflection. According to the law of reflection, the angle of reflection is always equal to the angle of incidence; that is, the angle at which the ray hits the surface is equal to the angle at which it is reflected from the surface.

Discussion Starter

- **What happens to light waves that strike the people and other things in this room?** Some light is absorbed, but much light bounces off the people and objects.

Responding to Individual Needs

Students Acquiring English Encourage students to look around the classroom, their homes, and their neighborhood for objects (other than mirrors) that show a reflected image. Students can list the objects, then look at themselves in each of these reflecting objects. Ask them to describe whether and how their images are changed. (Reflective objects might include spoons, shiny metal dishes, metal hubcaps, windows, or metal jewelry. Images formed will depend on whether the reflective surface is plane, convex, or concave.)

Bouncing Light

▲ **Image in a fun-house mirror**

You see objects because light coming from them enters your eyes. The Sun, lamps, and candles give off light, but

most objects don't. You can see such objects because of reflected light.

Reflection (ri flek′shən) is the bouncing back of light (or sound, or water) from a surface. Think of a lamp as it gives off light. Some of the light hits a chair. Part of the light that hits the chair is absorbed by the chair, but most of the light is reflected off the chair. Light that reflects off the chair to your eyes lets you see the chair.

Plane Mirrors

Any object with a very smooth surface, including still water and highly polished metals, can act as a mirror. The type of mirror you are most familiar with is called a plane mirror. A **plane mirror** is a mirror with a flat surface.

Light reflects from a plane mirror in the same pattern and at the same angle

▼ **Reflection in a plane mirror**

light ray

image

reflected ray

F22

▼ **Image in a plane mirror**

Investigate Further

Cultural Connection

SOLAR COOKERS **What to Do** Certain concave mirrors, known as parabolic mirrors, are used to capture the Sun's energy. A parabolic mirror focuses all incoming light into a single image point. These mirrors, when placed in solar cookers, can be used to cook food and boil water.

What's the Result? How could these mirrors be used to save energy? When other energy sources are not available, they could be used for cooking or to boil water to make it safe to drink. Solar energy doesn't cost anything to produce, so once people have a solar cooker, they don't have to pay for fuel. **How could using solar cookers help the environment of the area or country?** Use of solar cookers could keep people from having to burn fuel that pollutes the environment.

at which it strikes the mirror's surface. However, the light changes direction as it is reflected. If you stand in front of a mirror, light bouncing off your body strikes the mirror's surface. Some of this light is reflected off the mirror and back to your eyes. Because the light reflects off the mirror with the same pattern as the light that struck the mirror, you see an image.

The image you see in a plane mirror is right-side-up and the same size as the object being reflected. The image is not distorted, or out of shape. But it is reversed from left to right, so you don't see yourself exactly as others do.

Use the drawing on page F22 to follow the path that light takes to form an image in a plane mirror. Some light rays from the object travel toward the mirror. As these light rays strike the mirror, they are reflected. These rays enter your eye and form an image. Your brain forms a mental picture of where the light seems to come from. Because light travels in straight lines, the image seems to be behind the mirror.

Concave Mirrors

The images you see in curved mirrors often are distorted and are usually not the same size as the object. There are two kinds of curved mirrors. A **concave mirror** curves inward at the middle. A **convex mirror** curves outward at the middle.

Shaving and makeup mirrors are often concave. When an object is close to a concave mirror, the image formed in the mirror is larger than the object. Concave mirrors are also used as reflectors to concentrate light. The reflected light rays come together and are focused at one point. A concave mirror can be used to focus solar rays and cook food in a solar oven.

Convex Mirrors

A convex mirror produces an image that is smaller than the object. It also allows you to see much more of an area than other kinds of mirrors do. Because convex mirrors reflect light from such a wide area, they are useful as side-view mirrors on cars and trucks. ∎

▲ Concave mirror and the image it produces

▲ Convex mirror and the image it produces

F23

2. Guide the Discussion

Choose from the following strategies to facilitate discussion.

Making Comparisons

- **Why could you see your image in a piece of aluminum foil but not in a piece of paper?** Smooth, shiny foil reflects nearly all the light from your face in the same pattern back to your eyes. Paper reflects light in many directions.

Drawing Conclusions

◼ **How do you know that objects reflect light?** Because they can see the objects.

Connecting to the Activities

- *How Mirrors Affect Light, p. F20*
  Think back to How Mirrors Affect Light. **What is different about your reflection in a plane mirror?** Encourage students to realize the image is reversed.

- *How Mirrors Affect Light, p. F20*
  How does your image in a makeup or shaving mirror compare to the way it actually looks? It's larger. **How does the image change as you move away from the mirror?** It decreases in size.

👤 Responding to Individual Needs

Students Acquiring English Let students hold different types of mirrors and feel the shapes. Ask them to draw a cut-away picture of each mirror and label it in English.

Drawing Conclusions

◼ **If the side-view mirror on a car or truck reads "Objects are closer than they appear," what does this tell you about the size of the image?** The image produced must be smaller than it would be in a plane mirror.

3. Assess Understanding

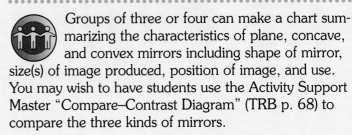 Groups of three or four can make a chart summarizing the characteristics of plane, concave, and convex mirrors including shape of mirror, size(s) of image produced, position of image, and use. You may wish to have students use the Activity Support Master "Compare–Contrast Diagram" (TRB p. 68) to compare the three kinds of mirrors.

Bending Light

Preview *Students focus on the behavior of light as it passes from one medium into another.*

1. Get Ready

Science Term refraction

Background

- When light passes from one medium into another, it is bent, or refracted. Early scientists knew about refraction and realized that it varied with different media. Many tried to make a mathematical law to show how much bending occurred. Ptolemy, a geographer who lived in the second century A.D., is believed to have developed a law of refraction. It worked in some cases, but not in others. The Arab scientist Alhazen also investigated refraction in the 12th century, but he couldn't predict how much light would bend. Not until 1621 was the problem solved by Snell's law. Willebrord Snell found that there was a characteristic ratio between a beam of light's angle before bending and its angle after bending. His law shows that the more a substance bends light, the higher its refractive index.

Discussion Starter

Have you even seen a "puddle" on the road ahead of you that disappeared as you approached? What causes such mirages? Allow students to speculate.

2. Guide the Discussion

Choose from the following strategies to facilitate discussion.

Connecting to the Activities

- *The Bending Pencil, p. F21*
  Think back to The Bending Pencil. **What caused the pencil to look broken in water?** Light waves changed direction as they moved from the water into the air.

Bending Light

A Change in Direction

In the activity on page F21, you saw that light passing through different materials can produce a strange image —like a broken ruler. The illusion occurs because light rays bend, or change direction, as they travel from one material into another. This bending of light as it passes from one material into another is called **refraction** (ri-frak'shən). In the activity, light was refracted as it passed from water into air.

The speed of light changes as it passes from one material into another. For example, light travels at close to 300,000 km/s (186,000 mi/s) in air and at 225,000 km/(140,000 mi/s) in water.

A Change in Speed

When light waves pass from air into water, they slow down. This change in speed of the light waves is what causes the light to refract, or change direction. You can see in the drawing on page F25 how light waves change direction as their speed increases when they pass from water into air.

Look at how a glass prism affects a beam of white light passing through it in the photograph below. The light slows down as it enters the prism, causing the beam of light to refract. But the different colors of light are bent at different angles. So a rainbow, or spectrum, is produced as the light leaves the prism.

▲ Refraction of light as it passes from air through a glass prism

F24

Integrating the Curriculum

Science & Math

SPEED OF LIGHT

What to Do The more light slows down or speeds up as it moves from one material into another, the more it is bent. Have students make a bar graph of the speed of light for: vacuum— 300,000 km/sec; diamond—124,000 km/sec; glass—197,000 km/sec; water—225,000 km/sec; air—299,000 km/sec; ice—229,000 km/sec. **What's the Result?** **In which case would light be refracted the most: passing from air into water or from air into ice?** Passing from air into ice, because the difference in the two speeds is greater. **In which case would light be refracted the least: passing from water into a diamond or from a vacuum into glass?** Passing from water into diamond, because the difference in the two speeds is smaller.

Tricks With Refracted Light

Have you ever tried to catch a fish in a fish tank? If you looked at the fish from above, you probably had trouble. The fish looks closer to the surface than it is. Look at the diagram of the fish tank. Light reflecting from the fish is refracted as it leaves the water. The light enters your eye, and your brain "assumes" that the light has traveled in a straight line. So your brain forms an image of where the fish seems to be. But that isn't where the fish really is! Refraction of light fools you.

If you have watched someone in a pet store try to net a fish, you probably noticed that the person looked at the fish through the side of the tank. By

▲ Refraction of light in water can fool you. Where is the fish?

looking straight into the water, that person had a better chance of catching the fish. When light rays move from one material to another along a line that is perpendicular to the surface, there is no refraction. Since the light rays don't bend, you don't get fooled.

SCIENCE IN LITERATURE

Bending light, bouncing light. Not only does light "bend" and "bounce," so do other forms of electromagnetic radiation. Radio waves are a familiar and useful form of electromagnetic radiation. These waves travel at the speed of light. Like light waves, radio waves can be bounced and bent.

Find out how radio waves behave and how they are put to use by reading *TUNING IN: The Sounds of the Radio* by Eve and Albert Stwertka. Do the "Try this . . . " activity on page 6 of *Tuning In*. Compare your results with those of your classmates.

TUNING IN
THE SOUNDS OF THE RADIO
by Eve and Albert Stwertka
Illustrated by Mena Dolobowsky
Julian Messner, 1993

F25

Drawing Conclusions

- **Why is it hard to catch a fish with a net in a pond?** Water refracts light, so the fish appear to be elsewhere.

- **How might early people who fished with spears have managed to catch fish?** They probably learned to adjust aiming the spear or to look straight down into the water.

SCIENCE IN LITERATURE

Tuning In: The Sounds of the Radio*
by Eve and Albert Swertka

If students do the Try this...on p. 6 of *Tuning In*, they will find that the number of stations and the variety of music, talk, and foreign languages will be larger in a metropolitan area than in a rural area, which may only have a few stations.

*Available in the Trade Book Library

3. Assess Understanding

Give groups of three or four a cup of water with a washer or screw nut on the bottom. Challenge them to pick up the washer with their pencil tip. Ask: **Why was it so difficult to locate and pick up the object?** Refraction made the object appear to be where it wasn't.

Science & Literature

What to Do Allow small groups of students to work together to perform the following activities from *Experimenting With Light and Illusions* by Alan Ward: "Bent Light," "More Evidence That Light Can Bend," and "Puzzles with Water-lenses," found on pp. 14, 15, and 16 of the book. To do these activities, students will need a penny, an opaque mixing bowl, water, a transparent box, a penlight flashlight, two hollow tubes, a glass jar, a ruler, and a Ping-Pong ball. **What's the Result?** Groups can compare their results and prepare a class summary.

Close the Investigation

 Critical Thinking Skills
Applying, Synthesizing, Solving Problems

1. The water refracted the light, causing your feet and legs to look closer to you and therefore shorter.

2. Both reflection and refraction change the direction of light waves. Reflection is the bouncing of light from a surface. Refraction is the bending of the light as it passes from one medium to another.

Challenge Read students the following scenario: Imagine that you're roller skating down a sidewalk when one skate goes off into the grass. That skate slows down, while the skate on the sidewalk keeps going fast. Your body turns in the direction of the slower skate, and you find yourself skating onto the grass at a slower speed. Ask students to explain how the roller skater is like a light wave being refracted.

Following Up

Baseline Assessment Return to the students' answers about evidence that light bounces off surfaces. Ask students if they would like to modify any of their responses and, if so, how.

Reteaching Students can work in small groups to devise a demonstration of how reflection and refraction occur. Groups can choose their own methods and materials and can present their demonstrations to the class.

 Use *Science Notebook* p. 294.

Investigation Review ▶
Use Investigation Review p. 136 in the *Assessment Guide*.

Air Bends Light

Have you ever ridden in a car on a hot, dry day and thought you saw a pool of water in the road? Was your mind playing tricks on you? Actually, the mirage you see is a result of light traveling at different speeds in cool air and warm air. Light from the Sun was refracted toward your eyes by the heated air near the road's surface. The pool you saw was really refracted sunlight. In effect, you were seeing an image of the sky on the road surface ahead of you. Your brain interprets the light as coming to you in a straight line from the road. ∎

Mirages are most common during summer months, when air near the ground is much warmer than air higher in the atmosphere. ▶

As light waves from above pass into the layer of warm air near the surface, the light bends, or refracts. If these light waves enter your eyes, you see an image of the sky, but you see it on the road surface. ▶

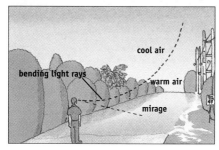

cool air
bending light rays
warm air
mirage

—————— **INVESTIGATION 3** ——————

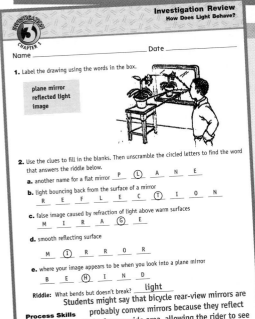

1. You are in water up to your waist in a local swimming pool. As you look down into the water, your legs and feet look short and stubby. You're really tall and thin. What happened?

2. Compare and contrast the reflection of light with the refraction of light.

F26

Assessment

Investigation Review
How Does Light Behave?

Name _____ Date _____

1. Label the drawing using the words in the box.

plane mirror
reflected light
image

2. Use the clues to fill in the blanks. Then unscramble the circled letters to find the word that answers the riddle below.
a. another name for a flat mirror P (L) A N E
b. light bouncing back from the surface of a mirror
R E F L E C (T) I O N
c. false image caused by refraction of light above warm surfaces
M I R A (G) E
d. smooth reflecting surface
M (I) R R O R
e. where your image appears to be when you look into a plane mirror
B E (H) I N D

Riddle: What bends but doesn't break? _____ light

Process Skills
Inferring

Suppose you want to buy a mirror to use on your bicycle to help you see images that are behind you while riding. What type of mirror—concave, convex, or plane—would you probably find in a bicycle shop? Explain your answer on a separate sheet of paper.

Students might say that bicycle rear-view mirrors are probably convex mirrors because they reflect light from a wide area, allowing the rider to see much more than the other two types of mirrors.

Portfolio

Make a Diagram Students can make labeled diagrams of light being reflected by a mirror and refracted by water.

REFLECT & EVALUATE

WORD POWER

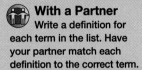

energy	frequency
hertz	plane mirror
vacuum	reflection
visible light	refraction
wavelength	wave
concave mirror	
convex mirror	
electromagnetic radiation	

 On Your Own
Review the terms in the list. Then write one new thing you learned about each term.

With a Partner
Write a definition for each term in the list. Have your partner match each definition to the correct term.

BUILD YOUR PORTFOLIO

Make several drawings of devices that use different kinds of electromagnetic radiation. If you prefer, make a collage of pictures of these devices cut from magazines.

Analyze Information

If you were the person on the pier in the drawing, where would the snorkeler appear to be?

Assess Performance

Examine a flashlight and locate the mirror near the bulb. What is the shape of the mirror? Turn on the flashlight and notice the path of the light. If possible, unscrew the front cover of the flashlight and get a better look at the mirror. Make a drawing to show how the mirror affects the light produced by the bulb.

Problem Solving

1. Describe and sketch the energy path that leads to light in a flashlight.

2. Make a sketch that shows a wave of red light and a wave of violet light. Label the sketch and explain how the waves differ.

3. Use a diagram to show that light travels in straight lines, even when it bends, or refracts, and when it reflects off a surface.

F27

REFLECT & EVALUATE

Word Power

On Your Own Students' sentences should reflect some new information related to each term.

With a Partner Clues should reflect an understanding of the meaning of the terms.

Analyze Information

Because light reflecting from the snorkeler is refracted as it leaves the water, the snorkeler would appear to be to the left of his actual position.

Assess Performance

Students' drawings should show a concave mirror that reflects the light from the flashlight's bulb into a beam.

Problem Solving

1. Students should show how electricity from the flashlight battery flows through a copper wire to a filament inside the light bulb. As the electricity heats the filament, the filament begins to glow, producing light.

2. The wavelength of red light is longer that of violet light. Drawings should indicate this difference by showing the peaks and troughs of the violet wave as closer together those of the red wave.

3. Students' diagrams should be similar to those on pp. F24 and F25, showing that light waves continue to travel in a straight line even after they enter a different material.

 Use *Science Notebook* pp. 295–296.

BUILD YOUR PORTFOLIO

Students' drawings might include microwave ovens, X-ray machines, heat lamps, devices operated by solar energy, or radio waves.

Chapter Test pp. 137–138 in the Assessment Guide

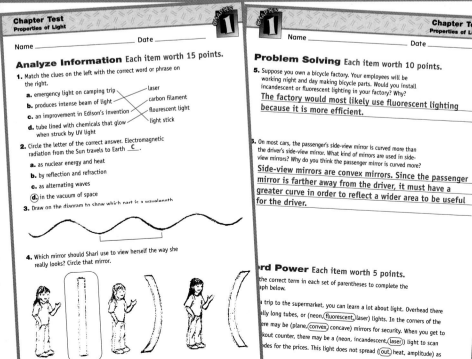

Chapter Test
Properties of Light

Name _____ Date _____

Analyze Information Each item worth 15 points.

1. Match the clues on the left with the correct word or phrase on the right.

a. emergency light on camping trip — laser
b. produces intense beam of light — carbon filament
c. an improvement in Edison's invention — flourescent light
d. tube lined with chemicals that glow when struck by UV light — light stick

2. Circle the letter of the correct answer. Electromagnetic radiation from the Sun travels to Earth __C__.
   a. as nuclear energy and heat
   b. by reflection and refraction
   c. as alternating waves
   d. in the vacuum of space

3. Draw on the diagram to show which part is a wavelength

4. Which mirror should Shari use to view herself the way she really looks? Circle that mirror.

Problem Solving Each item worth 10 points.

5. Suppose you own a bicycle factory. Your employees will be working night and day making bicycle parts. Would you install incandescent or fluorescent lighting in your factory? Why?
The factory would most likely use fluorescent lighting because it is more efficient.

6. On most cars, the passenger's side-view mirror is curved more than the driver's side-view mirror. What kind of mirrors are used in side-view mirrors? Why do you think the passenger mirror is curved more?
Side-view mirrors are convex mirrors. Since the passenger mirror is farther away from the driver, it must have a greater curve in order to reflect a wider area to be useful for the driver.

Word Power Each item worth 5 points.

the correct term in each set of parentheses to complete the ...graph below.

... a trip to the supermarket, you can learn a lot about light. Overhead there ...lly long tubes, or (neon, (fluorescent,) laser) lights. In the corners of the ...ere may be (plane, (convex,) concave) mirrors for security. When you get to ...kout counter, there may be a (neon, incandescent, (laser)) light to scan ...des for the prices. This light does not spread ((out,) heat, amplitude) as

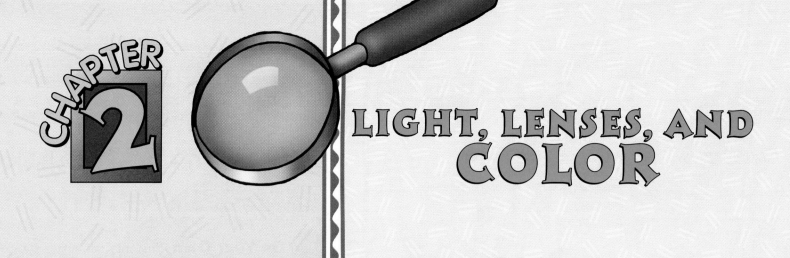

CHAPTER 2
LIGHT, LENSES, AND COLOR

Subconcepts	Activities	Materials

Investigation 1 How Do Lenses Help Control Light?

Lenses are used to change the direction of light, and are used in cameras and for correcting vision.

Suggested Pacing: 2–3 class periods

Standards
  p. 155

Benchmarks
  p. 45

Becoming Focused, p. F30
Science Processes: observe; infer; collect, record, and interpret data; identify and control variables

lens paper*, convex lens*, manila folder, flashlight*, D-cell batteries*, metric ruler*, newspaper, concave lens*, *Science Notebook* p. 300

Investigation 2 How Are Lenses Used in Telescopes and Microscopes?

In telescopes, lenses and sometimes mirrors enlarge and clarify the appearance of distant objects; in microscopes, lenses enlarge and clarify tiny objects or very thin slices of larger objects.

Suggested Pacing: 2–3 class periods

Standards
  p. 155

Benchmarks
  p. 45

Telescopic View, p. F36
Science Processes: observe, infer, make and use models

scissors, cardboard tubes*, metric ruler*, tape, convex lens *A**—15-cm focal length, convex lens *B**—5-cm focal length, modeling clay*, *Science Notebook* p. 304

Investigation 3 How Are Light and Color Related?

The color of an object depends on the colors of light absorbed and the colors of light reflected.

Suggested Pacing: 2–3 class periods

Standards
  p. 155

Circles of Light, p. F44
Science Processes: observe; predict; collect, record, and interpret data

Filtered Light, p. F46
Science Processes: observe; predict; collect, record, and interpret data; make hypotheses

flashlights*, D-cell batteries*, rubber bands*, cellophane* (red, blue, and green), *Science Notebook* pp. 306–307

assorted small objects of different colors (including a black object and a white object), cellophane* (red, green, and blue) for filters, *Science Notebook* pp. 308–309

Overview

In this chapter students investigate how lenses redirect light, explore the use of lenses in telescopes and microscopes, and probe the relationship between light and color.

Chapter Concept

Lenses, which change the direction of light, have many uses; the color of objects depends on how they absorb and reflect light.

Advance Preparation	Curriculum Connection	Assessment
Becoming Focused None	Integrating the Sciences TG p. F32 Math TG p. F33	**Chapter 2 Baseline Assessment:** *Science Notebook* pp. 297–298 **Investigation 1 Baseline Assessment:** TG p. F30 **Investigation 1 Review:** AG p. 139 **Think It/Write It,** p. F35; *Science Notebook* p. 303 **Following Up on Baseline Assessment:** TG p. F35 **Performance:** TG p. F35
Telescopic View Have students bring in cardboard tubes from rolls of paper towels.	Literature TG p. F38 Language Arts TG p. F39 Math TG p. F40 Science, Technology, & Society TG p. F41 Cultural Connection TG p. F42	**Investigation 2 Baseline Assessment:** TG p. F36 **Investigation 2 Review:** AG p. 140 **Think It/Write It,** p. F43; *Science Notebook* p. 305 **Following Up on Baseline Assessment:** TG p. F43 **Portfolio:** TG p. F43
Circles of Light Gather enough sheets of red, blue, and green cellophane for each group. Colored glass filters may be substituted for the cellophane. **Filtered Light** None	Language Arts TG p. F47 The Arts TG p. F48 Cultural Connection TG p. F49	**Investigation 3 Baseline Assessment:** TG p. F44 **Investigation 3 Review:** AG p. 141 **Think It/Write It,** p. F50; *Science Notebook* p. 310 **Following Up on Baseline Assessment:** TG p. F50 **Performance:** TG p. F50 **Chapter 2 Summative Assessment:** Reflect and Evaluate, p. F51 Chapter 2 Review/Test: AG pp. 142–143 *Science Notebook* pp. 311–312

TG= Teaching Guide   TRB= Teacher Resource Book   AG= Assessment Guide   *Materials in the Deluxe Equipment Kit

Chapter Overview

Chapter Concept Lenses, which change the direction of light, have many uses; the color of objects depends on how they absorb and reflect light.

Theme: Models

The wave model of light can be used to understand the phenomenon of color.

Common Misconceptions

Some students are likely to suggest that an object's color is the color of light it absorbs; this interpretation is based on the misconception that the eye somehow "sees out" to the object, rather than the fact that reflected light from the object travels to the eye.

Options for
Setting the Stage

Warm-Up Activity

Give all students a small piece of plastic wrap (about 5 cm, or 2 in square). Have them place the plastic wrap over the print on a book page. Ask if the plastic affects the appearance of the print. Have them place one large drop of water on the plastic wrap, slowly lift the plastic wrap, and observe what happens to the appearance of the type. The water drop acts as a lens.

Use *Science Notebook* pp. 297–298.

Discussion Starter:
A Young Astronomer

Use the text and photo to start a discussion about how astronomers use light and lenses.

- **Why can you see stars in the night sky?** Stars give off light that can be seen by the human eye.

- **How do astronomers use information carried by light?** Astronomers use telescopes to focus light from stars and planets to learn about them.

- **Career:** Astronomer

Astronomers study objects and phenomena beyond Earth's atmosphere. They apply knowledge of physics and mathematics and use instruments, including telescopes, to learn more about the universe.

LIGHT, LENSES, AND COLOR

Scientists seek to understand our planet, our solar system, and even the universe. This often involves getting the best possible view of things. Telescopes extend our vision to the galaxies. Microscopes help us see the tiny, complex world that is invisible to our unaided eyes. How is it possible for us to see so far and so much?

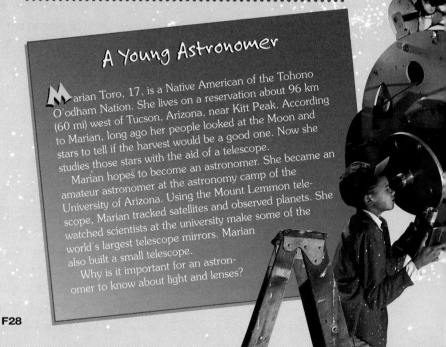

A Young Astronomer

Marian Toro, 17, is a Native American of the Tohono O'odham Nation. She lives on a reservation about 96 km (60 mi) west of Tucson, Arizona, near Kitt Peak. According to Marian, long ago her people looked at the Moon and stars to tell if the harvest would be a good one. Now she studies those stars with the aid of a telescope.

Marian hopes to become an astronomer. She became an amateur astronomer at the astronomy camp of the University of Arizona. Using the Mount Lemmon telescope, Marian tracked satellites and observed planets. She watched scientists at the university make some of the world's largest telescope mirrors. Marian also built a small telescope.

Why is it important for an astronomer to know about light and lenses?

F28

Home-School Connection

The Explore at Home activity "Over the Rainbow" helps students observe that white light is made up of many colors. Distribute the activity (TRB p. 29) when students have completed the chapter. Discuss what causes rainbows to appear in the sky and around waterfalls and sprinklers.

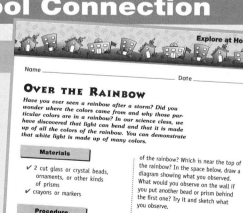

Explore at Home

Name _____ Date _____

OVER THE RAINBOW

Have you ever seen a rainbow after a storm? Did you wonder where the colors came from and why those particular colors are in a rainbow? In our science class, we have discovered that light can bend and that it is made up of all the colors of the rainbow. You can demonstrate that white light is made up of many colors.

Materials

✔ 2 cut glass or crystal beads, ornaments, or other kinds of prisms
✔ crayons or markers

Procedure

Hold the bead by a window in direct sunlight. Look for tiny rainbows on the walls around you. How many colors can you see? Which color is at the bottom part

of the rainbow? Which is near the top of the rainbow? In the space below, draw a diagram showing what you observed. What would you observe on the wall if you put another bead or prism behind the first one? Try it and sketch what you observe.

Results

The light bent as it passed through the prism and separated into various colors. Add the colors you saw to your drawings.

Data Table	
One prism	Two prisms

◀ A student observes the stars through the Mount Lemmon telescope.

F29

Technology Alert

CD-ROM

Meet The Waves! and **Mixing Colors** Enhance or replace Investigation 3

You can use the Scene Opener, **Meet The Waves!**, as a supplement to Chapter 2. In these activities, students observe that sound and light are produced by waves.

In **Mixing Colors** students become lighting designers and learn how to combine the three primary colors of light (red, green, and blue) to achieve different lighting effects on stage. First, they predict in the Writer the different colors they expect to achieve. They "click" on buttons for each combination of lights to determine which two primary colors of light mix together to produce a secondary color. The video features an interview with a lighting designer.

Chapter Road Map

*Pressed for Time?

As you work through the upcoming investigations, focus on the activities and resources identified by the clock.

Look for this symbol in front of questions that help develop Scientific Reasoning Skills.

HOW DO LENSES HELP CONTROL LIGHT?

Planner

Subconcept Lenses are used to change the direction of light, and are used in cameras and for correcting vision.

Objectives

- **Observe** light passing through a lens.
- **Experiment** and **hypothesize** about how convex and concave lenses are different.

Pacing 2–3 class periods

Science Terms lens, convex lens, focal point, concave lens, retina, contact lenses

Activate Prior Knowledge

Baseline Assessment **How will my eye look to you if I hold a magnifying glass up in front of it?** List students' predictions and save them for use later in Following Up.

Activity Becoming Focused

Preview *Students focus on how lenses affect light and should find that the size and position of images produced by convex lenses vary according to the distance of the object from the lens. Concave lenses always form images that are upright and reduced in size. Convex lenses focus light to a point. Concave lenses cause light rays to spread apart.*

1. Get Ready

Time about 30 minutes

Grouping groups of 4–6

HOW DO LENSES HELP CONTROL LIGHT?

Do you know someone who wears contact lenses? A contact lens changes the direction of light passing through it. This investigation should help you understand how lenses help a person see more clearly.

Activity
Becoming Focused

You've seen that as light passes from one material to another it can change direction. When a material such as glass is shaped into a lens, it directs—or redirects—the path of light. Explore how lens shape affects the way light passes into and out of the lens.

MATERIALS
- lens paper
- convex lens
- manila folder
- flashlight
- metric ruler
- newspaper
- concave lens
- *Science Notebook*

SAFETY /////
Be careful when handling glass lenses.

Procedure

1. In your *Science Notebook* make a chart titled "Comparing Convex and Concave Lenses." **Record** all observations during this activity in the chart.

2. Take a piece of lens paper and feel the shape of the convex lens through it. **Make a sketch** of the lens.

3. Darken the room. Using a manila folder as a screen, place a flashlight about 30 cm from the screen. Point the flashlight toward the screen.

4. Place the convex lens between the flashlight and the screen so that the light passes through the lens and shines onto the screen.

Step 4

F30

Responding to Individual Needs

Students Acquiring English Provide students with materials for creating a diagram of the activity they have just done. The diagram should include both the convex and concave lenses, and a dotted line indicating the effect of each type of lens on light that passes through it. Students can explain what is happening in their diagrams with explanations in their native languages. They can then rewrite the explanations, perhaps in simpler form, in English.

 Have students use the CD-ROM Painter and Writer to draw and label their diagrams.

5. **Observe** what happens on the screen as you move the lens back and forth between the light and the screen. **Infer** how the lens is affecting the light. **Record** your inference.

6. Stand with your back toward a window. Hold the lens in one hand and extend your arm so that the light from the window passes through the lens.

7. Have a classmate hold the screen so that the light passing through the lens shines on the screen. Move the screen and lens as needed until a clear image appears on the screen. Look at the image carefully and **record** your observations.

8. Place the convex lens on the print on a piece of newspaper. Raise the lens slowly and **observe** the print. **Record** your observations.

9. Repeat steps 2–8, using a concave lens. In the chart, **record** your observations about the concave lens.

Analyze and Conclude

1. In step 5, how did the appearance of the beam of light on the screen change for each lens?

2. Describe the image you saw on the screen as you moved each lens back and forth in step 7. What was unusual about the image?

3. How does a convex lens affect light when it focuses light to a point? How do convex and concave lenses differ in the way they affect light?

UNIT PROJECT LINK

Your group is going to put on a puppet show, using different colored lights to produce special visual effects. Cover a flashlight with cellophane of different colors. Experiment with blue, red, and green, in turn. Create situations to act out, using your puppets. Decide which colors of light to use to create the right emotion for each situation. Then give your show.

F31

Investigate Further

Unit Project Link

Students will find that light can greatly affect the mood of the stage set they construct. Bright yellow lighting (produced by using red and green cellophane) could simulate the outdoors on a summer day. Blue lighting could be used to simulate night or a dark room. Encourage students to brainstorm ideas on creating special lighting effects and to record their ideas in their *Science Notebook* on p. 301. Then use Unit Project Master F2 (TRB p. 100) to help students learn how to write a script for their show. You may wish to have students use the Activity Support Master "Compare-Contrast Diagram" (TRB p. 68) to compare concave and convex lenses.

 Collaborative Strategy One group member might record data while other students handle the lenses and flashlights.

Materials Hints Each group should have at least one concave lens and one convex lens.

Safety Review safety precautions with students. Be careful when handling glass lenses. Remind students not to look directly at sunlight through the lenses.

2. Guide the Procedure

- Carry out the activity in a room with windows that receive direct sunlight.

 Have students record and chart their data and answer questions on *Science Notebook,* p. 300.

 Have students use the CD-ROM Painter to illustrate how lenses function.

3. Assess Performance

Process Skills Checklist

- Did students accurately **collect** and **record data** on the effects of light passing through the lenses?
- Were students able to **infer** the difference between concave and convex lenses?

Analyze and Conclude

1. Students should observe that with a convex lens the beam of light becomes focused to a small point and then becomes unfocused as the lens is moved back and forth. The concave lens spreads the light out.

2. When the convex lens is used, the image formed on the screen is upside down and small. When the concave lens is used, there is no image formed on the screen.

3. The convex lens is causing the light rays to bend together and meet at a point. Students should conclude that convex lenses bend light rays inward, or focus light, while concave lenses bend light rays outward, or cause them to diverge.

You may wish to have students use the Activity Support Master "Compare-Contrast Diagram" (TRB p. 68) to compare concave and convex lenses.

Light and Lenses

 RESOURCE

Light and Lenses

Preview *Students focus on how light is affected when it passes through concave and convex lenses.*

1. Get Ready

Science Terms lens, convex lens, focal point, concave lens, retina, contact lenses

Background

- People have been wearing glasses—or corrective lenses—since the 1200s. Marco Polo reported people wearing glasses in China in about 1275. The demand for reading glasses increased dramatically after printed books became available in the late 1400s. In the 1500s people began wearing glasses to improve distance vision.

Discussion Starter

- **What do you think it must have been like for the first person who ever looked through a magnifying lens?** Encourage students to speculate about what a surprise it must have been for this individual to see something suddenly appear much larger.

- 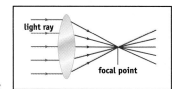 **How might this person have gone about finding out why the lens made objects look larger?** Students might speculate that conducting experiments like the one they have just done would be a good way to begin to learn about why a lens magnifies, and how light acts when it passes through a lens.

2. Guide the Discussion

Choose from the following strategies to facilitate discussion.

Making Comparisons

- **How are convex and concave lenses alike? How are they different?** Both lenses have curved surfaces and bend light. Both can produce images that are right side up. Convex lenses turn images upside down if the lens is far from the object. Convex lenses make an object viewed closely appear larger.

How Lenses Bend Light

You've probably had fun playing with a hand lens. Held close to an object, a hand lens lets you see details you didn't know were there. Held at arm's length, it shows a world turned upside down! What "magic" is at work here?

Actually, you already know something about this "magic." When light passes from one transparent material into another, the light bends, or changes direction. A **lens** is a transparent object with at least one curved surface. Lenses come in a variety of shapes, but all types refract light that passes through them.

Lens Shape

A lens that is thicker in the center than it is at the edges is called a **convex lens**. Such a lens brings parallel light rays together at a point known as the **focal point**. The thicker the lens, the more it bends light. So the thicker the lens, the closer the focal point is to the lens.

As you saw in the activity on lenses on pages F30 and F31, when you hold an object near a convex lens and look through the lens, you'll see a right-side-up image that is larger than the object. This is how hand lenses work. It's refraction, not magic, that produces a larger image. If a convex lens isn't very close to an object, the image that forms is small; it's also upside down!

A lens that is thicker at the edges than at its middle is called a **concave lens**. A concave lens causes parallel light rays to spread apart. The image of an object viewed through a concave lens is smaller than the object but the image formed is always right side up.

The Eye and a Camera

Both the human eye and a camera contain convex lenses. An important difference between your eyes and a camera is that a camera takes only one picture at a time. But your eyes are constantly "taking pictures." The lens of your eye focuses an image on the **retina** (ret'n ə). The retina is the light-sensitive layer at the back of the eye.

A convex lens brings light rays together at a focal point (*left*); a concave lens causes light rays to spread apart (*right*).

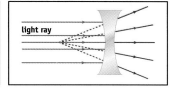

F32

Investigate Further

Integrating the Sciences

LIFE SCIENCE

What to Do Discuss the practical benefits the science of light and lenses (optics) has produced for ordinary people. Before corrective lenses existed, millions of people lived out their lives virtually blind. The impact of poor sight on both individual lives and society, both in the past and present, is significant. Survey the number of students in the class who wear some sort of corrective lenses.

What's the Result? What kinds of problems would people have if glasses or contact lenses weren't available? Responses might include such things as not being able to see the chalkboard in class, not being able to read a book, or not being able to drive.

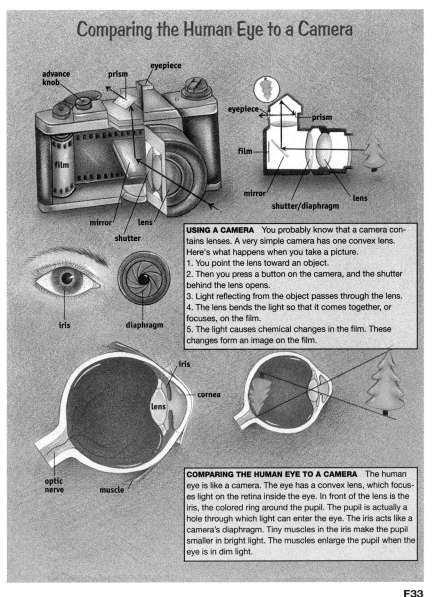

Comparing the Human Eye to a Camera

advance knob · prism · eyepiece · film · mirror · lens · shutter · iris · diaphragm

eyepiece · prism · film · mirror · shutter/diaphragm · lens

iris · cornea · lens · optic nerve · muscle

USING A CAMERA You probably know that a camera contains lenses. A very simple camera has one convex lens. Here's what happens when you take a picture.
1. You point the lens toward an object.
2. Then you press a button on the camera, and the shutter behind the lens opens.
3. Light reflecting from the object passes through the lens.
4. The lens bends the light so that it comes together, or focuses, on the film.
5. The light causes chemical changes in the film. These changes form an image on the film.

COMPARING THE HUMAN EYE TO A CAMERA The human eye is like a camera. The eye has a convex lens, which focuses light on the retina inside the eye. In front of the lens is the iris, the colored ring around the pupil. The pupil is actually a hole through which light can enter the eye. The iris acts like a camera's diaphragm. Tiny muscles in the iris make the pupil smaller in bright light. The muscles enlarge the pupil when the eye is in dim light.

F33

Integrating the Curriculum

Science & Math

GRAPHING **What to Do** To get an idea of how much lenses affect everyday life, have students gather data on corrective lenses. They should ask, "Do you wear some sort of corrective lenses? If so, are they contact lenses or glasses?"
What's the Result? Students can make a bar graph of their findings
Have students use the CD-ROM Grapher to prepare their graphs.

Multi-Age Classroom Groups can analyze data by adding up the total number who wear glasses and the number who wear contact lenses. List the data collected for each class on the chalkboard and have students make bar graphs.

Connecting to the Activities

- **Becoming Focused, pp. F30–F31**
Think back to Becoming Focused. **What effect did you create in the activity for which you would use the term focal point?** Students should infer that focal point refers to the spot where the light passing through the lens becomes concentrated into a dot.

Making Inferences

What might happen if a lens were not perfectly smooth? How would the effect of a lens on light change? Encourage students to conclude that if a lens were imperfect, it might not be possible to focus light because the lens would not bend all light rays to a point.

Making Comparisons

- **How is the operation of a camera like that of an eye? How is it different?** Encourage students to notice that both the camera and the eye use lenses to focus light and they both form images. A camera lens, however, moves in and out to change its focus, while the lens in the human eye changes its shape.

You may wish to have students use the Activity Support Master "Compare-Contrast Diagram" (TRB p. 68) to compare and contrast a camera and the human eye.

Responding to Individual Needs

Students Acquiring English Students can choose key terms in this resource and write them in English and their native languages.

Thinking Critically

- **In what way is an eye more like a movie camera than a still camera?** Students should suggest that because an eye is constantly forming images and processing them, it is more like a movie camera than a still camera, which records a single image.

Making Inferences

Sometimes cameras are equipped with telephoto lenses. What do you think a telephoto lens might do? What makes you think so? Students should infer that a telephoto lens combines the features of a telescope and a regular camera lens, allowing for close-up shots of distant objects.

Thinking About the Data

- **What type of corrective lens would you need if you were nearsighted? What type would help farsightedness?** Students should note that a nearsighted person would use concave lenses, while a farsighted person would use convex lenses.

Making Comparisons

- **Why can contact lenses be so much smaller than regular corrective lenses?** Responses should indicate that because the contact lens is so much closer to the eye, the light does not need to be bent as much to make the correction.

3. Assess Understanding

Students can work in groups of three or four. Half the groups can work together to create a drawing or diagram of a camera, with labels indicating its basic parts. The other groups can make the same type of diagram of the human eye. Then have "camera" and "eye" groups link up, put their diagrams together, and connect with pieces of colored yarn the labeled parts of cameras and eyes that have similar functions.

It sends nerve impulses to the brain along the optic nerve. The brain then interprets the pictures and figures out what you're seeing.

Another difference between your eyes and a camera is in how the eyes focus. You can focus on objects that are close to you and on objects that are far away, but the eye's lens can't move in and out the way a camera lens does. Instead, the lens of the eye changes shape. When you look at something nearby, muscles in the eye pull on the edges of the lens and make it thinner. When you look at something far away, the muscles relax, and the lens gets thicker again.

Correcting Vision

Many people wear glasses. Nearsighted people see nearby things clearly, but cannot see distant objects clearly. As the drawings below show, the eyes of a nearsighted person focus images in front of the retina. Glasses with concave lenses correct such a condition by spreading out the light rays before they enter the eye. The eye's lens then focuses the light rays on the retina.

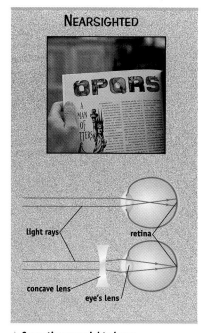

▲ Correcting nearsightedness

▲ Correcting farsightedness

Investigate Further

Experiment

Students should note that in bright light the iris contracts, while in dimmer light it opens wide. Challenge the students to think of various conditions under which they can repeat their experiment. They might see if the iris of a person wearing glasses or contact lenses reacts any differently to dim and bright light. They might see how the eye reacts after sunglasses are removed. Have the students record their observations of all similarities and differences as they experiment with the behavior of the iris. They should record their observations in their *Science Notebooks* on p. 302.

People who are farsighted see far-away objects clearly, but they have trouble seeing nearby things. This condition is corrected with convex lenses, which bring the light rays closer together before they enter the eye. The lens of the eye then properly focuses the light rays on the retina.

Contact Lenses

Many people wear contact lenses instead of eyeglasses. **Contact lenses** are clear, thin lenses that are placed on the eye in front of the cornea. Contact lenses don't contact, or touch, the eye. They stick to a thin layer of tears that covers the cornea.

Like eyeglasses, contact lenses change the path of light. But with contact lenses, concave lenses are used for both nearsighted and farsighted people. Because contact lenses are so close to the eye, they don't need to be thick to bend the light enough to correct a person's vision.

The earliest contact lenses were made of rigid plastic and were often uncomfortable. In 1965, soft contact lenses were invented. These lenses are flexible and more comfortable than the older lenses. Most soft contact lenses must be

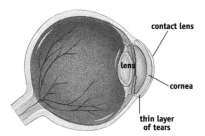

▲ A contact lens floating on a layer of tears

removed and cleaned each day. The removal also allows oxygen to reach the living tissue of the cornea. Some soft contact lenses let oxygen pass through, so they can be worn for many days at a time. When they are taken out, they also must be carefully cleaned. ■

INVESTIGATE FURTHER!

EXPERIMENT

To see how the iris responds to the brightness of light, work with a partner. Take turns observing each other's eyes in dim light. Then turn on bright lights or move toward a sunny window. Observe the pupils of your partner's eyes. How did the pupils look in dim light? How did they change in bright light?

INVESTIGATION 1

1. A convex lens projects an image that is upside down. If the image on your retina is upside down, why doesn't the world look upside down to you?

2. Compare and contrast the way light is changed as it moves through convex and concave lenses.

F35

Critical Thinking Skills
Generating Ideas, Analyzing

1. Students should hypothesize that the brain adjusts the image so that we perceive it right side up.

2. Answers should include the observation that convex lenses tend to focus light while concave lenses tend to spread out light.

Challenge To explore in more depth how contact lenses function, suggest that students write letters requesting free pamphlets or other printed information on contact lenses from local optometrists, ophthalmologists, or manufacturers of lenses. Remind them to ask specifically for graphic materials that illustrate how different kinds of contact lenses work. Students can use the information they obtain to create their own detailed illustrations. Students can work in groups to write their letters.

Following Up

Baseline Assessment Return to the list of students' responses about how the magnifying glass will make your eye look and why it appears that way. Have students modify their responses, if necessary, based on what they have learned in the investigation.

Reteaching Discuss the investigation subconcept with students. On the board write any remaining questions students still have about how lenses work. Then have volunteers who have grasped the concept attempt to answer the questions for those who have not yet fully understood it.

Use *Science Notebook* p. 303.

◄ **Investigation Review**
Use Investigation Review p. 139 in the *Assessment Guide*.

Assessment

Portfolio

Make a Word Web Challenge students to create a word web that illustrates everything they have learned about lenses and how they affect light. Suggest that an eye or camera might make an excellent starting point. Encourage students to include in their word webs the terms they have learned, followed by brief descriptions of the function related to each term.

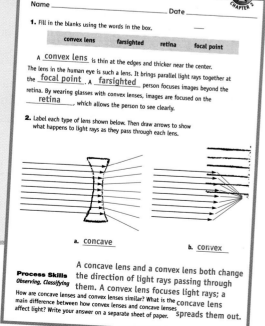

Investigation Review
How Do Lenses Help Control Light?

Name _____
Date _____

1. Fill in the blanks using the words in the box.

| convex lens | farsighted | retina | focal point |

A ___convex lens___ is thin at the edges and thicker near the center. The lens in the human eye is such a lens. It brings parallel light rays together at the ___focal point___. A ___farsighted___ person focuses images beyond the retina. By wearing glasses with convex lenses, images are focused on the ___retina___, which allows the person to see clearly.

2. Label each type of lens shown below. Then draw arrows to show what happens to light rays as they pass through each lens.

a. ___concave___   b. ___convex___

Process Skills
Observing, Classifying

How are concave lenses and convex lenses similar? What is the main difference between how convex lenses and concave lenses affect light? Write your answer on a separate sheet of paper.

A concave lens and a convex lens both change the direction of light rays passing through them. A convex lens focuses light rays; a concave lens spreads them out.

HOW ARE LENSES USED IN TELESCOPES AND MICROSCOPES?

Planner

Subconcept Telescopes, lenses, or sometimes mirrors, enlarge and clarify the appearance of distant objects; in microscopes, lenses enlarge and clarify tiny objects or very thin slices of larger objects.

Objectives

- **Observe** how telescopes and microscopes work.
- **Evaluate** how we use telescopes and microscopes.

Pacing 2–3 class periods

Science Terms refracting telescope, reflecting telescope, simple microscope, compound microscope, electron microscope

Activate Prior Knowledge

Baseline Assessment Ask: **What kind of lens would you use to build a telescope?** Save the answers for Following Up.

Activity Telescopic View

Preview *Students focus on how lenses affect light. They should observe that a telescope makes distant objects appear larger and more distinct.*

1. Get Ready

Time about 45 minutes

Grouping groups of 4–6

Collaborative Strategy Group members should take turns using the telescope and then comparing their findings with one another.

INVESTIGATION 2 — HOW ARE LENSES USED IN TELESCOPES AND MICROSCOPES?

Lenses can be used to show us things too small or too far away to be seen with our unaided eyes. Much of what we know about life on Earth and objects in space is a result of combining lenses and mirrors.

Activity
Telescopic View

Back in the early 1600s, lens makers in Europe began experimenting with lenses. Before long, several lens makers had placed two lenses of different sizes in a tube, forming a telescope. You can build a telescope very much like the ones built hundreds of years ago.

MATERIALS
- scissors
- cardboard tubes
- metric ruler
- tape
- convex lens A, 15 cm focal length
- convex lens B, 5 cm focal length
- modeling clay
- *Science Notebook*

SAFETY
NEVER LOOK DIRECTLY AT THE SUN! Be careful when handling glass lenses.

Procedure

1. Use scissors to cut a cardboard tube into two pieces: one piece 12 cm long, the other piece 15 cm long.

2. In the shorter tube, make a lengthwise cut as shown. Turn the cut edges inward, forming a slightly tapered tube. Tape the cut edges as shown in the drawing on page F37.

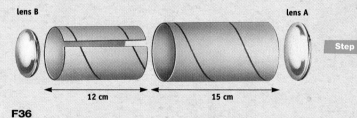

lens B   lens A

Step 2

|← 12 cm →| |← 15 cm →|

F36

Responding to Individual Needs

Kinesthetic Activity Help students act out how a telescope works. Clear a space large enough for several students to move around in. Have one student represent the eyepiece lens, and another the objective lens. Tell the remaining students that they will represent the object being viewed. At first, there should be only two or three students standing directly in line with the two "lenses." Instruct the student representing the objective lens to move closer to the object being viewed. For every step he or she takes, two more students should join the "object," thus making it "larger." Let the objective lens student try moving back and forth, as the class did with the telescope in the activity. As the "objective lens" moves back a step, two students should leave the group.

3. Use modeling clay and tape to attach lens A to one end of the longer tube. Use more clay to attach lens B to one end of the shorter tube.

4. Place the open end of the shorter tube into the open end of the longer tube. You have just made a simple telescope!

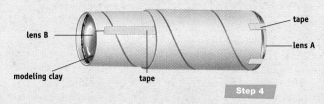

lens B
tape
lens A
modeling clay
tape

Step 4

5. Hold the telescope up to your eye and look through the lens that is in the shorter tube.

6. Use the telescope to **observe** various objects outdoors.

7. Move the shorter tube back and forth inside the longer tube until the image of the object you are observing is clear.

Analyze and Conclude

1. Describe in your *Science Notebook* how the objects you observed looked when viewed through your telescope.

2. Make sketches of how several objects look when viewed directly and when viewed through a telescope.

INVESTIGATE FURTHER!

EXPERIMENT

Look in your daily newspaper to find out which planets are visible at this time. Then use your telescope to observe the Moon and these planets.

F37

Safety Review safety precautions with students. Never look directly at the Sun. Be careful when handling glass lenses.

2. Guide the Procedure

- For best results, conduct the activity in a room with windows that receive direct sunlight.

 Have students record their data and answer questions on *Science Notebook,* p. 304.

 You may wish to have students use the CD-ROM Painter to create a diagram of the telescope they have constructed.

3. Assess Performance

Process Skills Checklist
- Did students follow directions to **make** and **use a model** of the telescope.
- Did students **infer** how the telescope works?

Analyze and Conclude
1. Students should say that objects appear larger and upside down when viewed through the telescope.

2. Students' drawings should show the objects larger, but inverted, when viewed through the telescope. When seen directly, the objects are smaller and right side up.

Investigate Further

Experiment

Make students aware that while their telescopes do not have nearly the power of standard models, they are still real telescopes and should provide noticeable magnification of what they see in the night sky. Students should be able to detect details in the lunar surface that they cannot see with the unaided eye. They should also notice increased brightness from planets they locate with the field guide. Remind students to record their observations in their *Science Notebooks* p. 304.

 Have students research the moon and planets using the Astronomical Bodies Data Pack on the CD-ROM.

The Telescope — From Galileo to Hubble

Preview *Students focus on when telescopes were invented and on the differences in types of telescopes.*

1. Get Ready

Science Terms
refracting telescope, reflecting telescope

Background

- The large telescopes currently used by astronomers are installed in special structures called observatories. These are often located at high altitudes to eliminate distortion of atmospheric haze and city lights. Also, to reduce movement, observatories are often built on bedrock. The world's largest reflecting telescope, with a mirror 600 cm (236 in.) in diameter, is located in Zelenchukskaya, Russia. The Yerkes Observatory in Williams Bay, Wisconsin, has the world's largest refracting telescope, with a lens 102 cm (40 in.) in diameter.

Discussion Starter

- **Why do you think the inventors of telescopes used them as they did?** Students may speculate that, because the inventors were often lens grinders with an interest in the natural world, their purpose in developing these devices was to investigate their surroundings.

- **How might powerful space telescopes like the Hubble tell us about our past? Why is this important?** Students might realize that by looking deep into the universe, space telescopes can pick up clues about how galaxies formed and can even witness such events as the collapse of distant stars. This information helps scientists understand the nature of the universe and our place in it.

The Telescope— From Galileo to Hubble

No one knows for certain who made the first telescope. Evidence suggests that it was probably constructed in Holland in the early 1600s.

Galileo (gal ə lē'ō) Galilei was the first person to use a telescope to study the sky. An Italian scientist who lived from 1554 to 1642, Galileo built his first telescope in 1609. He had been studying the stars and planets for many years and was eager to get a better look. Galileo's telescope magnified by 32

times what he saw. But with the telescope he was able to see mountains and craters on the Moon. When he studied the planet Jupiter through his telescope, he discovered four of its moons.

Galileo's telescope was a **refracting telescope**. As the name suggests, this telescope used lenses that refracted light to make an image. The drawing on the next page shows a refracting telescope that uses two lenses. Light from a faraway object first passes through the objective lens, or lens

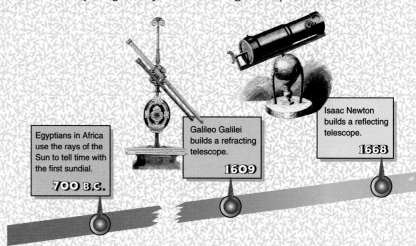

Egyptians in Africa use the rays of the Sun to tell time with the first sundial.
700 B.C.

Galileo Galilei builds a refracting telescope.
1609

Isaac Newton builds a reflecting telescope.
1668

F38

Integrating the Curriculum

Science & Literature

A BIOGRAPHY

What to Do Have interested students read *Rooftop Astronomer: A Story About Maria Mitchell* by Stephanie Sammartino McPherson, a biography of the first woman astronomer in the United States. Encourage groups of students to discuss her life, especially her use of telescopes.

What's the Result? How did Maria Mitchell become an astronomer? She read books on math and science while working as a librarian. **What was her first discovery? How did she make it?** In 1847, while helping her father survey the sky, she discovered a comet. **What kinds of things did she study?** sunspots, comets, double stars, solar eclipses, and the moons of Saturn and Jupiter.

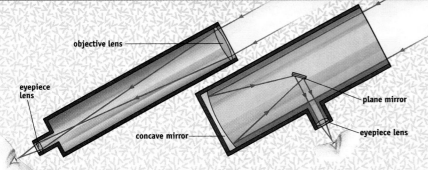

objective lens

eyepiece lens

concave mirror

plane mirror

eyepiece lens

▲ A simple refracting telescope

▲ A simple reflecting telescope

closer to the object, forming a very small image. Then the eyepiece, or lens nearest the eye, magnifies the first image.

In 1668, Isaac Newton made a reflecting telescope, using a concave mirror. In a **reflecting telescope**, light strikes a mirror and is reflected to a focal point, where an image forms. A small flat mirror is used to reflect this image to a lens that magnifies the image.

The mirror in Newton's telescope had a diameter of only about 3 cm

(1.2 in.). A larger mirror can focus on smaller or more distant objects. The reflecting telescopes used by modern astronomers are much larger than Newton's.

The Hubble Space Telescope, also a reflecting telescope, is in orbit above Earth's atmosphere. The advantage of having a telescope in orbit is that the light from distant objects is not changed by passing through air. The Hubble Space Telescope was named in honor of Edwin P. Hubble. ■

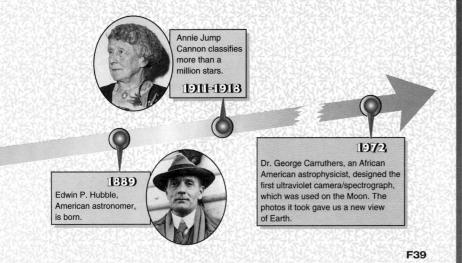

Annie Jump Cannon classifies more than a million stars.
1911-1918

1889
Edwin P. Hubble, American astronomer, is born.

1972
Dr. George Carruthers, an African American astrophysicist, designed the first ultraviolet camera/spectrograph, which was used on the Moon. The photos it took gave us a new view of Earth.

F39

Science & Language Arts

WORD ORIGINS **What to Do** Students may enjoy working in small groups and finding out the origins of the new words they are learning. Suggest that each group create a chart with the science terms from this investigation. For each word, ask students to include on their charts its pronunciation, origin, and dictionary meaning.

What's the Result? From what languages do most of the words originally come? Answers will vary, but many scientific terms have their origins in Latin and Greek.

Have students use the CD-ROM Spreadsheet to prepare their chart.

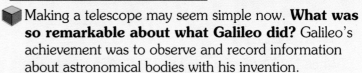

2. Guide the Discussion

Choose from the following strategies to facilitate discussion.

Connecting to the Activities
- ***Telescopic View, pp. F36–F37***
How is the telescope you made like Galileo's? Students should note that both telescopes are refracting telescopes, using two lenses together in a movable tube.

Making Judgments
Making a telescope may seem simple now. **What was so remarkable about what Galileo did?** Galileo's achievement was to observe and record information about astronomical bodies with his invention.

Making Comparisons
- **How were Galileo's and Newton's telescopes alike? How were they different?** While both telescopes performed the same function and had eyepiece lenses, Galileo's telescope was a refracting telescope and Newton's was a reflecting telescope.

Identifying and Solving Problems
- The mirror in Newton's telescope was only 3 cm in diameter. The largest telescope now has a mirror of 600 cm. **How many times larger is it in diameter?** Students should calculate that the telescope is 200 times larger in diameter.

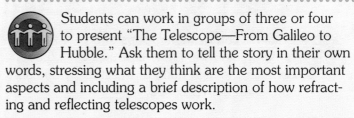 **Responding to Individual Needs**
Students Acquiring English Students can make and use flash cards that show difficult terms from the resource written in English on one side and in their native language on the other.

3. Assess Understanding

Students can work in groups of three or four to present "The Telescope—From Galileo to Hubble." Ask them to tell the story in their own words, stressing what they think are the most important aspects and including a brief description of how refracting and reflecting telescopes work.

Lyman Spitzer and His Magnificent Dream

Preview *Students focus on the development of the Hubble Space Telescope.*

1. Get Ready

Background

- When NASA was founded in 1958, America was involved in a fierce competition to be the first nation to send astronauts into space.

Discussion Starter

- **What are some ways that improved telescopes like the Hubble may change our future?** Students may speculate that one day advanced telescopes might tell us about life elsewhere in the universe, or help us to discover what has happened or will happen in our universe.

2. Guide the Discussion

Use the following strategy to facilitate discussion.

Connecting to the Activities

- **Telescopic View, pp. F36–F37**
  If you put the telescope you constructed into outer space, would it work any better? Students should infer that just as the Hubble Space Telescope has superior performance in the airless conditions of space, so would theirs.

3. Assess Understanding

Students can work in groups of 3 or 4 to collaborate on a drawing that illustrates what they consider the high point of the story of Lyman Spitzer and the Hubble telescope.

Lyman Spitzer and His Magnificent Dream

In 1946, Lyman Spitzer wrote that a telescope in space could provide the information needed to answer some very difficult questions: How big is the universe? What is the structure of galaxies? What is the nature of the planets?

In 1957 the Soviet Union launched the *Sputnik* satellite. The American space agency, the National Aeronautics and Space Administration (NASA), was started the following year. In the 1960s and 1970s, two observatories carrying telescopes were placed in orbit by NASA. The success of these telescopes in space showed that Spitzer's idea for a large space telescope could work.

▲ **Lyman Spitzer**

In 1977, NASA's space telescope project was approved. In 1990 the telescope, known to the world as the Hubble Space Telescope, was finally placed in orbit.

While it did give scientists some good information, the telescope had problems. The mirror had not been shaped correctly. During a space shuttle mission in December 1993, astronauts successfully repaired the telescope. Since that time, the telescope has taken photographs of Pluto and its moon. It has also found a black hole at the core of a galaxy.

Spitzer's dream has become a reality. The information needed to answer his questions is now being gathered. ■

▼ **The Hubble Space Telescope**

F40

Integrating the Curriculum

Science & Math

LARGE NUMBERS

What to Do The numbers used in astronomy are often so huge that they are difficult to fathom. To give students an idea of "billions," have them try to calculate in miles the distance light travels in a year. Explain that light travels at about 186,000 miles per second. With 60 seconds in a minute, 60 minutes in an hour, 24 hours in a day, and 365 days in a year, the product of all these multiplications will be the distance light travels in one year.

What's the Result? How far does light travel in one year? About 6 trillion miles; explain that a jet flying at 500 miles per hour would have to remain airborne for about 1.3 million years to travel one light-year.

The Microscope

During the 1600s, grinding lenses was a popular hobby. Anton van Leeuwenhoek (än'tôn vän lā'vən-hōōk) was a Dutch cloth merchant and lens grinder. From one of the many lenses he ground, he made a **simple microscope**. The photo at right shows a model of this microscope, which had only one lens that was held between two metal plates. The object to be examined was stuck on the end of a pin placed beside the lens. A person using the microscope had to bring it up close to the eye. The lens could magnify objects more than 200 times their normal size.

With his microscope, Leeuwenhoek looked at insect parts, hair, ivory, and droplets of pond water. In the water, he found tiny organisms that could not be seen with only the human eye. He called these organisms *tierken*, which in Dutch means "little animals."

After Leeuwenhoek reported that he had found parasites on fleas, the English poet Jonathan Swift wrote:

So naturalists observe, a flea
Has smaller fleas that on him prey;
And these have smaller still
  to bite em;
And so proceed *ad infinitum*.

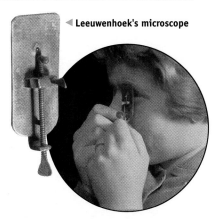

◄ **Leeuwenhoek's microscope**

What do you think he meant by these four lines of poetry?

A few years prior to Leeuwenhoek, Zacharias Janssen had invented a compound microscope. The **compound microscope** uses two convex lenses. A mirror reflects light toward an object that is on a clear glass slide. Light reflecting from the object enters the microscope tube containing the lenses. Light passing through the objective lens forms the first image. Light rays from this image pass through the eyepiece lens, which enlarges the image.

Robert Hooke, an English scientist, studied many objects through a compound microscope that he built. In

F41

Investigate Further

 ### Science, Technology & Society

SPACE TRAVEL **What to Do** Explain to students that NASA astronaut Franklin Chang-Diaz began his career in physics and mechanical engineering, working with special microscopes to work with atoms in atomic fusion. His first flight on the shuttle was in 1986, during which he conducted experiments in astrophysics and videotaped a shuttle tour in Spanish for broadcast in Latin America and the United States. Encourage students to write their ideas on the research shuttle astronauts may conduct in space and how they might use telescopes and microscopes. **What's the Result?** Invite students to share their ideas with the class.

How do you think the work the astronauts do might benefit people on Earth? Students may mention research that would help people understand Earth's environment and the origin of Earth.

The Microscope

Preview *Students focus on how microscopes were developed and what they are like today.*

1. Get Ready

Science Terms simple microscope, compound microscope, electron microscope

Background

• One of the great achievements of the early microscope inventors was their ability to produce careful illustrations of exactly what they saw through the lenses.

Discussion Starter

What are some ways the development of microscopes may have changed the way we live today? Using microscopes has enabled us to identify the causes of many diseases and thereby to save many lives. It has also given us an in-depth view of the fine structure of many of Earth's living things.

2. Guide the Discussion

Choose from the following strategies to facilitate discussion.

Connecting to the Activities

• *Telescopic View, pp. F36–F37*
What features are common to both the telescope you built and Janssen's compound microscope? Students should indicate that both used an objective lens and an eyepiece lens.

Responding to Individual Needs

Students Acquiring English Suggest that students make a drawing of a microscope and label the parts in their native language. Then have them work with an English-proficient partner to label the parts in English.

Making Comparisons

• **How are standard compound microscopes and electron microscopes alike? How are they different?** Both microscopes magnify an image, but one uses light while the other uses streams of electrons. You may wish to have students use the Activity Support Master "Compare-Contrast Diagram" (TRB p. 68) to compare standard compound microscopes and electron microscopes.

SCIENCE IN LITERATURE

Extremely Weird Micro Monsters
by Sarah Lovett

Students could present their favorite micro monster to the class, either through an oral presentation, a story, an audiotape, or a drawing.

Thinking Critically

Just as modern telescopes are hundreds of times more powerful than their predecessors, so too are electron microscopes vastly more powerful than Leeuwenhoek's and Janssen's. How might looking as deeply into the world of small things tell us as much about our origins as looking out to the edges of the universe? Investigating the structure of living things might give us clues to how life first began on Earth.

3. Assess Understanding

Students can work in small groups to draw a time line of microscope improvements. Time lines should depict the microscopes students read about in the resource. The main features of each microscope should be labeled. Students may need to tape several sheets of paper together to depict the whole time span, which should stretch from 1590 to the present.

1665, Hooke published a book, *Micrographia*, that contained his drawings of the things he had seen. One of the objects he had looked at was cork. Hooke noticed that the cork was made of tiny boxes. He called the boxes *cells*. The cells Hooke saw weren't living. What he saw were the outer parts of the cells that had once been alive.

The compound microscope made it possible for people to see the structures of living things. People saw tiny living things that they had never known about. Scientists have also used microscopes to study organisms that cause diseases. In fact, microscopes have had a far greater impact on human life than most people realize.

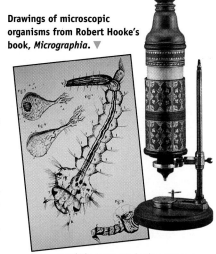
Drawings of microscopic organisms from Robert Hooke's book, *Micrographia*. ▼

Hooke's compound microscope ▲

SCIENCE IN LITERATURE

EXTREMELY WEIRD MICRO MONSTERS
by Sarah Lovett
John Muir Publications, 1993

Are you ready for the microscopic world? It can be pretty scary! Powerful light microscopes—and even more powerful electron microscopes—can take pictures that make incredibly small creatures look downright monstrous! You can take a look at 22 colorful microscopic portraits in *Extremely Weird Micro Monsters* by Sarah Lovett.

Choose your favorite creatures and then read all about them. Do you get the feeling that microscopes make the world seem much more crowded?

F42

Investigate Further

Cultural Connection

GLOBAL MEDICINE **What to Do** Discuss how advances in microscope technology have led to remarkable results in Third World medicine. Have students work in groups to research a disease, such as amoebic dysentery, malaria, African sleeping sickness, cholera, or histoplasmosis. They should draw a picture of the disease-causing organism, describe the symptoms of the disease, and tell how it is treated.
What's the Result? Each group can present its findings to the class and then display the drawings.
Multi-Age Classroom Provide resource materials at different levels of difficulty, so that each student can find information at his or her own reading level.

Flu virus seen with this microscope ▼

Insect seen with this microscope ▼

▲ Transmission electron microscope

▲ Scanning electron microscope

Modern compound light microscopes can magnify as much as 2,000 times. An **electron microscope** can make things appear hundreds of thousands of times bigger than they actually are. The electron microscope uses a beam of electrons instead of a beam of light. In 1935 the first commercial model of an electron microscope became available. Since that time this powerful microscope has been much improved and refined.

There are two kinds of electron microscopes. A transmission electron microscope passes electrons from an electron gun through the object and onto a fluorescent screen. The microscope often displays the object in white against a black background. The flu virus shown here had color added to it.

A scanning electron microscope moves electrons across the object being viewed. Then the electrons enter a collector and produce an enlarged image on what looks like a television screen. This kind of microscope is excellent for showing objects in three dimensions. ■

INVESTIGATION 2

1. One way to study a leaf is to look at very thin slices of the leaf under a compound microscope. Why is it important to view a thin slice and not the whole leaf?

2. How are microscopes and refracting telescopes similar? How are they different?

F43

Assessment

Portfolio

Write Science Journal Entries Ask students to imagine being an early scientist who uses one of the first telescopes or microscopes. Ask them to write several pages of a journal that this scientist keeps. Encourage them to include descriptions of what they see and do, as well as their thoughts about their discoveries.

Investigation Review
How Are Lenses Used In Telescopes and Microscopes?

Name _____ Date _____

1. Sequence the sentences in each exercise below by putting them in the order in which they happened.

   a. A lens magnifies the star's image. Light from a star strikes a concave mirror. The star's image is reflected by a flat mirror.
   <u>Light from a star strikes a concave mirror. The star's image is reflected by a flat mirror. A lens magnifies the star's image.</u>

   b. The first commercial electron microscope is made available. Janssen invents a compound microscope. The Hubble Space Telescope is set in orbit.
   <u>Janssen invents a compound microscope. The first commercial electron microscope is made available. The Hubble Space Telescope is set in orbit.</u>

2. Briefly describe the difference between each of the following pairs of instruments.

   a. simple reflecting telescope, simple refracting telescope <u>A simple reflecting telescope uses mirrors and a lens; a simple refracting telescope uses only a lens.</u>

   b. compound microscope, electron microscope <u>A compound microscope uses light; an electron microscope uses a beam of electrons.</u>

Process Skills
Inferring Students' answers should include a discussion of focal point. The lengths of the telescope tubes could be adjusted to sharpen the image.
A friend is looking through a telescope at some star patterns. When you look into the telescope, the image is fuzzy. Why? What can you do to make the image more clear? Write your answer on a separate sheet of paper.

Close the Investigation

Critical Thinking Skills
Solving Problems, Analyzing, Synthesizing

1. A thin slice allows light to pass through, making tiny structures visible.

2. Both refracting telescopes and microscopes use objective and eyepiece lenses to bend light and magnify images, and a movable tube for focusing. With a microscope, the object to be viewed is very close to the objective lens, but with the telescope, it is distant.

Challenge Encourage students to do further research on how electron microscopes achieve such powerful magnification. Form "Investigation Task Forces," with each member assigned to learn about a different aspect of electron microscopes. Each task force member should discover as much as possible about his or her assignment in the "research mission." Then each member should report to the team, which in turn will create a diagram of the microscope and a brief presentation for the class. Consider assigning half the groups to transmission electron microscopes and half to scanning electron microscopes.

 Have students use the CD-ROM Painter to create their diagrams of the microscope.

Following Up

Baseline Assessment Have students review their choices of lens for building a telescope and modify their answers if needed.

Reteaching Discuss the investigation subconcept with students. On the board, write any questions students still have about how telescopes and microscopes open up unseen worlds. Then lead the class in a discussion of the questions.

 Use *Science Notebook* p. 305.

◄ **Investigation Review**
Use Investigation Review p. 140 in the *Assessment Guide*.

HOW ARE LIGHT AND COLOR RELATED?

Planner

Subconcept The color of an object depends on the colors of light absorbed and the colors of light reflected.

Objectives

- **Predict** what new colors different combinations of primary colored lights will produce.
- **Deduce** an object's color based on the light it reflects and absorbs.

Pacing 2–3 class periods

Science Terms opaque, transparent, translucent, filters

Activate Prior Knowledge

Baseline Assessment Ask: **What color or colors of light does a red apple absorb?** Make a class list of students' responses and save it for use in Following Up.

Activity Circles of Light

Preview *Students discover that mixing red and blue light creates magenta; mixing red and green light creates yellow; mixing blue and green light creates cyan; and mixing red, blue, and green light creates white light.*

Advance Preparation *See p. F28b.*

1. Get Ready

Time about 30 minutes

Grouping groups of 4–6

Collaborative Strategy One group member should record data while another holds the flashlight and others handle the filters.

Materials Hints Colored glass filters may be substituted for the cellophane.

HOW ARE LIGHT AND COLOR RELATED?

Have you ever been at a school show where red or blue lights were shone on the stage? A stage crew probably used filters of different colors. Did the performers and scenery change color, too? How do you think filters cause color changes?

Activity
Circles of Light

MATERIALS
- 3 flashlights
- 3 rubber bands
- red, blue, and green cellophane
- *Science Notebook*

You have probably mixed paints of different colors together. Think back to what happened. Do you think the same colors will result when you mix different colors of light? Try this activity and find out.

Procedure

1. Cover the lens of a flashlight with red cellophane. Fasten the cellophane tightly over the lens with a rubber band.

2. Repeat step 1 with the remaining two flashlights. Cover one flashlight with blue cellophane and cover the other flashlight with green cellophane.

Step 2

F44

Responding to Individual Needs

Gifted and Talented Activity Interested students might want to find out how the three colors of light used in the activity are used to create the picture on a color television set. A good source for information is *The Way Things Work* by David Macaulay. Suggest that students share their information with the class. Have them include an explanation of how the adjustment buttons or knobs change the hue and tint of the colors.

3. Darken the room. Direct the light from the flashlight covered with red cellophane onto a white wall or screen. Repeat with each of the other two flashlights.

4. **Observe** the wall and **record** your findings in your *Science Notebook*.

5. **Predict** what will happen when you direct red and green light from the flashlights onto the wall or screen so that the circles of light overlap. Try it. **Record** your observations.

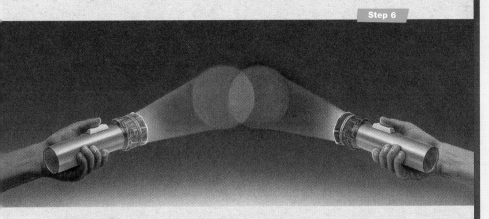

Step 6

6. Repeat step 5, using all the possible combinations of two colors of light. **Record** your results.

7. **Predict** what will happen if you make all three circles of color overlap. Then overlap the circles of color. **Observe** what happens and **record** your results.

Analyze and Conclude

1. Did your predictions of what would happen match what actually happened? If they did not, explain why.

2. What color light results from mixing red and blue light? red and green light? blue and green?

3. What color light results from mixing all three lights?

4. What conclusion can you draw about white light?

INVESTIGATE FURTHER!

RESEARCH

Find out about the color filters photographers use on their camera lenses to achieve various effects. What are these filters made of? What are some of the effects of using filters?

F45

Investigate Further

Research

Photographic filters are made of colored, plasticlike gelatin or colored glass in a lens holder. Ultraviolet filters are used to reduce haze. They are also useful for photographing distant objects and for taking photos at high altitudes. Polarizing filters screen out glare from shiny surfaces, such as glass and water. Color filters are used mainly to deepen the contrast in black-and-white photographs. Have students record their findings in their *Science Notebooks* on p. 307.

Safety Review safety precautions with students.

2. Guide the Procedure

- For best results, conduct the activity in a darkened room.
- Depending on the quality of the colored cellophane, it may have to be doubled to obtain the expected results.

Have students record their data and answer questions on *Science Notebook*, pp. 306–307.

You may wish to have students use the CD-ROM Painter to illustrate what happens when the different colors of light are mixed.

3. Assess Performance

Process Skills Checklist

- Did students carefully **observe** the effects of combining different colored lights?
- Did students accurately **collect** and **record data** about light and color?
- Did students make reasonable **predictions** about what colors would be produced by various combinations of light?

Analyze and Conclude

1. Students should have a grasp of what may have gone wrong with their predictions. Check their responses for reasonableness.

2. Mixing red and blue light results in magenta; mixing red and green light results in yellow; mixing blue and green light results in cyan. Students may not recognize this color by name; accept such answers as blue-green but explain that the correct name of the color is cyan.

3. Mixing all three colors of light results in white light.

4. Students should recognize that white light is a mixture of all the colors of light.

Activity   Filtered Light

Preview *Students focus on how light causes objects to appear colored and how the objects' color is affected by the filter they are seen through.*

1. Get Ready

Time about 30 minutes

Grouping groups of 4–6

 Collaborative Strategy One group member might record data while others handle the materials.

Materials Hints Glass filters may be used.

2. Guide the Procedure

- For best results, fold cellophane filters double.

 Have students record their data and answer questions on *Science Notebook* pp. 308–309.

You may wish to have students use the CD-ROM Painter to illustrate how the different objects absorb and reflect different colors of light.

3. Assess Performance

Process Skills Checklist
- Did students carefully **observe** the objects through different colored filters?
- Did students **collect** and **record data** about how objects appear to be different colors?
- Did students make reasonable **predictions** of what colors objects would appear?

Analyze and Conclude
1. Objects appear their natural color when viewed through a filter of that same color.
2. Objects that are not white appear black when viewed through a filter of a color different from their natural color. White objects appear to be the same color as the filter they are viewed through.
3. Hypotheses should suggest that objects are the color of the light they reflect and they absorb all other colors.
4. Answers should hypothesize that some objects absorb all colors and thus are black, while other objects reflect all colors and thus are white.

Activity
Filtered Light

Why is a red apple red and a green apple green? Can the eye be fooled into seeing another color when an object is red or green?

Procedure

1. Place an assortment of small colored objects on a piece of white paper. In your *Science Notebook*, record the name and color of each object.

2. Predict how the objects will look if they are seen through filters of different colors. Discuss your predictions with other students. Then look through the blue filter at the objects. Record your observations of the appearance of the objects.

3. Repeat step 2, using the green filter.

4. Repeat step 2, using the red filter.

5. Predict how the objects will look if they are seen through several filters at one time. Discuss your predictions. Then repeat step 2, using combinations of the filters. Record your observations.

Step 2

Analyze and Conclude

1. How does each filter affect the appearance of objects that are the same color as the filter?

2. How does each filter affect the appearance of objects that are of different colors from the filter?

3. The white light shining on objects contains many colors. Knowing this, suggest a hypothesis to explain why most objects seem to have only one color.

4. Use your hypothesis to explain why some objects are black and some are white.

F46

Responding to Individual Needs

Students Acquiring English Students can make color drawings of their observations and label them in their native languages. They can then write the English words for the labels. If appropriate, invite the students to present what they have drawn to the rest of the class.

Have students use the CD-ROM Painter and Writer to draw and label their diagrams.

Seeing Color

"Look, a rainbow!" That brilliant, multicolored band arching across the sky usually causes people to stop and stare. You probably know that a rainbow comes from white light. White light is made up of all the colors of the visible spectrum. Sunlight passing through water droplets in the air is refracted by these "natural" prisms, or lenses. The different colors are refracted in different amounts, so the colors spread out and are then reflected off the droplets to your eyes—treating you to a rainbow.

You can make a rainbow by shining light through a prism. When you do this, you separate white light into red, orange, yellow, green, blue, indigo, and violet.

As you saw earlier, the color of visible light is related to its wavelength. Violet light has the shortest wavelength. Red light has the longest wavelength. So your eyes and your brain are really responding to differences in wavelengths of light and interpreting these differences as colors.

The Colors of Objects

When you look at a red apple, what color of light is reaching your eye? You may need to think about this question for a moment. The answer involves knowing what happens to the light that strikes an object.

Most objects are **opaque** (ō pāk′), which means that they do not let light pass through them. Wood, books, and apples are opaque. When light strikes an opaque object, some of the light is absorbed, or taken in, by the object. This light changes to heat in the object, warming it. Some of the light is reflected. If the object is a red apple, red light is reflected and the other colors are absorbed. What color of light is reflected by a green apple? Some objects, including lenses, are **transparent**.

white light

prism

A prism separates white light into a rainbow. ▶

F47

Integrating the Curriculum

Science & Language Arts

WRITING STORIES **What to Do** Suggest that students write a brief fairy tale for children in the manner of Dr. Seuss that explains something they now know about color. Different colors may appear as characters. Incidents in the story may hinge on facts about how colors are created. Stress that the science in the story must be correct, and that student should remember that they are writing for a younger audience.
What's the Result? Have students read aloud their stories to the class. Discuss the scientific accuracy of each story.
Multi-Age Classroom Encourage students to work in teams to do the activity. Add their stories to the classroom library.

Seeing Color

Preview *Students focus on how light and color interact to produce an object's color.*

1. Get Ready

Science Terms
opaque, transparent, translucent, filters

Background

- Not all light waves have the same wavelength. When you see colors, you are seeing light of different wavelengths. Sunlight—called white light—appears to be colorless but is really a mixture of different colors, or wavelengths of light. Isaac Newton discovered that white light is made up of all the colors of the spectrum by passing light through a glass prism. When he passed the colors of the visible spectrum through a second prism, the colors recombined, forming white light. The shortest wavelengths humans can see are violet (wavelength: 350 nm). Ultraviolet waves are shorter than those of violet light. The "black lights" sometimes seen in novelty stores are actually ultraviolet, although they look blue.

Discussion Starter

What are some things you observe about sunlight? How does it make you feel? Does it ever take on different colors? Why might this be so? Students might observe that sunlight produces heat, and that from time to time—especially at dawn and sunset—sunlight takes on a more orange-red color. Students may speculate that the position of the sun in the sky —and the dust particles through which the light passes—has something to do with the different colors sunlight takes on.

2. Guide the Discussion

Choose from the following strategies to facilitate discussion.

Making Comparisons

- **What is the shortest wavelength of light you can see? What is the longest?** Violet is the shortest wavelength visible, and red is the longest.

▲ An opaque screen   ▲ A translucent screen

Responding to Individual Needs

Students Acquiring English Students can color or paint a copy of the visible spectrum and label each color with its name in both English and their native language. They should also label the color with the longest wavelength and the shortest wavelength.

Drawing Conclusions

- **What happens to light that strikes an object?** Light that is absorbed changes to heat, warming the object that absorbs it; some of the light is reflected. If the object is transparent or translucent, some light will pass through; the light may be refracted.

Thinking About the Data

- **If you wanted to be warm on a cold, sunny day, which color jacket should you wear—white or black?** A black jacket **Why?** Because it absorbs all colors of light and turns the light into heat.

Connecting to the Activities

- ***Circles of Light, pp. F44–F45, Filtered Light, p. F46*** **Which term would best describe the filters you used in the activities—opaque, translucent, or transparent?** Transparent

Making Inferences

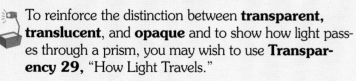 **What tells you that deep water reflects at least some light?** Students should suggest that since large bodies of water can look blue or green they must be reflecting light.

Thinking Critically

- **How is translucent glass the opposite of a convex lens?** Students should realize that while a convex lens focuses and concentrates light, translucent glass scatters it.

- To reinforce the distinction between **transparent, translucent,** and **opaque** and to show how light passes through a prism, you may wish to use **Transparency 29,** "How Light Travels."

Light passes through them. Transparent matter is said to transmit light. Clear glass and shallow water are transparent. They absorb very little light. They do reflect some light, but most light passes through. In the photos above, which object lets the most light pass through?

Colored glass is partially transparent. It allows only certain colors of light to pass through. Red glass absorbs all colors of light except red. Some red light is reflected, but most passes through the glass. Remember, an object's color is the color that reflects off or passes through the object. It's the color that reaches your eye.

Translucent objects, such as frosted glass and wax paper, let light pass through them. However, the light does not follow straight-line paths through the material. It is scattered in many directions. This makes it impossible for you to see clearly through translucent materials, even though the colors of objects behind the translucent material can be seen.

F48

Making Colors by Adding Light

During a live stage show, colored lights are often used to create special effects. Stage lights have a colored transparent material in front of the bulb. These colored materials, or **filters,** absorb some colors of light and let others pass through. Each kind of filter transmits a different color. The

▲ Examples of color addition, the mixing of light

Integrating the Curriculum

Science & the Arts

LIGHTING A PLAY

What to Do Students might enjoy working in small groups to make a simple puppet stage from the cardboard box. The stage area should be lined with white paper. Students can draw characters for the play on drawing paper and color the characters' costumes. Each character should then be cut out and taped onto a plastic straw. Groups can create a scene from a play and decide how they will light it with a flashlight to create the mood they want to achieve. This puppet stage can also be used for the folk tale they're staging.

What's the Result? How would you light a scene that takes place on an eerie night? With dark blue lighting

▲ A transparent glass

most common filters used are red, blue, and green. By shining several of these different-colored lights on the same spot, the stage crew can make other colors, or even white light.

Look at the overlapping circles of light on these pages. Mixing red light and green light produces yellow light. Combining red light and blue light

makes magenta light. Combining blue light and green light makes a blue-green color called cyan (sī´ən). Mixing colored light in this way is called color addition because colored lights are combined, or added together. The "Circles of Light" activity included experiments on color addition.

As the photograph on page F50 shows, shining red, green, and blue light onto the same area of a screen produces white light. These three colors are called primary colors because you can mix them to make other colors.

Subtracting Light

Recall how filters absorb some colors of light. Instead of adding light, a filter takes some light away. So filters make light by color subtraction. Opaque materials, including paints and dyes, are color subtractors.

A white object appears white because it reflects all colors of light. A black object, on the other hand, appears black because it absorbs all colors and reflects no light. If you paint a white object red, the object will reflect red light but will absorb other colors.

Suppose you're wearing your favorite red sweater. You know it looks red in a well-lighted room, but what happens under colored light? If you look at your red sweater under red light, the sweater still appears red. But in blue light or green light, the sweater will look black! Remember that the sweater reflects only red light. The sweater cannot reflect blue or green light. Since no red light is reflected, the sweater looks black.

F49

Investigate Further

Cultural Connection

MAKING PAINT

What You Need red cabbage, spinach leaves, or any other vegetables that can be used to make color, plus cotton balls, water, pot, stove

What to Do Share with students that paints were used thousands of years ago. Cave paintings found in France date from the Stone Age. The paints were ground from colored earths and clays and mixed with animal fat. By the Middle Ages, artists and cloth makers were using pigments from colored minerals and plants. Trade links with China brought new pigments to Europe. If you have access to a stove, invite students to help you boil cabbage and spinach leaves or other plants to create vegetable dyes.

What's the Result? Invite students to dip cotton balls in the cooled water and describe the colors they see.

Making Inferences

- In order to have color, an opaque object must reflect at least one color of light. **What happens when an object reflects two or more colors of light?** Students should infer that such an object simply takes on a color that is a combination of the colors it reflects.

■ **What color would an object appear if it reflected both red and blue light?** Magenta. **How do you know?** Because red and blue light combine to make magenta

■ **What color would an object appear if it reflected both red and green light?** Yellow. Red and green light combine to make yellow.

■ **When many colors of light are mixed, the result is white light; when many colors of paint come together the result is black. Why do you think this is?** Students may speculate that since all the colors together would absorb just about every color of light and reflect none, the paint would look black.

Responding to Individual Needs

Gifted and Talented Activity Students might enjoy finding out what the primary colors of paint are and how mixing primary colors of paint differs from mixing primary colors of light. They could share their information with the class.

3. Assess Understanding

Have students work in groups of three or four to develop rules for a flash-card game based on colored lights and filters. Explain that the game may work however students wish, but must be based on what students know about color subtraction and addition. Hint that the simpler the rules, the more fun the game will be.

You may wish to have students use the Activity Support Master "Compare-Contrast Diagram" (TRB p. 68) to compare and contrast the addition of colored lights and the addition of color pigments.

Close
the Investigation

Critical Thinking Skills
Solving Problems, Analyzing, Applying

1. Students should note that the red in the shirt would appear black because there is no red light, but the yellow part would appear yellow. A magenta and blue shirt would look blue, since there would be no red light to create magenta.

2. The blue portion of the flag would reflect blue and absorb all other colors; the white stars and white stripes would reflect all colors and absorb none; and the red stripes would reflect only red and absorb all other colors.

Challenge Ask students to suggest two ways to prove that white light is made of colors. Then have them demonstrate their proofs.

Following Up

Baseline Assessment Return to the class list of what colors of light a red apple would absorb. Ask students if they would like to revise any of their responses.

Reteaching Using flashlights covered with red, blue, and green cellophane, ask students to predict what color various objects in the room will appear when light from one of the flashlights is shined on them. Then ask what color various objects will appear if combinations of the lights are used instead. You may want to have students draw diagrams on the chalkboard showing which colors are absorbed and which are reflected by various classroom objects.

 Use *Science Notebook* p. 310.

Investigation Review ▶
Use Investigation Review p. 141 in the *Assessment Guide*.

Color subtraction also occurs when filters are combined. A cyan, or blue-green filter, lets blue light and green light pass through while it absorbs red light. Now suppose you put a yellow filter on top of the cyan filter. Which light can pass through both filters?

Only green light can pass through both cyan and yellow filters. A cyan filter lets blue light and green light pass through. A yellow filter lets red light and green light pass through. The only color that can pass through both filters is green. So you would see green light. ■

▲ **The effect of overlapping light**

1. Sodium-vapor street lamps are used in some cities. The light that comes from the bulbs in these lamps does not contain any red light. How would a red-and-yellow striped shirt look under such light? How would a magenta-and-blue striped shirt look?

2. What colors of light are reflected and absorbed by the different areas of the American flag?

F50

Assessment

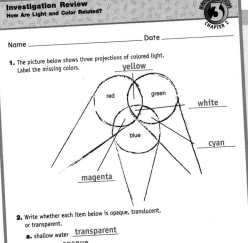

Investigation Review
How Are Light and Color Related?

Name _____ Date _____

1. The picture below shows three projections of colored light. Label the missing colors.

yellow
red   green   white
blue   cyan
magenta

2. Write whether each item below is opaque, translucent, or transparent.
a. shallow water transparent
b. wood opaque
c. clear glass transparent
d. waxed paper translucent
e. rocks opaque
f. frosted glass translucent

Students should infer that the windshields are darkened to filter out some of the sunlight that shines into the car. The dark filters reduce some of the glare caused by sunlight,

Process Skills
Inferring
Have you noticed that the top portion of some car windshields are darkened? Why do you think this is done? Write your answer on a separate sheet of paper. which can make driving difficult.

Performance
Demonstration Ask students to create their own presentation showing a beam of white light going through three distinct phases as colors are successively added and subtracted, arriving back at white light. Students' presentations can be made on a tag board, with different colors of paper illustrating each stage.

CHAPTER 2 REVIEW — REFLECT & EVALUATE

WORD POWER

filter   lens
compound microscope
concave lens
contact lenses
convex lens
electron microscope
focal point
opaque
reflecting telescope
refracting telescope
retina
simple microscope
translucent
transparent

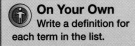 **On Your Own**
Write a definition for each term in the list.

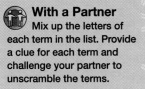 **With a Partner**
Mix up the letters of each term in the list. Provide a clue for each term and challenge your partner to unscramble the terms.

PORTFOLIO

Write a story about what things around you would look like if sunlight contained only yellow light.

Analyze Information

Study the drawing. Then use the drawing to describe, in your own words, how light is absorbed, reflected, or transmitted by the objects. Tell if each object is transparent, translucent, or opaque.

Assess Performance

Design and carry out an experiment to see how a convex lens projects an image from a night-light bulb. Vary the distance of the lens from the bulb and note the changes in the image. Compare your results with those of others. What do the results tell you about convex lenses?

Problem Solving

1. The eye is able to focus an image of both nearby and distant objects, but not at the same time. Make sketches showing the lens shape when focused on a nearby object and when focused on a distant object.

2. Microscopes have become more and more powerful. How do you think this has affected the kinds of things scientists study with microscopes?

3. Color film contains three different light-sensitive chemicals. Each one is sensitive to a different color. Which three colors, do you think, does film record? Explain your answer.

F51

Chapter Test pp. 142–143 in the Assessment Guide

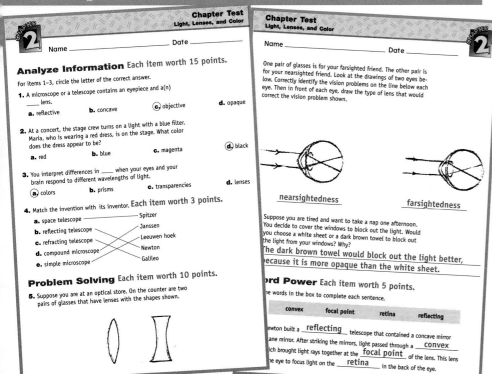

CHAPTER 2 REVIEW

REFLECT & EVALUATE

Word Power

 On Your Own Have students use the Glossary to check definitions.

 With a Partner Clues should reflect an understanding of the meaning of the terms.

Analyze Information

The mirror is opaque and reflects nearly all of the light falling on it. The flower is also opaque and reflects some colors while absorbing others. The vase and water are transparent and transmit light. The sandwich and box are opaque, absorbing some light and reflecting some. The wax paper is translucent, transmitting but scattering light.

Assess Performance

Near the nightlight, an enlarged right-side-up image is seen through the lens. As the lens is moved away, a small upside-down image forms that can be projected onto a screen. A convex lens can magnify objects.

Problem Solving

1. To see nearby objects, the muscles contract and the lens becomes thicker. To see distant objects, the muscles relax; the lens becomes thinner.

2. Scientists can study small organisms.

3. Red, green, and blue, mixing red, green, and blue will make all other colors.

 Use *Science Notebook* pp. 311–312.

PORTFOLIO

Students might mention that the only colors they could see would be red or green or combinations of red and green. All blue objects would appear black because there would be no blue light for an object to reflect.

REFLECT & EVALUATE **F 51**

CHAPTER 3 — PROPERTIES OF SOUND

Subconcepts	Activities	Materials
Investigation 1 What Is Sound?		
Sound, which is produced by vibrations, is a form of energy that travels through matter as a wave; sounds can be characterized by the wave's wavelength, frequency, and amplitude. *Suggested Pacing: 2–3 class periods* **Standards** p. 155	**Rubber-Band Banjo,** p. F54 *Science Processes:* observe; collect, record, and interpret data; define operationally; make hypotheses; make and use models **Waves and Sound,** p. F55 *Science Processes:* observe, communicate, predict, make and use models	goggles*, rubber band*, ruler*, pencils, *Science Notebook* p. 315 goggles*, pieces of string*, coil spring toy*, pieces of colored yarn*, *Science Notebook* p. 316
Investigation 2 How Does Matter Affect How Sound Travels?		
Sound travels more quickly through solids than through liquids and more quickly through liquids than through gases; sound also travels more quickly through matter as the temperature of the matter is raised. *Suggested Pacing: 2–3 class periods* **Standards** p. 155	**Ear to the Wall,** p. F60 *Science Processes:* observe; infer; collect, record, and interpret data; define operationally; make and use models **A String Phone,** p. F61 *Science Processes:* observe; infer; collect, record, and interpret data; make hypotheses; make and use models	plastic cup, empty aluminum can, *Science Notebook* p. 319 paper cups*, sharpened pencil, 6 m of strong string*, paper clips, *Science Notebook* p. 320
Investigation 3 How Do High Sounds Differ From Low Sounds?		

Pitch, or the highness or lowness of sound, depends on the frequency of the sound waves.
 	
Suggested Pacing: 3–4 class periods
Standards
  p. 155
Benchmarks
  p. 45
	Highs and Lows, p. F64
	Science Processes: observe; infer; collect, record, and interpret data; make hypotheses; make and use models
	
	Changing Pitch, p. F65
	Science Processes: observe; infer; collect, record, and interpret data; identify and control variables; make and use models
		identical small-necked plastic bottles, water, *Science Notebook* p. 323
		
		goggles*, rubber bands* (thin, medium, thick), cardboard box, small wooden dowel* (10 cm long), *Science Notebook* p. 324

Overview

In this chapter students investigate the wave nature of sound, look at the effect of matter on the speed of sound, and explore such characteristics of sound as pitch and frequency.

Chapter Concept

Sound, a form of energy that travels in waves, can be described by its wavelength, frequency, amplitude, speed, and pitch.

Advance Preparation	Curriculum Connection	Assessment
Rubber-Band Banjo None **Waves and Sound** Cut enough 30-cm pieces of string so that each group has two pieces. Cut enough 10-cm pieces of yarn so that each group has ten pieces.	Language Arts TG p. F56 Integrating the Sciences TG p. F57 The Arts TG p. F58	**Chapter 3 Baseline Assessment:** *Science Notebook* pp. 313–314 **Investigation 1 Baseline Assessment:** TG p. F54 **Investigation 1 Review:** AG p. 144 **Think It/Write It,** p. F59; *Science Notebook* p. 318 **Following Up on Baseline Assessment:** TG p. F59 **Performance:** TG p. F59
Ear to the Wall None **A String Phone** None	Math TG p. F62	**Investigation 2 Baseline Assessment:** TG p. F60 **Investigation 2 Review:** AG p. 145 **Think It/Write It,** p. F63; *Science Notebook* p. 322 **Following Up on Baseline Assessment:** TG p. F63 **Portfolio:** TG p. F63
Highs and Lows Collect enough 1- and 2-liter plastic bottles so that each group has three bottles of the same size. **Changing Pitch** Cut enough 10-cm long wooden dowels so that each group has one. Collect enough small cardboard boxes, shoeboxes, or tissue boxes so that each group has one box.	Cultural Connection TG pp. F66, F68 Literature TG p. F69 Science, Technology, & Society TG p. F71	**Investigation 3 Baseline Assessment:** TG p. F64 **Investigation 3 Review:** AG p. 146 **Think It/Write It,** p. F72; *Science Notebook* p. 328 **Following Up on Baseline Assessment:** TG p. F72 **Performance:** TG p. F72 **Chapter 3 Summative Assessment:** Reflect and Evaluate, p. F73 Chapter 3 Review/Test: AG pp. 147–148 *Science Notebook* pp. 329–330

TG= Teaching Guide   TRB= Teacher Resource Book   AG= Assessment Guide   *Materials in the Deluxe Equipment Kit

Chapter Overview

Chapter Concept Sound, a form of energy that travels in waves, can be described by its wavelength, frequency, amplitude, speed, and pitch.

Theme: Models

Models provide an opportunity to experience a variety of vibrating systems and show some of the properties of sound waves.

Common Misconceptions

Some students might think that sound travels only through air (gases) and not through solids and liquids. This chapter gives students examples of sound transmission through different materials.

Options for
Setting the Stage

Warm-Up Activity

Provide each small group of students with a cardboard tube and a cork that will fit relatively snugly inside the tube. Attach the cork to a pencil. Have students take turns moving the cork up and down while blowing across the top of the tube to observe what happens to the sound.

Use *Science Notebook* pp. 313–314.

Discussion Starter:
Big Eyes/Big Ears

Use the photo and text to discuss sounds students hear in their community.

- **What sounds do you usually hear in the morning before you get to school?** *Ringing alarm clocks, running water, radio or television, people's voices, traffic sounds, or sirens*

- **Career:** *Acoustical Architect*
The field of architectural acoustics deals with making rooms and buildings quiet and/or providing good conditions for listening to speech or music. Acoustical architects design such things as auditoriums, churches, halls, libraries, and music rooms, and might also be concerned with environmental acoustics, which involves the control of noise pollution.

PROPERTIES OF SOUND

The community where you live has landmarks that make it special and give it character. Your community also has soundmarks. A soundmark is a unique sound that people recognize and remember. It might be a sound made by a clock, bell, whistle, or horn. What are some soundmarks in your community?

Big Eyes/Big Ears

Bill and Mary Buchen are sonic architects. They design and build interactive sound sculptures, games, and playgrounds. One of their playgrounds is at Public School 23 in the South Bronx area of New York City. Another is at Candlestick Point Recreation Area in San Francisco.

At each playground or playspace, children can explore a variety of instruments, including the wind gamelan, an instrument played by the wind. Another is the sound observatory, a series of stainless steel drums played with the feet.

These playgrounds have equipment that allows children to explore the sounds of their neighborhoods. Big Eyes/Big Ears is an echo chamber 3 m (10 ft) above the children's heads that amplifies and transmits captured sounds to the children on the ground. If the chamber were in your neighborhood, what captured sounds would you hear?

F52

Home-School Connection

In the Explore at Home activity "Sound Vibrations," students demonstrate that sound travels in waves. Distribute the activity (TRB p. 30) when students have completed the chapter. Ask what causes sounds to be produced on violins, drums, or pianos.

Explore at Home

Name _____ Date _____

GOOD VIBRATIONS!

Have you ever played or watched someone play a guitar? How were high and low notes made? How was the music made louder? In our class, we have been investigating sound, finding out how it travels, and how low sounds differ from high sounds. You can do this demonstration to show how sound vibrations travel in waves.

Materials

✔ cardboard paper towel or toilet paper roll
✔ balloon
✔ rubber band
✔ scissors

Procedure

Cut the neck off the balloon. With the help of a family member, stretch the balloon over one end of the cardboard roll. Make sure the balloon fits tightly and secure it with a rubber band. Hold the cardboard roll in one hand and place the other hand lightly on the balloon. Speak loudly into the open end of the cardboard roll.

then speak softly, yell, whisper, and hum. Have your family member try it. What did each of you feel?

Results

Your hand felt the sound vibrations on the balloon produced by speaking into the tube. Did the vibrations change speed when you changed how you were speaking? What does this tell you about how sound interacts with materials? How might this be similar to what happens in your ear when you hear sounds? For a similar effect, place a radio or cassette player on its back and sprinkle scraps of tissue paper on top. Turn up the volume. Try to explain what you observe.

Coming Up

WHAT IS SOUND?
. . . . F54

HOW DOES MATTER AFFECT HOW SOUND TRAVELS?
. . . . F60

HOW DO HIGH SOUNDS DIFFER FROM LOW SOUNDS?
. . . . F64

▶ A student explores the sounds that can be made on steel drums.

F53

Chapter Road Map

What Is Sound?

Activities	**Resources**
✳ Rubber-Band Banjo Waves and Sound	✳ The Nature of Sound

How Does Matter Affect How Sound Travels?

Activities	**Resources**
✳ Ear to the Wall A String Phone	✳ When Sound Travels and When It Doesn't

How Do High Sounds Differ From Low Sounds?

Activities	**Resources**
Highs and Lows ✳ Changing Pitch	Wind Instruments Around the World ✳ Pitch Synthesizing Sound

Technology Alert

CD-ROM

Meet The Waves! and Speed Up Enhances or replaces Investigation 2

The Scene Opener, **Meet The Waves!**, can be used with this chapter. The activities are designed to introduce students to sound and light waves. They "click" on individual light and sound sources for a concert in an amphitheater and hear audios of the individual sounds. They observe the basic features of a wave.

In **Speed Up** students investigate how fast sound travels through air, water, and other materials. They use Speed of Sound and Density Probes to observe the relationship between density and the speed of sound in different materials. They enter their findings in a Spreadsheet and record their findings in the Writer.

✳ **Pressed for Time?**

As you work through the upcoming investigations, focus on the activities and resources identified by the clock.

◼ Look for this symbol in front of questions that help develop Scientific Reasoning Skills.

WHAT IS SOUND?

Planner

Subconcept Sound, which is produced by vibrations, is a form of energy that travels through matter as a wave; sounds can be characterized by the wave's wavelength, frequency, and amplitude.

Objectives

- **Observe** how sounds are produced.
- **Build a model** and **draw conclusions** about how sound waves move through matter.
- **Describe** three main characteristics of a sound.

Pacing 2–3 class periods

Science Terms vibration, sound, compression, rarefaction, crest, trough, wavelength, frequency, amplitude, overtone, timbre

Activate Prior Knowledge

Baseline Assessment Ask: **Have you ever heard drums played so loudly that you could** *feel* **the drum beat? Why could you feel a sound?** List student responses for use in Following Up.

Have you ever sat perfectly still and listened to the sound around you? Try it sometime and you may be amazed at what you hear. In this investigation you'll see how sound is produced and how it travels. In the process, you may hear some sweet—and sour—sounds!

Activity
Rubber-Band Banjo

How are sounds produced? Construct a simple banjo and use it to find out.

MATERIALS
- goggles
- rubber band
- ruler
- 2 pencils
- *Science Notebook*

SAFETY //////
Wear goggles during this activity.

Procedure

Stretch a rubber band lengthwise over a ruler. Then insert a pencil under the rubber band at each end of the ruler so that the rubber band is lifted away from the surface of the ruler. Pluck the rubber band at any point between the two pencils. **Observe** what happens. **Record** what you see and hear in your *Science Notebook*. Press your finger at different points along the rubber band, plucking it each time. **Describe** the sounds produced.

Analyze and Conclude

1. Hypothesize how the rubber band produces sound.

2. How did the sound change when you pressed the rubber band at different points on the ruler?

F54

Activity Rubber-Band Banjo

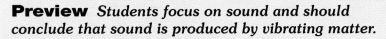

Preview *Students focus on sound and should conclude that sound is produced by vibrating matter.*

1. Get Ready

Time about 30 minutes

Grouping groups of 4–6

Collaborative Strategy One student can pluck the rubber band and another student can observe and record what happens.

Materials Hints Rubber bands should be broad enough to prevent breaking under tension.

Safety Review safety precautions with students.

2. Guide the Procedure

Have students record their data and answer questions on *Science Notebook* p. 315.

You may wish to have students use the Spreadsheet to organize and display their data.

3. Assess Performance

Process Skills Checklist
- Did students **hypothesize** that sound is produced by the vibrating rubber band?

Analyze and Conclude
1. The rubber band produces sound because it vibrates when plucked.
2. The sound became higher or lower when the rubber band was held at different points along the ruler.

Activity
Waves and Sound

Sound is a form of energy that travels through different objects and materials. In this activity you'll build a model of the way a sound wave moves.

MATERIALS
- goggles
- 2 pieces of string, each about 30 cm long
- 1 coil spring
- 10 pieces of colored yarn, each 10 cm long
- *Science Notebook*

SAFETY
Wear goggles during this activity.

Procedure

1. Use a piece of string to tie one end of a coil spring to a table leg. Stretch the coil spring and use another piece of string to tie the other end to another table leg. Make sure that the spring is stretched tightly enough so that it doesn't touch the floor.

2. Fold pieces of yarn in half. Starting at one end of the spring, hang a piece of yarn on every tenth coil.

3. **Predict** what will happen to the yarn if you pinch five end coils together and then release them. **Discuss** your prediction with your group. **Record** your prediction in your *Science Notebook*.

4. Pinch together five coils at one end of the spring and quickly release them. **Record** your observations of the coil spring and the yarn.

5. Repeat step 4 several times. **Record** your observations each time.

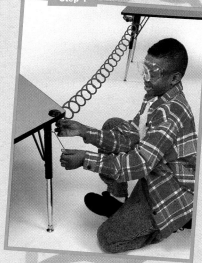

Step 1

Analyze and Conclude

1. Write a general statement about the way the spring coil behaved when you pinched and then released the five end coils.

2. What evidence did you observe that energy was transferred along the coil?

F55

Responding to Individual Needs

Inclusion Activity To make sure that students understand that their model represents the way in which a sound wave moves, have them orally describe what occurs in each step of the activity and correlate the spring's action to the movement of a sound wave through matter. Tape record their oral descriptions. Play them back for each student. Ask if they want to change anything in their descriptions. If so, re-record their new descriptions.

Activity Waves and Sound

Preview *Students focus on sound as a form of energy and should conclude that energy moves along the coil when it is compressed and released.*

Advance Preparation *See p. F52b.*

1. Get Ready

Time about 30 minutes

Grouping groups of 4–6

Collaborative Strategy One student might record data while the others experiment with the coil.

Materials Hints Coil springs can be found at most toy stores.

Safety Review safety precautions with students. To prevent injury, instruct students not to release the stretched spring rapidly. Remind students to wear their goggles at all times.

2. Guide the Procedure

 Have students record their data and answer questions on *Science Notebook* p. 316.

 You may wish to have students use the Spreadsheet to organize and display their data.

3. Assess Performance

Process Skills Checklist
- Did students **use the model** correctly?
- Were students able to accurately **predict** the outcome when coils are compressed and released?
- Did students make careful **observations** of the behavior of the spring?

Analyze and Conclude

1. The five end coils moved forward past their original positions, causing the coils in front of them to move; the coils then moved back beyond their original position. A wave moved along the coils of the spring.

2. Evidence for the transfer of energy was that the yarn hanging over every tenth coil moved—in succession.

The Nature of Sound

Preview *Students focus on the ways in which frequency and amplitude affect sound.*

1. Get Ready

Science Terms vibration, sound, compression, rarefaction, crest, troughs, wavelength, frequency, amplitude, overtone, timbre

Background

- Sound waves are characterized by their wavelength, their frequency, and their amplitude. *Frequency* refers to the number of waves that pass a given point in a given period of time. The standard unit for measuring frequency is the hertz (Hz), which represents one wave passing a given point per second. The frequency of a sound wave can be calculated by dividing the speed of the wave by its wavelength.

Discussion Starter

- **What do you think the difference is between music and noise?** Students might answer that music is pleasant to listen to, while noise is unpleasant.

- **How are music and noise alike?** They both consist of sounds.

- **How do you think that sound can be made into music?** Encourage speculation; students might respond that musicians make certain sounds with their instruments and use these sounds to make melodies.

Responding to Individual Needs

Students Acquiring English Introduce vocabulary for Spanish-speaking students that is similar in English and Spanish (sound—*sonido*; amplitude—*amplitud*; frequency—*frecuencia*; vibrations—*vibraciones*; music—*música*).

The Nature of Sound

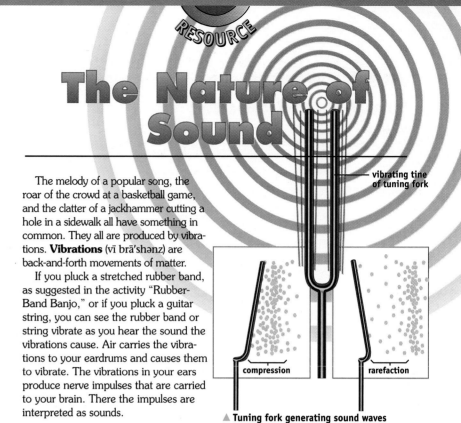

The melody of a popular song, the roar of the crowd at a basketball game, and the clatter of a jackhammer cutting a hole in a sidewalk all have something in common. They all are produced by vibrations. **Vibrations** (vī brā'shənz) are back-and-forth movements of matter.

If you pluck a stretched rubber band, as suggested in the activity "Rubber-Band Banjo," or if you pluck a guitar string, you can see the rubber band or string vibrate as you hear the sound the vibrations cause. Air carries the vibrations to your eardrums and causes them to vibrate. The vibrations in your ears produce nerve impulses that are carried to your brain. There the impulses are interpreted as sounds.

vibrating tine of tuning fork

compression   rarefaction

▲ **Tuning fork generating sound waves**

Sound Waves

Sound is a form of energy that travels through matter as waves. Anything that is in motion has energy, and sound is certainly in motion. If you tap a tuning fork with a rubber hammer, you transfer energy from the moving hammer to the tines of the tuning fork.

Parts of a sound wave ▼

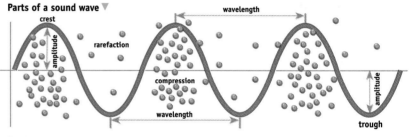

F56

Integrating the Curriculum

Science & Language Arts

"SOUNDS" LIKE **What to Do** Working in small groups, let students consult a thesaurus and dictionary to make an A-to-Z list of words related to or synonymous with sound. Encourage students to share their lists with the class.

What's the Result? Which words do you think best represent particular sounds? Answers will vary but might include words like *buzz, hum, click, snap, ring, zap, meow, bow-wow*, and so on.

The back-and-forth motion of the tines pushing against air particles around them creates sound waves that travel outward from the tuning fork. The region where the particles have been pushed closer together is called a **compression** (kəm presh′ən). Air pressure is greater than usual in this region. The region where there are fewer particles than normal is called a **rarefaction** (rer ə fak′shən). Air pressure is lower than usual in this region. A sound wave is a series of compressions and rarefactions moving outward from the source of a vibration.

A sound wave can be represented as a more familiar up-and-down wave, as shown at the bottom of page F56. In the drawing, the **crests** represent the compressions of a sound wave, or regions of greater air pressure. The **troughs** (trôfs) represent the rarefactions, or regions of lower air pressure.

When a sound wave travels from its source to your ear, the particles that carry the wave do not travel along with the wave. Like the coils of the spring in the activity "Waves and Sound," the particles in air move back and forth. But after the wave passes, they are still in the same general location, much as the coils remained where they were. (Think back to the pieces of yarn in the activity.)

Measuring Sound Waves

The distance from one compression to the next is the **wavelength** of a sound wave. Wavelength depends on the frequency of vibration of the source of the sound. **Frequency** is the number of complete waves produced in a unit of time, such as a second. A high sound is one that has a high frequency. A great many waves are produced each second. A low sound is one that has a low frequency. Fewer waves are produced each second.

The **amplitude** (am′plə tōōd) of the wave in the drawing represents the difference in air pressure between the

Sound wave of a loud sound, such as a moving freight train ▼

Sound wave of a soft sound, such as a whisper ▼

F57

Investigate Further

Integrating the Sciences

EARTH SCIENCE **What to Do** Students can use index cards to make a "house." Explain that mining companies sometimes set explosives in rocks to loosen materials they are mining. The vibrations produced by the explosions travel through the ground. Students can simulate this by dropping a book on the table at the end opposite where their house of cards is located.

What's the Result? Ask: **How do you know that the vibrations traveled through the table?** The house of cards was knocked down.

What do you think might happen if houses are built too close to a mine where explosives are used? The houses could be damaged by the vibrations.

2. Guide the Discussion

Choose from the following strategies to facilitate discussion.

Connecting to the Activities

- *Rubber-Band Banjo, p. F54*
  What happened when the rubber band banjo's string was plucked? It vibrated back and forth. **When it vibrated, what was happening to the air particles near the band?** The air particles near the rubber band were alternately squeezed together and spread apart.

- *Waves and Sound, p. F55*
  In the activity, Waves and Sound, what do you think represented compression? Compression occurred when the coils were squeezed together. **What represented rarefaction?** Rarefaction occurred when the coils were released.

Making Inferences

If the movement of the coil in the activity represented compression and rarefaction, what do you think the coil itself represented? The coil represented the matter that the sound wave was traveling through.

Thinking Critically

Can you see sounds? Students should respond that they cannot see sounds but can sometimes see the vibration that causes sound.

Have students research the nature of sound using the Sound, Light & Waves Data Pack on the CD-ROM.

To reinforce students' understanding of the nature of sound waves, you may wish to use **Transparency 30,** "Transmission of Sound." Use with **Transparency 1,** "Moire Overlay," for a special visual effect.

Students Acquiring English Have students draw a sound wave, labeling the crest, trough, and amplitude in both English and their native language. Have students work in pairs, with an English-proficient student in each pair. Encourage teams to pronounce terms in both languages.

3. Assess Understanding

Have students place their fingers against their throats as they sing the national anthem. What do they feel? Discuss with students how air is pushed over their vocal cords when they speak or sing. Encourage students to outline, step-by-step, what occurs when air passes over the vocal cords. **How could they change the wave patterns of the sounds they produce?** Student responses might indicate that wave patterns can be changed by altering the shape of the inside of the mouth and by changing the shape of the lips. Some students may realize that changing the length of the vocal cords and the amount of air passing over them will change the wave patterns.

SCIENCE IN LITERATURE

Tuning In: The Sounds of the Radio*
by Eve and Albert Stwertka

Students can create a poster or other graphic to show the steps taken in broadcasting a radio show. They might also contact a local radio station and request a tour of its facilities.

*Available in the Trade Book Library.

---

compressions and the rarefactions. It is a measure of the amount of energy in a sound wave. A loud sound is represented by a sound wave with a large amplitude. A soft sound is represented by a sound wave with a small amplitude.

Quality of Sound—Timbre

The drawing on page F56 of the up-and-down sound wave is simple. It represents a pure sound made by a tuning fork. A tuning fork may produce a note, or tone, with a single frequency and a simple wave pattern. But most of the sounds you hear, such as music on the radio and TV, are very complex. They are made up of several waves, which combine to form complex sounds.

Whether produced by a vibrating string or a vibrating air column, every musical tone is mixed with other, fainter tones known as **overtones**. The blending of these tones produces a unique quality that makes the sounds of different instruments, or the voices of different people, unique. Even if two instruments are producing the same note, you can tell that one sound comes from a flute, for example, and one comes from a trumpet. The quality of a musical tone is called its **timbre** (tim′bər). Musicians often use words such as *mellow, bright,* or *tinny* to describe differences in the timbre of sounds.

Noise

You may disagree with your family and friends about what is "good" music. But you'll probably agree that the tones and overtones of music combine in very

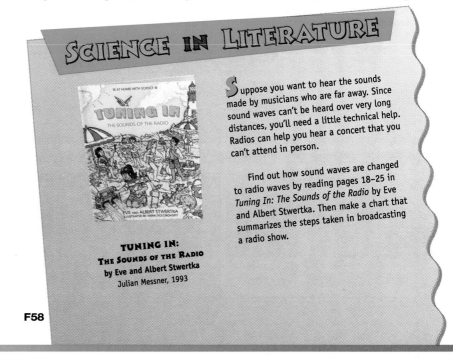

SCIENCE IN LITERATURE

Suppose you want to hear the sounds made by musicians who are far away. Since sound waves can't be heard over very long distances, you'll need a little technical help. Radios can help you hear a concert that you can't attend in person.

Find out how sound waves are changed to radio waves by reading pages 18–25 in *Tuning In: The Sounds of the Radio* by Eve and Albert Stwertka. Then make a chart that summarizes the steps taken in broadcasting a radio show.

TUNING IN:
THE SOUNDS OF THE RADIO
by Eve and Albert Stwertka
Julian Messner, 1993

F58

Integrating the Curriculum

Science & the Arts

What to Do On a tape recorder play for students examples of four different taped sounds (soft music, loud music, soft noise, loud noise). Have them draw a design, using colored markers, that represents each of the sounds.

What's the Result? **How did the way you represented music differ from the way you represented noise?** Music might be shown with patterns that are smoother than those of noise; music might be represented by pastel colors rather than by bold, dark colors. **How did the way you represented loud sound differ from how you represented soft sounds?** Loud sounds might be shown with designs having big patterns and bold colors.

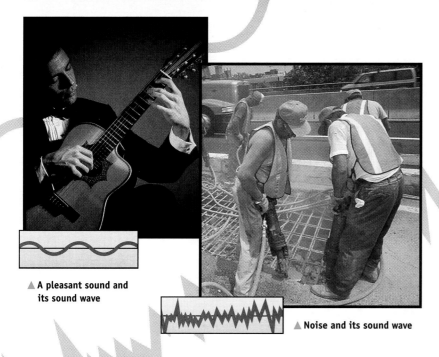

▲ A pleasant sound and its sound wave

▲ Noise and its sound wave

pleasant ways. Many sources of sound produce combinations of waves that are unpleasant. You would probably agree that the sounds of jackhammers, squealing brakes, or a tray of dishes being dropped are unpleasant. Unpleasant

sounds, or noises, have irregular sound waves. From the drawings below the photographs, you can see that the wave pattern of music is smooth and forms a repeating pattern. The wave pattern of noise is irregular. ■

━━━━━ INVESTIGATION 1 ━━━━━

THINK IT WRITE IT

1. Describe three main characteristics of a sound.

2. Make sketches of sound waves to represent
   (a) a shout and a whisper,
   (b) a bird's chirp and a lion's roar, and
   (c) music and noise.

F59

THINK IT WRITE IT

Critical Thinking Skills
Synthesizing, Analyzing, Applying, Expressing Ideas

1. Frequency—the number of complete sound waves produced in a unit of time; wavelength—the distance from one compression to the next; amplitude—a measure of the amount of energy in the sound wave

2. Description of sound waves: Shout vs. whisper— shout has large amplitude; whisper has small amplitude; bird's chirp vs. lion's roar—chirp is regular, even, with small amplitude; roar is irregular with large amplitude; music vs. noise—music is even and regular; noise is irregular.

Challenge Students can work in groups of four or five. Obtain tuning forks of at least two different sizes. Then fill two pans of the same size with water. Have students set the two forks in motion by striking each with a rubber mallet. As soon as the forks are vibrating, have students touch the forks to the surface of the water in each of the two pans. Tell them to observe the waves that are set up by the vibrating tuning fork. Have students time the motion of the waves and compare the waves formed in each of the pans. Encourage students to explain how the water waves are similar to and different from sound waves.

Following Up

Baseline Assessment Return to the class list of why students can feel sounds. Ask students to supplement their original responses with information learned in the investigation.

Reteaching On a tabletop, arrange four marbles in a line. Tap a fifth marble so that it gently strikes the first marble. Encourage students to infer that the marbles represent particles of matter; their movement represents the transfer of energy from particle to particle.

Use *Science Notebook* p. 318.

◄ **Investigation Review**
Use Investigation Review p. 144 in the *Assessment Guide.*

Assessment

Performance
Demonstration Students can work in small groups to create percussion instruments from common materials such as bottles and coffee cans. Have each group perform for the class, then explain how each instrument relied upon vibration to make its sound. Encourage students to discuss the amplitude and wave patterns that they think each instrument produces.

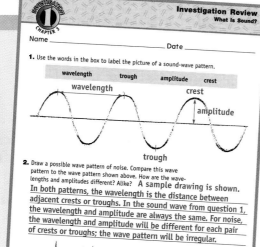

INVESTIGATION 1 CHAPTER 3

Investigation Review
What Is Sound?

Name _____ Date _____

1. Use the words in the box to label the picture of a sound-wave pattern.

| wavelength | trough | amplitude | crest |

wavelength

crest

amplitude

trough

2. Draw a possible wave pattern of noise. Compare this wave pattern to the wave pattern shown above. How are the wavelengths and amplitudes different? Alike? **A sample drawing is shown.** In both patterns, the wavelength is the distance between adjacent crests or troughs. In the sound wave from question 1, the wavelength and amplitude are always the same. For noise, the wavelength and amplitude will be different for each pair of crests or troughs; the wave pattern will be irregular.

Process Skills
Making a Hypothesis

How does the sound of a guitar change when the strings are tightened and loosened? How is the frequency of the sound affected by these changes? Write your answer on a separate sheet of paper.

Tightened guitar strings create a higher sound; loosened strings create a lower sound; the tightened strings create sounds with shorter wavelengths and a higher frequency. The loosened strings create sounds with longer wavelengths and a lower frequency.

HOW DOES MATTER AFFECT HOW SOUND TRAVELS?

Planner

Subconcept Sound travels more quickly through solids than through liquids and more quickly through liquids than through gases; sound also travels more quickly through matter as the temperature of the matter is raised.

Objectives

- **Analyze** how sound travels through matter.
- **Draw conclusions** about the way in which matter affects how sound travels.

Pacing 2–3 class periods

Activate Prior Knowledge

Baseline Assessment Encourage students to recall a time when they were under water. Ask: **Can sounds travel through water? How do you know?** Make a class list and save it for use in Following Up.

 **2 HOW DOES MATTER AFFECT HOW SOUND TRAVELS?**

Have you ever gone swimming and noticed that sounds are different under water? As you experiment with sound, you'll find out how the material through which sound passes affects the properties of sound.

Activity
Ear to the Wall

MATERIALS
- plastic cup
- empty aluminum can
- *Science Notebook*

Press your ear to a wall. What can you hear? Does sound travel better through some materials than through others?

Procedure

Tap your fingernails on your desk. Then place your ear on your desktop. Again, tap your fingernails. **Compare** the two tapping sounds. **Record** your observations in your *Science Notebook*. Next, place an empty plastic cup upside down on the desk. Press your ear against the bottom of the cup. Tap lightly on the cup. Repeat, using an empty aluminum can. **Discuss** your observations with your group. **Record** your findings.

Analyze and Conclude

1. What can you infer about how well sound travels through wood, plastic, and metal?

2. Why can you often hear a conversation in another room when you press your ear to the wall?

F60

Activity — Ear to the Wall

Preview *Students focus on how sound more readily travels through solids than through gases.*

1. Get Ready

Time about 30 minutes

Grouping groups of 4–6

 Collaborative Strategy Each group member should try all parts of the activity and join in the discussion.

Safety Review safety precautions with students.

2. Guide the Procedure

 Have students record their data and answer questions on *Science Notebook* p. 319.

You may wish to have students use the Spreadsheet to organize and display their data.

3. Assess Performance

Process Skills Checklist
- Were students able to **infer** that sound travels more readily through solids than through gases?

Analyze and Conclude
1. Sound travels better through solids than through the air and better through metal and wood than through plastic.
2. Because the sound is traveling through the solid wall and then to your ear.

Activity

A String Phone

MATERIALS
- 2 paper cups
- sharpened pencil
- 6 m of strong string
- 2 paper clips
- *Science Notebook*

You might have made string telephones when you were younger. In this activity you'll figure out how they work.

Procedure

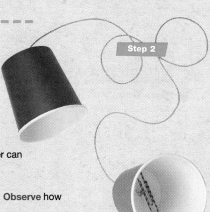

Step 2

1. Use a pencil to punch a hole in the center of the bottom of two paper cups.

2. Put one end of a piece of string through the hole in one cup and tie the string around a paper clip on the inside of the cup.

3. Repeat step 2 with the other end of the string and the other cup.

4. Find a quiet area where you and a partner can stand far enough apart so that the string is stretched tightly.

5. Have your partner say something quietly. **Observe** how well you can hear what your partner says.

6. Now hold the cup up to your ear. Have your partner quietly say something into the other cup. **Record** your observations in your *Science Notebook*.

7. While your partner is speaking into the cup, pinch the string about 30 cm from your end. Listen carefully to the sound produced. **Record** your observations.

8. Reverse roles with your partner and repeat steps 5 through 7.

Analyze and Conclude

1. **Compare** how well you could hear your partner with and without the string phone.

2. Through what did the sound travel to reach your ear each time? What happened when you pinched the string?

3. **Hypothesize** how you could improve this telephone. Test your hypothesis.

INVESTIGATE FURTHER!

RESEARCH

Naval vessels often used air tubes to communicate from one part of a ship to another part. What are the advantages of an air-tube system? How do modern intercom systems work?

Investigate Further

Research

The advantages of air-tube systems are that they are simple and inexpensive. Modern intercom systems work when a person at one end of the intercom speaks and vibrations are converted to electrical impulses that travel on wires to the receiving end. At the receiving end of the intercom, the impulses are again converted to vibrations, which are interpreted as sound. Remind students to record their findings on *Science Notebook* p. 321.

Activity — A String Phone

Preview *Students use the ability of sound to travel through solids to make a usable string telephone.*

1. Get Ready

Time about 45 minutes

Grouping groups of 4–6

Collaborative Strategy Students should take turns experimenting with the string phone and recording data.

Materials Hints Clean yogurt cups may be substituted for paper cups.

2. Guide the Procedure

- For best results, students should pull the string taut. Remind them to speak quietly into the cups.

 Have students record their data and answer questions on *Science Notebook* p. 320.

You may wish to have students use the CD-ROM Spreadsheet to organize and display their data.

3. Assess Performance

Process Skills Checklist

- Did students follow instructions when they **made and used a model** of a string telephone?

- Did students make careful **observations** about how well they could hear on the string telephone? Did they accurately **collect and record data**?

- Did students **infer** that sound travels more easily through solid matter than through air?

- Did students make a reasonable **hypothesis** about how to improve their string phone?

Analyze and Conclude

1. Students were better able to hear what their partners said when the string phone was used.

2. Sound traveled through a solid (the string). When the string was pinched, the sound was fainter or not heard.

3. Students might suggest replacing the string with metal wire. Wire transmitted sound well in the previous activity.

When Sound Travels and When It Doesn't

Preview *Students focus on variables that affect how sound travels through matter.*

1. Get Ready

Background

• The Doppler effect causes sounds that are approaching the observer to seem higher in pitch, and those moving away from the observer to seem lower in pitch. This occurs because the source of the sound is moving, causing the sound waves ahead of it to compress and those behind it to spread out.

Discussion Starter

 What do you think you would hear if there were no air in the room? Why? In the absence of air to conduct the sound, no sound would be heard.

2. Guide the Discussion

Choose from the following strategies to facilitate discussion.

Connecting to the Activities

• ***Ear to the Wall, p. F60***
How did the sound traveling through air compare with the sound traveling through solid matter? It was louder in the solids.

Responding to Individual Needs

Gifted and Talented Activity Students can investigate the Doppler effect to answer this question: Why does the siren of a moving fire engine seem to drop to a lower note after it passes you?

3. Assess Understanding

Encourage students to design a bar graph or pictogram to present the data on p. F63 in another way.

When Sound Travels and When It Doesn't

The pitcher winds up and then releases the ball. The batter swings, and the bat connects with the ball right over home plate. But you don't hear the bat hit the ball until about a second later. Why does this happen?

Sound waves travel much more slowly than light waves do. The speed of sound in air is about 346 m/s (1,125 ft/s). The speed of light is about 300 million m/s (985 million ft/s)—almost 900,000 times greater than the speed of sound!

The speed of sound varies with the material through which it moves. The table on page F63 compares the speed of sound in several different materials. Recall in the activity "Ear to the Wall" that the sound of your fingers tapping on the desk was much louder when you placed your ear directly on the desktop. Sound travels faster through wood than it does through air. The closely packed particles in the wooden desk transmit the sound more quickly than do the particles in air. Less sound energy is changed to other forms of energy in the wood. So the sound of your fingers tapping is louder.

The speed of sound also varies with the temperature of the material through which the sound moves. From the table, compare the speed of sound in air at 0°C and at 25°C. Particles of matter move faster at higher temperatures than at lower temperatures. Why does this difference affect the rate at which

◀ **Why don't you *hear* the bat hit the ball at the same time that you *see* it?**

Integrating the Curriculum

 ### Science & Math

SOUND SPEED **What You Need** Have pairs of students use a tape measure to measure the distance from one end of the school sports field to the other. One student should stand at one end of the field with two wooden blocks over his head, while the other stays at the opposite end holding a stopwatch. The student with the blocks should strike them together sharply. When the other student *sees* the blocks hit, the stopwatch should be started. When the sound reaches the student, the stopwatch should be stopped and the time recorded to the nearest tenth of a second. Repeat two or three times to calculate an average time. The speed of sound can be calculated by dividing the distance by the time.

What's the Result? Ask: **Why did you repeat the activity several times and then calculate an average?** To make sure it was accurate.

THE SPEED OF SOUND IN DIFFERENT MATERIALS	
Material	**Speed (m/s)**
Air at 0°C	331
Air at 20°C	343
Air at 25°C	346
Water at 25°C	1,498
Sea water at 25°C	1,531
Copper	3,100
Brick	3,650
Glass	4,540
Steel	5,200

The drawings below show that sound waves cannot travel through a vacuum. If you put a ringing alarm clock inside a jar filled with air, you'll hear the alarm going off. Then if you slowly pump air from the jar, you'll find that the sound gets fainter and fainter until you can no longer hear it. So the girl in the drawing does not hear the ringing clock. ■

▲ Sound waves travel through air.

sound travels? As the temperature rises, particles take less time to collide with one another. As a result, they pass along the wave energy more quickly.

Unlike light waves, sound waves can travel only when there is matter to carry them. You can see the light from the Sun because it travels through the vacuum of space. But you don't hear the roaring nuclear explosions that are the source of the Sun's energy. You can't hear them because sound waves require matter for their transmission.

▲ Sound cannot travel through a vacuum.

— INVESTIGATION 2 —

1. Explain how the matter through which sound travels affects the sound. Give a specific example to support your explanation.

2. After lunch you put your head down on your desk to rest. You hear very loud footsteps that you hadn't noticed before. Why are the footsteps so loud now?

F63

Assessment

Portfolio

Write a Story Encourage students to imagine that they are a sound that must be heard. Have them write a creative story telling how they reach their destination. What obstacles do they face? What will help them on their way to be heard?

Investigation Review
How Does Matter Affect How Sound Travels?

Name _____ Date _____

1. Use words and phrases from the box to complete the sentences below.

sound	at different speeds	through a vacuum	light

Sound waves travel _at different speeds_. Light waves can travel _through a vacuum_. The speed of _light_ is much greater than the speed of _sound_.

2. For each pair of phrases, write which wave travels faster and why.

a. sound in air, sound in steel
Sound in steel; steel particles are closely packed and transmit sound more quickly than do particles in air.

b. sound at 15°C, sound at 30°C
Sound at 30°C; the particles of matter move faster at higher temperatures because, as the temperature rises, the particles take less time to collide and pass along the wave energy.

Process Skills
Inferring

Suppose you are walking past the assembly hall in your school and hear a noise coming from inside. You want to know what the noise is, but the door is locked. What is one thing you could do to hear the noise better? Explain your answer. _By putting your ear to the door or wall, you could hear the noise more clearly and loudly. This is because sounds are louder when they travel through solids, such as a door, than through gases, such as air._

Close
the Investigation

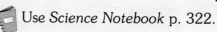

Critical Thinking Skills
Analyzing, Applying

1. Sound travels more easily through solids than through liquids. It travels more easily through liquids than through gases. Sound traveled better through the string telephone than through the air.

2. The footsteps sound louder because the sound waves are traveling through the floor and then through the desktop to your ears rather than through the air. Sounds travel faster (better) through solids.

Challenge Have students recall how traffic noise is amplified during a rain shower. **Why does this occur? What happens to traffic noise when snow, rather than rain, is on the pavement? How can these differences be explained?** Even though both rain and snow are essentially water, snow is formed of crystals surrounded by air spaces. Sound does not travel as well through air as it does through liquid, so the sounds are muffled in snow.

Following Up

Baseline Assessment Return to students' speculations on whether sounds travel through water. Ask students to modify and explain their statements with information learned in this investigation.

Reteaching Let students participate in a simple experiment that illustrates this investigation's concept. Carefully place the eraser end of a pencil against a student's cheek while gently flicking your finger against the pencil. What does the student hear? Then pull the pencil slightly away from the cheek and flick it again. Is the sound as loud this time? Encourage students to explain the difference in the sounds produced.

Use *Science Notebook* p. 322.

◀ **Investigation Review**
Use Investigation Review p. 145 in the *Assessment Guide*.

How Do High Sounds Differ From Low Sounds?

Planner

Subconcept Pitch, or the highness or lowness of sound, depends on the frequency of the sound waves.

Objectives
- **Compare** high and low sounds.
- **Investigate** and **infer** which variables affect pitch.

Pacing 3–4 class periods

Science Terms pitch, frequency, hertz, octave, sound synthesizer

Activate Prior Knowledge

Baseline Assessment Ask: **What do you think makes one person's voice different from someone else's?** Make a list of responses and save it for use in Following Up.

How Do High Sounds Differ From Low Sounds?

When your best friend calls you on the telephone, you know his or her voice right away. You can also tell the difference between a guitar and a trumpet. What makes sounds different? How can you tell one sound from another?

Activity
Highs and Lows

The pitch of a sound is its highness or lowness. What are some ways you can vary pitch?

MATERIALS
- 3 identical small-necked plastic bottles
- water
- *Science Notebook*

SAFETY
Clean up any spills immediately.

Procedure

Get three identical bottles. Leave one bottle empty, fill a second halfway with water, and fill the third almost to the top with water. **Predict** what will happen if you blow across the top of each bottle. **Discuss** your prediction with your group. Then blow across the top of each bottle until you hear a clear tone from it. **Infer** why there were differences between the tones. **Record** your observations in your *Science Notebook*.

Analyze and Conclude

1. How did the sounds in the three bottles compare? How did the quantity of water affect the pitch?

2. **Infer** what was vibrating—the water, the air, or the bottle. Explain your inference.

3. **Hypothesize** about what causes the pitch of a sound to vary.

F64

Activity Highs and Lows

Preview *Students focus on pitch and should find that an empty bottle produces a low-pitched sound, while a full bottle produces a higher-pitched sound.*

Advance Preparation *See p. F52b.*

1. Get Ready

Time about 30 minutes

Grouping groups of 4–6

Safety Review safety precautions with students.

2. Guide the Procedure

- Add food coloring to make the water level easier to see.

 Have students record their data and answer questions on *Science Notebook* p. 323.

 You may wish to have students use the Spreadsheet and CD-ROM Painter to organize and display their data.

3. Assess Performance

Process Skills Checklist
- Did students accurately **predict** what would happen and **collect and record their data** accurately?

Analyze and Conclude
1. Empty bottle—low sound; half-filled bottle—higher sound; nearly full bottle—highest sound. The greater the quantity of water, the higher the pitch of the sound.
2. The air above the water was vibrating; the empty bottle produced the sound of lowest pitch because the column of air in the empty bottle was greatest.
3. The height of the air above the water varied the pitch.

Activity
Changing Pitch

In this activity you'll explore ways to change the pitch of a vibrating rubber band. What do you think some of the ways might be?

MATERIALS
- goggles
- 3 rubber bands (1 thin, 1 medium, 1 thick)
- cardboard box
- small wooden dowel, 10 cm long
- *Science Notebook*

SAFETY
Wear goggles when working with rubber bands.

Procedure

1. Stretch three rubber bands lengthwise over a box as shown in the picture.

2. **Predict** how the pitch of each of the three rubber bands, when plucked, will differ. **Discuss** your predictions with your group.

3. Pluck each rubber band and listen to the pitch. **Record** your observations in your *Science Notebook*.

4. Select one of the rubber bands and twist a dowel near one end of the rubber band to tighten it. Pluck the rubber band and **record** your observations.

5. Repeat step 4 three times, each time turning the dowel a little bit more. **Record** your observations.

6. Repeat steps 4 and 5 with each of the other rubber bands. **Record** your observations.

Step 1

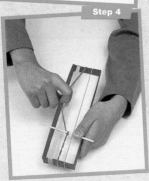
Step 4

Analyze and Conclude

1. How is the thickness of a rubber band related to the pitch of the sound it produces when plucked?

2. **Compare** the sounds produced by the rubber bands in steps 3 and 4. What can you conclude about any differences?

3. What did you do to the rubber band when you twisted the dowel? How did this affect the pitch of the sound produced when it was plucked?

4. Imagine that the rubber bands are strings on a guitar. What general statements can you make about the pitches of sounds produced by guitar strings?

F65

Responding to Individual Needs

Students Acquiring English Encourage students to think of a stringed instrument native to their country. Have them draw a picture of it, labeling its parts in both English and their native language. Have them write a sentence in English and their native language stating how the instrument is similar to the cardboard box guitar. Invite them to demonstrate the instrument.

Activity
Changing Pitch

Preview *Students focus on pitch and should observe that shortening rubber bands raises the pitch of the sound.*

Advance Preparation *See p. F52b.*

1. Get Ready

Time about 30 minutes

Grouping groups of 4–6

Collaborative Strategy One student might record data while the others experiment with the model.

Materials Hints Tissue boxes or shoeboxes may be substituted for cardboard gift boxes.

Safety Review safety precautions with students.

2. Guide the Procedure

- For best results, allow at least 1 cm (about 1/2 in.) space between the rubber bands.

Have students record their data and answer questions on *Science Notebook* p. 324.

Students can use the CD-ROM Spreadsheet and Painter to organize and display their data.

3. Assess Performance

Process Skills Checklist

- Did students follow instructions when **making and using models?**
- Were students able to accurately **predict** the different sounds produced by the rubber bands?
- Were students able to **infer** that decreasing the length of the rubber bands increased pitch?

Analyze and Conclude

1. Thicker rubber bands produce lower-pitched sounds.

2. The twisted rubber band produced a higher sound.

3. The rubber band was shortened, thus increasing the pitch of the sound.

4. Thicker guitar strings produce lower-pitched sounds when plucked. When a guitar string is tightened or the length of the string is decreased (by pressing on it), the pitch is raised.

Wind Instruments Around the World

Preview *Students focus on how the various woodwind instruments produce sounds of differing pitch and timbre.*

1. Get Ready

Background

- Wind instruments, also called aerophones, include all those that produce their sounds by causing a column of air enclosed in a pipe or cone to vibrate. Wind instruments have existed since ancient times. Reed pipes, double pipes, and end-blown flutes date back to about 2500 B.C. in Sumerian and Egyptian civilizations. Bamboo flutes are described in Chinese texts as early as the 10th century B.C. The instruments of the flute and reed groups were the first to become highly developed, since finger holes are easily pierced along their length.

Wind instruments, including flutes, whistles, oboes, and trumpets, have long played an important role in the traditional music of African peoples. Flutes, made from bamboo, wood, clay, and bones are common throughout the sub-Saharan region. Panpipes are common in central Africa, while globular flutes, made from gourds or hard-shelled fruits are found in parts of southern Africa.

Discussion Starter

- **When you think of a marching band, what instruments come to mind?** Answers might include trumpets, tubas, trombones, and flutes.

- **How are these instruments alike?** Students should respond that they all make sounds by vibrating air.

- **How do these instruments differ from one another?** Students might respond that they are shaped differently and produce different sounds.

Wind Instruments
Around the World

In Japan, it's called a *fuye* (fōō'yä); in South Africa it's known as the *naka ya lethlake* (nä'kä yä le-lä'kä); in China, the *ti-tzu* (di dzōō). What is it? All of these words describe the same thing—the musical instrument you know as the flute. Wind instruments in different parts of the world vary in shape and sound. But they are all alike in one way—they depend on a vibrating column of air to produce sound.

The pitch made by the vibrating air depends on the length of the air column, as you observed in the activity on page F64. A shorter column produces a sound with a higher pitch; a longer column produces a lower pitch.

Reed Instruments

The orchestral clarinet uses a reed to produce sounds. A reed is a short, thin piece of wood attached to the mouthpiece. When you blow into the mouthpiece, the reed vibrates, and this vibration causes the column of air inside the clarinet to vibrate. The mouthpiece is attached to a cylindrical tube with holes in it. Covering and uncovering the holes changes the length of the column of air, thereby changing the note that is played. The sound comes out the

bell at the base of the tube.

Compare the orchestral clarinet with the zummara (zōō mä'rə), shown below. The zummara, an instrument played with a reed, has two joined pipes. Made of cane, the zummara has twelve holes, six in each pipe. It is played in Tunisia, a country in northern Africa.

Brass Instruments

You have seen that a wind instrument such as the clarinet uses a reed to make the air vibrate. Brass instruments such as the trumpet and the trombone have no reeds. The player's lips vibrate against the mouthpiece, causing the air in the instrument to vibrate.

Orchestral clarinet▶

Zummara, a double-pipe reed instrument from Tunisia

F66

Investigate Further

Cultural Connection

What to Do Students can investigate panpipes, simple instruments that have been used for thousands of years worldwide. According to Greek mythology, the first pipes were invented by Pan, the god of woods and pastures. Have students answer these questions: **How do panpipes work? Do people in different countries make their pipes from different materials?**

What's the Result? How do panpipes differ among civilizations or countries? In the Aztec civilization wood pipes were played only by enslaved people or by boys about to be sacrificed. The shaman of Tibet used a pipe made from a human leg bone. Pipes have been made from materials ranging from bird bones to tree trunks. The pipe's size can vary according to the materials from which it is made.

The orchestral trumpet uses valves to control the length of the air column and to control the pitch of the sound. The trombone has a slide that changes the length of the air column. In some parts of the world, musicians play trumpets that do not use valves. Instead, the trumpeters use only the vibration of the their lips to change the pitch. Such an instrument is the neku, shown below.

Kinds of Flutes

Flutes also lack reeds. A narrow opening cut in the tube produces sound when air passes over it or through it. In an orchestral flute, this opening is on the side of a long, thin tube. The multiple flute has more than one pipe. This *dvojnice* (dvoi'nē tsə) has a twin pipe carved from a block of wood. Like the orchestral flute, this flute has a mouthpiece and finger holes. However, it does not have keys, and the air is blown in from the top rather than from the side.

Wind instruments from around the world look and sound different. A flutist living in the United States might not be familiar with an African flute. However, people from any country can enjoy the music from these instruments. ■

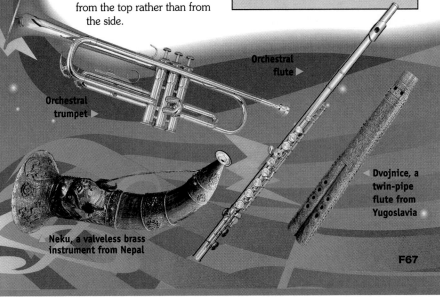

Orchestral flute ▶

◀ Orchestral trumpet

Neku, a valveless brass instrument from Nepal

Dvojnice, a twin-pipe flute from Yugoslavia

F67

UNIT PROJECT LINK

Instruments and other devices are used to create music and sound effects in shows. Work with your team to plan a show based on a folk tale, using the puppets from the puppet show in Chapter 2. After you decide which folk tale you'll use, try telling the tale from a different point of view. Plan the sound effects that you will need. You may even want to build your own instruments and sound-effects devices. Add lighting, using the cellophane-covered flashlights. When your plans are complete, begin your rehearsals.

Unit Project Link

Encourage students to brainstorm ways to provide sound effects and music for the puppet show that they are preparing. Have students determine how they will provide the proper lighting for each scene of the show. Let students record their plans in their *Science Notebooks* on p. 326. Suggest that students use Unit Project Masters F3 – F7 (TRB pp. 101 – 105) for instructions on building simple instruments from different parts of the world and in creating other kinds of sound effects. Students can use the instruments to provide the musical accompaniment to their puppet show. Set aside time for students to rehearse their narration, sound effects, and music.

2. Guide the Discussion

Choose from the following strategies to facilitate discussion.

Connecting to the Activities

- *Highs and Lows, p. F64*
  What wind instruments have you made in the activities in this chapter? Students should recall the bottles used in Highs and Lows.

- **How did you change the pitch with these instruments?** The pitch of the sounds produced by the bottles depended on the amount of water (actually, the length of the vibrating column of air).

Making Comparisons

- **Were your bottle instruments more like a clarinet or a flute? Why do you think so?** More like a flute, since air is blown over a mouthpiece from above; they don't have a reed as a clarinet does.

Identifying and Solving Problems

How do you think that you could make an instrument from *one* tube and still be able to make different-pitched sounds? Encourage speculation; students, especially those who play in the school band, may know that musicians can open and close valves in a tube to produce a tone of the desired pitch.

Responding to Individual Needs

Auditory Activity Play an audiotape of various wind instruments or have students demonstrate them. Ask students to describe how the instruments sound different from one another. Encourage them to use creative adjectives to describe the sounds.

3. Assess Understanding

Let students make "funnel music" by placing the narrow end of a plastic or metal funnel to their lips and blowing into the funnel while making the lips vibrate. Discuss which group of instruments their funnels most resemble (brass instruments, such as the trumpet). Encourage students to write a paragraph describing how their funnel horns differ from the clarinet and flute.

Pitch

Preview *Students focus on the variables that affect the pitch of a sound.*

1. Get Ready

Science Terms pitch, frequency, hertz, octave

Background

- Musical pitch is determined by the number of times a sound-producing medium vibrates per second. An international standard adopted in 1939 places A above middle C at 440 vibrations per second, also expressed as 440 cycles per second, or 440 Hz. This is usually accepted by instrument makers, although some exceptions continue. In the past, a variety of pitch levels existed. The baroque era (17th century) had different standard pitches for secular vocal music, church music, and chamber music. Instrumental pitch in the 18th and early 19th centuries was a half-step lower than the present level. Therefore, people now hear the symphonies of Haydn, Mozart, and others at a different pitch than originally intended.

Discussion Starter

- **What is the difference between the sound of a small child's voice and an adult's voice?** The child's voice is higher pitched.

- **What do you think causes this difference?** Encourage student speculation; remind students of the rubber band banjo activity. Guide students to recall that vibration of something shorter in length produces higher sounds. Lead students to the idea that children have higher-pitched voices than adults because their vocal cords are shorter and thinner than those of adults.

Pitch

Singing the national anthem is not easy for many people, especially when it comes to hitting the high notes. But a good singer can sing the notes having the highest and lowest pitches. **Pitch** is the highness or lowness of sound. It is related to the frequency of the sound waves produced. The frequency of a sound wave is the number of waves passing a location, such as your eardrum, each second. High-pitched sounds produce many sound waves per second and so have a high frequency. Low-pitched sounds produce fewer sound waves per second and so have a lower frequency.

The frequency of a sound wave is measured in a unit called the **Hertz** (Hz), or cycles per second. Humans have a certain range of frequencies that they can hear and a range that they can produce, as shown in the graph below. Also shown is what certain other animals can hear and produce. People can hear sounds as low as 20 Hz and as high as 20,000 Hz. How does this compare with what bats can hear and produce?

Ranges of frequencies heard and produced by certain animals and humans ▼

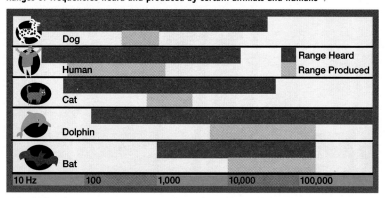

F68

Investigate Further

Cultural Connection

MUSIC NOTES

What You Need cassette or CD player, tapes or CDs of Japanese and Middle Eastern music, western guitar music, and chants (available in many public libraries)

What to Do Play tapes of music from various cultures. Ask students to suggest what instruments they think were used to make the music. Discuss with students the differences between major and minor chords. Invite them to describe their impressions. Then suggest that music can also be made without musical instruments. Play chants or a cappella singing. Discuss any changes in pitch and volume they hear.

What's the Result? Invite students to select a familiar song and sing it as a class without any accompaniment. Discuss with students how the song differs when sung with instruments and without.

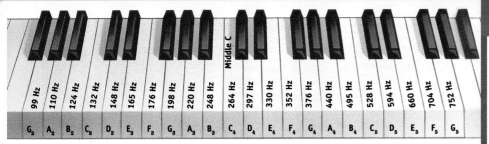

The frequency of notes on a piano keyboard. Middle C, which has a frequency of 264 Hz, is in the center of the keyboard.

Pitch and Music

Do you play the piano, organ, or electric keyboard? If you do, you know that the keyboard is divided into octaves. Each series of eight notes makes up an **octave** (äk'tiv). The keyboard above shows the frequencies of notes of several octaves. Notice that middle C, which has a frequency of 264 Hz, is written as C_4. The note that is one octave below middle C is another C, written C_3. The note C that is one octave above middle C is written C_5. A similar method is used to show octaves for other notes.

Look at the frequencies of C_3, C_4, and C_5. Note how the frequencies are related. Each time you go up an octave, the frequency of the note doubles. How might this explain why we hear all these notes as C? Is this pattern also true of other notes that are one or two octaves apart, such as E_3 and E_4 or G_3 and G_4? Check the frequencies of the notes on the keyboard to find out.

The graph below shows the frequency range for a number of musical instruments and for human voices. In general, men have longer, thicker vocal cords than women. As a result, men find it

Range of frequencies produced by various instruments and the human voice ▼

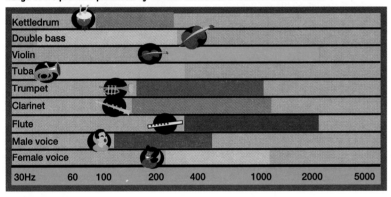

	30Hz	60	100	200	400	1000	2000	5000
Kettledrum								
Double bass								
Violin								
Tuba								
Trumpet								
Clarinet								
Flute								
Male voice								
Female voice								

F69

Integrating the Curriculum

Science & Literature

What You Need Read "On Playing the Mammoth," pp. 230-231, from *The Way Things Work*, by David Macaulay. Show students the drawings that illustrate the section. Following the discussion, ask students to write and illustrate a similar type of story.
What's the Result? When their illustrated stories are finished, encourage students to read them aloud and explain how the illustrations enhance the text.
Multi-Age Classroom Students can work in pairs and should collaborate on ideas for the story and what aspects might be illustrated. As they work, one student can be the writer and the other the illustrator.

---

2. Guide the Discussion

Choose from the following strategies to facilitate discussion.

Connecting to the Activities

• *Highs and Lows, p. F64*
Think back to *Highs and Lows*. When you blew into the bottles to make different sounds, which bottle produced the sound with the highest frequency? The lowest frequency? The bottle with the most water in it produced the sound with the highest frequency, while the bottle with the least amount of water in it made the sound with the lowest frequency.

• *Changing Pitch, p. F65*
When you made the box guitar, which rubber bands produced the lowest sounds? The highest? The thickest rubber band produced the lowest sound, while the thinnest produced the highest sound. **Which sounds had the highest frequency?** The sounds with the highest pitch

• **How did you change the pitch of the sounds?** Shortening the bands produced higher-pitched sounds. **How did you change amplitude?** By plucking harder

Drawing Conclusions

• **What can you conclude about frequency and how high or low a sound is?** Students should conclude that a high frequency produces a high-pitched sound, while low frequency produces a lower-pitched sound.

Thinking About the Data

• **How does the range of sounds bats can hear compare with the range for humans?** Humans can hear sounds from 20 to 20,000 Hz, while bats can hear sounds from 1,000 to 120,000 Hz.

• **Do you think a colony of bats roosting in the top of a barn would be disturbed by people talking in the barn? Explain.** They probably wouldn't be disturbed because most human voices produce sounds lower than the lowest sounds a bat can hear.

• **How does the hearing range of dogs compare with that of humans?** Dogs can hear lower sounds than humans and higher sounds than humans.

Making Comparisons

- **How do the frequencies of notes that are an octave apart compare?** Each time you go up an octave, the frequency of the note doubles.

- **Look at the keyboard diagram on p. F69. What would be the frequency of the A above the highest A shown on the diagram? How do you know?** The frequency would be 880 Hz because it would be double 440 Hz.

Thinking About the Data

- **Look at the chart on p. F69. Which instrument in the chart has the widest range of frequencies produced? Which instrument has the narrowest range of frequencies produced?** The violin has the widest range and the kettledrum has the narrowest range.

- **Which instrument's range of frequencies is closest to that of the human voice?** The range of frequencies of the trumpet and clarinet are closest to that of the human female voice.

Responding to Individual Needs

Kinesthetic Activity Encourage interested students to make a drum by stretching and securing a piece of strong plastic, cloth, or paper over a plastic bowl. They can use a wooden dowel or spoon to tap the drums. Have students investigate how changing the tightness of the drumhead affects the pitch of the sound produced. They might also investigate how the pitch changes when they use a smaller bowl and a larger bowl. Have students present their findings to the class.

Connecting to the Activities

- *Changing Pitch, p. F65*
  How is the way a guitar string's pitch is changed similar to the way you changed the pitch of the rubber bands in the activity? When the strings or the rubber bands are made shorter, the pitch is higher. When the strings or rubber bands are tightened, the pitch becomes higher.

3. Assess Understanding

Use a simple demonstration to reinforce the investigation concept. As students observe, pour water from a pitcher into a bottle. How does the sound change as the water level increases? Review how the length of the column of air is related to pitch, and how pitch is related to frequency.

1 When the guitarist strums the full length of a string, she produces a low note.

2 When she presses her finger on a string, she shortens it, and produces a higher note.

easier to sing notes with lower pitches. Women can more easily sing notes of higher pitches. Because the vocal cords of children are shorter than those of adults, children tend to speak and sing at higher pitches than adults.

Musical Highs and Lows

If you've ever played a guitar, you know that the thicker strings produce the lower notes, and the thinner strings produce the higher notes. The guitar player changes the length of a string by holding the string down against the frets, the bars on the guitar neck. When a string is held against a fret, the part of the string that vibrates is shorter, so the pitch is higher. At the top of the guitar are the pegs that change the tension on the strings. If a string is tightened, the pitch gets higher. If the string is loosened, the pitch gets lower. How does this compare with what you observed in the activity on page F65?

The pitch of the sounds produced by wind instruments depends on the length of the vibrating column of air. The shorter the column, the greater the frequency of vibration and the higher the pitch. As the graph on page F69 shows, the frequency ranges of instruments differ.

Controlling Loudness

The amplitude of the sound waves produced by musical instruments is heard as loudness. For stringed instruments, the loudness depends on how a string is plucked or bowed. The harder you pluck or bow the string, the louder the sound. For wind instruments, the harder the musician blows, the louder the sound. For percussion instruments, such as drums and cymbals, the loudness depends on how forcefully the instruments are struck. ■

INVESTIGATE FURTHER!

EXPERIMENT

Place a plastic ruler on a table, with about half the ruler extending beyond the edge of the table. Hold the ruler firmly on the table top. Use your free hand to "pluck" the free end of the ruler. Note the rate of vibration and the pitch of the sound you hear. Think of a way to change the pitch of the sound produced by plucking the ruler. Discuss this idea with other students and then try it out.

F70

Investigate Further

Experiment

Students should find that the pitch of the sound produced by the ruler increases as the length of ruler extending beyond the edge of the table decreases. Remind students to record their findings on *Science Notebook* p. 327.

Synthesizing Sound

A **sound synthesizer** is an electronic device that can produce a wide variety of sounds. The first electronic sound synthesizer was developed by Harry Olson and Herbert Belar at Radio Corporation of America (RCA) in 1955. Olson and Belar built the synthesizer to carry out research on the properties of sound. But a number of composers recognized the great potential for sound synthesizers to produce real music.

Music Synthesizers

Today synthesized music is produced using a keyboard or a sound bank that creates specific groups of sound waves. Synthesizers can produce sounds

Music synthesizer ▶

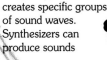

that resemble many traditional instruments, such as pianos and flutes, and they can also combine tones to form new sounds. Some synthesizers can also produce special effects, including echoes and reverberations.

A synthesizer can produce the sounds of every known musical instrument fairly well. So it can sometimes be used to replace an orchestra, and it has become a popular means of providing music for radio, television, and movies.

Speech Synthesizers

Did you ever call directory assistance for a telephone number and hear a robot-like voice? That was synthesized speech! Synthesized speech has many uses. It can provide instructions to children on how to use a computer. It can alert pilots, astronauts, and drivers about conditions that may need their attention. A speech synthesizer can be used by people with various kinds of disabilities.

How does a speech synthesizer work? It stores sounds that are later combined to produce words and sentences that sound like those spoken by a human voice. Most speech synthesizers use the basic sounds of a language such as English. Each of the sounds, when spoken into a microphone,

F71

Science, Technology & Society

SYNTHESIZERS **What to Do** Explain that speech synthesizers are finding wider application in the world today. Cars, telephone systems, airline navigation systems, public announcement systems, and computer tutorials all make use of synthesized speech. Synthesized speech can provide warnings, instruction, or information. Encourage students to investigate current applications of speech synthesizers.

What's the Result? **What uses for synthesized speech do you think you might see in the future?** Responses might include talking appliances to tell you that a pot is boiling over or the washing machine has finished a load; a door that reminds you to close it.

Synthesizing Sound

Preview *Students focus on how synthesizers are used to produce sound.*

1. Get Ready

Science Terms sound synthesizer

Background

- The direct creation of sound by computers was first developed in 1963 at Bell Telephone Laboratories. The system used an IBM 7094 computer and represented each complex sound as a sound pressure-wave.

Discussion Starter

- **How can a single musician take the place of an entire orchestra?** A musician playing a music synthesizer can produce the sound of an orchestra.

2. Guide the Discussion

Choose from the following strategies to facilitate discussion.

Connecting to the Activities

- *Changing Pitch, p. F65*
  How are synthesized sounds like the sounds you made with rubber bands? All are caused by vibration of matter.

Responding to Individual Needs

Musical Activity Interested students could research groups or artists who use music synthesizers. They might bring in tapes or CDs that contain examples of synthesized music to share with classmates.

3. Assess Understanding

Students can work together to design a web drawing showing the ways synthesized speech is used in everyday activities. Encourage students to share their drawings with the class.

INVESTIGATION 3

Close
the Investigation

Critical Thinking Skills
Analyzing, Synthesizing, Applying, Expressing Ideas

1. Low-pitched sounds have a lower frequency than high-pitched sounds; they produce fewer sound waves per second than higher-pitched sounds. If you look at the vibrating part of a ruler hanging over the edge of a table, you can see that when the ruler vibrates faster, the pitch is higher.

2. A piccolo produces higher sounds than a flute because the vibrating column of air in a piccolo is shorter than the column of air in a flute.

Challenge Encourage students to invent and construct their own wind instruments. They should be able to explain and demonstrate how their instruments are played.

Following Up

Baseline Assessment Return to the class list of explanations for differences among people's voices. Encourage students to supplement their list with information they have learned in the investigation.

Reteaching Let students make reeds from drinking straws. Flatten one end of the straw, and cut off the corners to form a point. (The straw will be in the shape of a sharpened pencil.) Students can hold the cut end of the straws between their lips and blow gently. Encourage students to experiment by shortening the straw. Discuss how the sounds are produced.

 Use *Science Notebook* p. 328.

Investigation Review ▶
Use Investigation Review p. 146 in the *Assessment Guide.*

▲ Simulated speech at the supermarket

produces a distinct electric current that can be stored in a computer as part of a magnetic pattern. A set of rules, also stored, is used to put the sounds back together. Following these rules, the computer can produce syllables, words, and sentences. The speech synthesizer can then produce the sounds of a human voice.

When you hear a speech synthesizer, you can usually tell that it is not a real person speaking. But the computer programs of synthesizers are improving, and the voices are becoming more humanlike in quality.

Recognizing Voices

The sound waves that form when people speak can be changed to electrical pulses by a microphone. Some computers have been successfully programmed to respond to the electrical signals produced by voice commands. Instead of typing commands, a person can ask the computer to bring up a certain file. For example, with some telephone systems, you can just say someone's name into the phone, and the system finds that person's number in your directory. You don't even have to dial! ∎

The boy is learning to use a speech synthesizer. ▼

INVESTIGATION 3

1. Explain what causes a high sound to differ from a low sound. Give examples to support your answer.

2. A piccolo is an instrument that looks like a short flute. Would you expect a piccolo to produce higher or lower sounds than a flute? Explain your answer.

F72

Assessment

Investigation Review
How Do High Sounds Differ From Low Sounds?

CHAPTER 3

Name _____ Date _____

1. Use the clues below to unscramble each word. Write the word on the line that follows each clue.

a. ZETHR: Unit used to measure sound frequency ___hertz___

b. VETOCA: Series of eight notes ___octave___

c. HPTCI: Highness or lowness of sound ___pitch___

2. Complete the chart below about the different sounds produced by musicians in a band.

Musician	Activity	Resulting Sound
singer	shortens vocal cords	Pitch goes ___up___.
flute player	shortens length of air column	Pitch goes ___up___.
trumpet player	blows harder	Amplitude ___increases___. Pitch goes ___down___.
bass guitarist	plays thick, long strings	
keyboard player	plays frequencies of 132 hertz and 264 hertz at the same time	Pitches are 1 ___octave___ apart.

The sounds made by the bottles filled halfway should be the same low sound because the pitch made by the vibrating air depends on the length of

Process Skills
Hypothesizing, Inferring

Suppose you have four identical glass bottles. You fill one bottle halfway with water and another almost to the top with water. Then you fill a third bottle halfway with cooking oil and the fourth almost to the top with oil. Then you blow across the top of each bottle. How will the sounds differ? How will they be the same? Explain your answer on a separate sheet of paper.

the air column, not the type of liquid used to fill the bottle. The bottles filled almost to the top should also produce the same high sound for the same reason.

Portfolio
Make a Concept Map
Encourage students to make a concept map centered on the idea of pitch. The concept map should illustrate how pitch is related to frequency and how frequency is related to the length of the column of air and length of a string.

REFLECT & EVALUATE

WORD POWER

amplitude
compression
crest
frequency
hertz (Hz)
octave
overtone
wavelength

pitch
rarefaction
sound
sound
  synthesizer
timbre
trough
vibration

 On Your Own
Review the terms in the list. Then use as many terms as you can in a paragraph about sound.

With a Partner
Mix up the letters of each term in the list. Provide a clue for each term and challenge your partner to unscramble the terms.

PORTFOLIO

Make a graph of the frequencies of the notes of one octave of a musical scale. Make a second graph showing a different octave. How do the patterns of the two octaves compare?

Analyze Information

Study the photograph of the recorder, a simple wind instrument. Then use the photograph to explain how the recorder produces the highest pitch and the lowest pitch.

Assess Performance

Can you make a glass xylophone? Get several drinking glasses of the same size. Put different amounts of water in the glasses. Adjust the amounts until you can play a song by tapping the glasses with a pencil. How does the amount of water in a glass affect the pitch of the sound?

Problem Solving

1. Why would a motorboat sound closer when you're underwater than it actually is when you come to the surface?

2. The keys of a piano are attached to strings. Imagine that you are looking inside a grand piano. Compare the appearance of the strings that produce low notes with that of the strings that produce high notes.

3. In many science-fiction movies, a *whooshing* sound is heard as a spacecraft moves by. The spacecraft and the sound are the products of special effects. Imagine you are in a spacecraft and another flies by. Explain whether you would—or would not—hear a sound.

F73

Chapter Test pp. 147–148 in the Assessment Guide

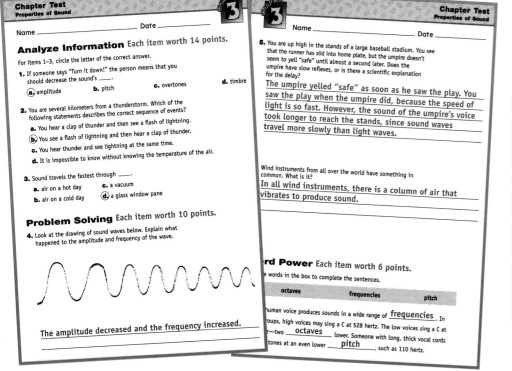

Chapter Test
Properties of Sound

Name _____ Date _____

Analyze Information Each item worth 14 points.
For items 1–3, circle the letter of the correct answer.

1. If someone says "Turn it down!" the person means that you should decrease the sound's ____.
(a.) amplitude   **b.** pitch   **c.** overtones   **d.** timbre

2. You are several kilometers from a thunderstorm. Which of the following statements describes the correct sequence of events?
a. You hear a clap of thunder and then see a flash of lightning.
(b.) You see a flash of lightning and then hear a clap of thunder.
c. You hear thunder and see lightning at the same time.
d. It is impossible to know without knowing the temperature of the air.

3. Sound travels the fastest through ____.
a. air on a hot day   **c.** a vacuum
b. air on a cold day   **(d.)** a glass window pane

Problem Solving Each item worth 10 points.

4. Look at the drawing of sound waves below. Explain what happened to the amplitude and frequency of the wave.

The amplitude decreased and the frequency increased.

5. You are up high in the stands of a large baseball stadium. You see that the runner has slid into home plate, but the umpire doesn't seem to yell "safe" until almost a second later. Does the umpire have slow reflexes, or is there a scientific explanation for the delay?
The umpire yelled "safe" as soon as he saw the play. You saw the play when the umpire did, because the speed of light is so fast. However, the sound of the umpire's voice took longer to reach the stands, since sound waves travel more slowly than light waves.

Wind instruments from all over the world have something in common. What is it?
In all wind instruments, there is a column of air that vibrates to produce sound.

Word Power Each item worth 6 points.
Use words in the box to complete the sentences.

| octaves | frequencies | pitch |

human voice produces sounds in a wide range of **frequencies**. In groups, high voices may sing a C at 528 hertz. The low voices sing a C at two **octaves** lower. Someone with long, thick vocal cords tones at an even lower **pitch**, such as 110 hertz.

REFLECT & EVALUATE

Word Power

 On Your Own Students' use of the terms should reflect an understanding of their meanings.

 With a Partner Students' clues should reflect an understanding of the meanings of the terms.

Analyze Information

The lowest pitch is produced when all of the holes are covered or closed. As holes are uncovered, progressively higher tones are produced for one octave. (Above that octave, higher pitches are reached by "cross fingering.")

Assess Performance

The amount of water in a glass determines the height of the column of air above it. The different lengths of columns of air in the glasses produce different notes. Long columns of air produce low notes; short columns produce high notes.

Problem Solving

1. Sound travels faster in water than in air, and less of the sound energy is changed to other forms of energy in water. Therefore, the motorboat seems closer because the sound is louder.

2. Strings producing low notes are thick and long; those producing high notes are thin and short.

3. If the spacecraft were beyond the atmosphere, no sound would be heard because sound cannot travel in a vacuum.

 Use *Science Notebook* pp. 329–330.

PORTFOLIO

Check students' bar or line graphs for accuracy. The patterns of the two octaves should be the same.

CHAPTER 4 HEARING AND RECORDING SOUND

Subconcepts	Activities	Materials

Investigation 1 How Can You Control Sound?

The intensity, or volume, of sound can be controlled by various materials and devices. *Suggested Pacing: 2–3 class periods* **Standards** p. 155 **Benchmarks** pp. 45, 49	**Directing Sound,** p. F76 *Science Processes:* infer; collect, record, and interpret data; experiment **Muffling Sound,** p. F77 *Science Processes:* measure/use numbers; predict; collect, record, and interpret data; identify and control variables; experiment; make and use models	meterstick*, large piece of construction paper, *Science Notebook* p. 333 small empty cardboard box with top removed*, wind-up clock with loud ticking sound*, meterstick*, sound-absorbing materials (cloth, cotton, bubble-packing*, shredded newspaper, plastic-foam peanuts*), *Science Notebook* pp. 334–335

Investigation 2 How Do People Hear?

Sound waves are transmitted through the structures of the ear to the auditory nerve, where nerve impulses are produced and transmitted to the brain; these impulses are interpreted by the brain as sound. *Suggested Pacing: 3–4 class periods* **Standards** p. 155 **Benchmarks** pp. 45, 54, 197	**Identifying Sounds,** p. F82 *Science Processes:* communicate; infer; collect, record, and interpret data	blindfold, assorted sound makers (bells*, whistles, clickers*, rattles), *Science Notebook* pp. 337–338

Investigation 3 How Is Sound Transmitted and Recorded?

Various electronic devices are used to amplify, record, and transmit sound. *Suggested Pacing: 2–3 class periods* **Standards** p. 155 **Benchmarks** pp. 45, 50, 54, 55, 197, 198	**Magnetic Sounds,** p. F88 *Science Processes:* observe; infer; collect, record, and interpret data **Tape-Recording,** p. F89 *Science Processes:* observe; predict; collect, record, and interpret data; make hypotheses	blank audiocassette*, bar magnet, *Science Notebook* p. 341 blank audiocassette*, tape recorder, bar magnet, pencil, *Science Notebook* pp. 342–343

Overview

In this chapter students investigate various ways to control sound, find out about the human ear and how to help hearing loss, and look into old and new methods of transmitting and recording sound.

Chapter Concept

The ear and auditory nerve, which are responsible for hearing, can be protected by controlling sounds; a variety of inventions have changed the way people record sounds.

Advance Preparation	Curriculum Connection	Assessment
Directing Sound None **Muffling Sound** Have students bring in shoeboxes and a variety of sound-absorbing materials, such as newspapers and plastic foam "peanuts."	Math TG p. F78 Science, Technology, & Society TG p. F79 Integrating the Sciences TG p. F80	**Chapter 4 Baseline Assessment:** *Science Notebook* pp. 331–332 **Investigation 1 Baseline Assessment:** TG p. F76 **Investigation 1 Review:** AG p. 149 **Think It/Write It,** p. F81; *Science Notebook* p. 336 **Following Up on Baseline Assessment:** TG p. F81 **Performance:** TG p. F81
Identifying Sounds None	Language Arts TG p. F84 Integrating the Sciences TG pp. F85, F86	**Investigation 2 Baseline Assessment:** TG p. F82 **Investigation 2 Review:** AG p. 150 **Think It/Write It,** p. F87; *Science Notebook* p. 340 **Following Up on Baseline Assessment:** TG p. F87 **Portfolio:** TG p. F87
Magnetic Sounds None **Tape-Recording** None	Science, Technology, & Society TG p. F90 Language Arts TG p. F91 Cultural Connection TG p. F92 Social Studies TG p. F93	**Investigation 3 Baseline Assessment:** TG p. F88 **Investigation 3 Review:** AG p. 151 **Think It/Write It,** p. F94; *Science Notebook* p. 344 **Following Up on Baseline Assessment:** TG p. F94 **Performance:** TG p. F94 **Chapter 4 Summative Assessment:** Reflect and Evaluate, p. F95 Chapter 4 Review/Test: AG pp. 152–153 *Science Notebook* pp. 345–346

TG= Teaching Guide   TRB= Teacher Resource Book   AG= Assessment Guide   *Materials in the Deluxe Equipment Kit

Chapter Overview

Chapter Concept The ear and auditory nerve, which are responsible for hearing, can be protected by controlling sounds; a variety of inventions have been developed to record sound.

Theme: Systems

The human ear, a hearing aid, sign language, a tape recorder, and a television are each a system made of things and/or processes that interact to perform some function. Thinking about things as systems includes identifying the parts and how one part connects to or affects other parts.

Common Misconceptions

Students might think that sound exists only when they can hear it. Remind students that some sounds cannot be heard by humans. Point out that hearing ability varies from person to person and from one animal to another.

Options for
Setting the Stage

Warm-Up Activity

Play an audiotape of various television voices students might be familiar with and ask them to identify as many voices as they can. Then discuss how they were able to identify the voices.

Use *Science Notebook* pp. 331–332.

Discussion Starter:
In Your Ear

Use the photo and text to start a discussion about hearing aids.

- **How is your hearing tested?** The person being tested wears a set of headphones attached to a device that gives off tones of various pitches and loudness. The person signals, usually by raising a hand, when he or she hears a tone.

- **Career:** *Audiologist*
An audiologist is a person specially trained to detect and diagnose hearing problems. An audiologist uses an audiometer that produces vibrations of various frequencies and intensities to test hearing.

HEARING AND RECORDING SOUND

Some of the things that people enjoy most in life are sounds. We hear a special person's voice, the laughter of a child, our favorite music. All these are possible because of the existence of sound.

In Your Ear

There are about 28 million Americans who have some type of hearing impairment that could be helped by the use of a hearing aid. But only one in four of these people actually gets one. Many people simply don't like the looks of the traditional hearing aid that rests in the cup of the outer ear. Now scientists, led by electrical engineer Henri Garcia, have developed the first "invisible" hearing aid. It consists of a tiny cylinder about .64 cm (.25 in) wide and 1.3 cm (.5 in) long.

This hearing aid is so small that it can be planted inside the ear canal, almost touching the eardrum, where no one can see it. It is crafted from spongy, flexible material. This design allows it to fit comfortably inside the ear while protecting the delicate electronic parts of the device itself.

A hearing aid makes sound louder. In what other ways can sound be changed or controlled?

F74

Home-School Connection

The Explore at Home activity "A Sound Disguise" guides students to experiment with ways to muffle or absorb sound. Distribute the activity (TRB p. 31) when students have completed the chapter. Ask students to suggest reasons that people might want to muffle or absorb sound.

Explore at Home

Name _____ Date _____

A SOUND DISGUISE

If a sound is too loud, how do you soften it? We have been exploring how sound is controlled, how people hear, and how sound is transmitted and recorded. You can experiment with ways sound can be absorbed.

Materials

✔ small film canister or plastic container with lid
✔ cotton balls
✔ small objects (coins, paper clips)
✔ thin cardboard, or thick paper
✔ tape

Procedure

Place one or two small objects in the film canister and close the lid. Shake the canister. Listen to the sounds the objects make. In the data table below, write a sentence describing the sound. Now remove the objects and line the inside of the canister with cardboard or paper. Use tape to secure the lining. Use the same objects and shake the canister again. Record your observations. Finally, remove the cardboard, leaving the objects inside the canister. Tape cotton around the outside of the canister, then shake it. Record your observations.

Results

Did the cardboard or the cotton absorb the sound more effectively? What other materials do you think might be good for muffling sound? Find a way to use what you found out.

Data Table	
Canister	Sound I Heard
without cardboard or cotton	
with cardboard	
with cotton	

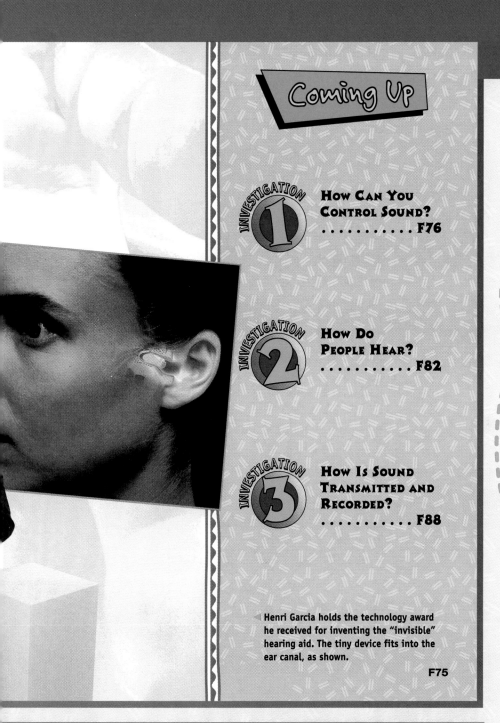
Henri Garcia holds the technology award he received for inventing the "invisible" hearing aid. The tiny device fits into the ear canal, as shown.

F75

Chapter Road Map

How Can You Control Sound?

Activities
* Directing Sound
  Muffling Sound

Resources
* Turn Up the Sound

How Do People Hear?

Activities
* Identifying Sounds

Resources
American Sign Language
* How the Ear Works
  Help for Hearing Loss

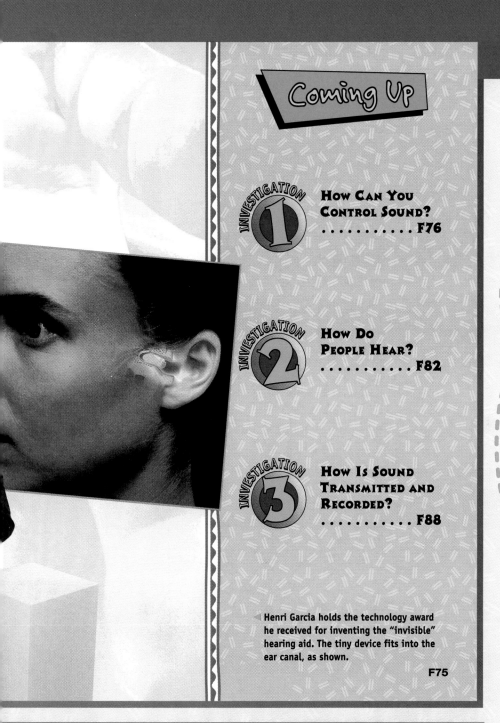

How Is Sound Transmitted and Recorded?

Activities
* Magnetic Sounds
  Tape-Recording

Resources
* Recorded Sound
  Delivering Information

Technology Alert

CD-ROM

Ears to You Enhances or replaces Investigation 2

The activities in **Ears to You** encourage students to think about how they hear sounds; the activities also identify the body parts used in hearing. First, students see an anatomical view of the outer, middle, and inner ears and their relationship to the nose, mouth, and throat. They label the path of sound waves traveling through the parts of an ear. They "click" on labels to hear how each part of the ear functions in order for humans to hear. Students drag labels to identify each part in sequence. In the Writer, students record how they think each structure is adapted to its function. They can view a video in which an ear, nose, and throat doctor explains how hearing aids help correct hearing impairment or loss.

*Pressed for Time?

As you work through the upcoming investigations, focus on the activities and resources identified by the clock.

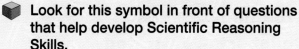
Look for this symbol in front of questions that help develop Scientific Reasoning Skills.

HOW CAN YOU CONTROL SOUND?

Planner

Subconcept The intensity, or volume, of sound can be controlled by various materials and devices.

Objectives
- **Investigate** how sound can be controlled.
- **Describe, identify,** and **classify** materials that can control sound.
- **Infer** how volume is measured and how loud sounds can affect health.

Pacing 2–3 class periods

Science Terms volume, intensity, decibel, noise pollution

Activate Prior Knowledge

Baseline Assessment Drop a paper clip and ask students if they heard it fall. Ask: **How could this sound be made louder?** Record and save students' responses for use in Following Up.

INVESTIGATION 1

HOW CAN YOU CONTROL SOUND?

Have you ever been to a rock concert? If you have, you know how loud sounds can be made. People are often controlling sound—making it louder, softer, higher, or lower. In this investigation you will explore some of the ways sound can be controlled.

Activity

Directing Sound

MATERIALS
- meterstick
- large piece of construction paper
- *Science Notebook*

Outdoors, bands sometimes play in front of a curved band shell. How does a band shell control sound?

Procedure

With your class, go to an open area outdoors. Have one student stand about 50 m away, face the class, and make an announcement, such as "The football team will practice at 3 P.M." Record how well you heard him or her. Next have the student cup both hands around his or her mouth and repeat the announcement at the same volume. Record how well you heard the announcement.

Finally, have the student roll a piece of construction paper into a megaphone, or cone shape. Have the student place the megaphone up to his or her mouth and again make the announcement. Record how the sound of the student's voice compares to the two other times he or she spoke.

Analyze and Conclude

1. When could you best hear the student speak? Why?
2. Where are megaphones used? What is their purpose?
3. How are a megaphone and a band shell alike?

F76

Activity Directing Sound

Preview *Students focus on ways to direct sound using the principles of a megaphone and should find that a megaphone amplifies a sound.*

1. Get Ready

Time about 20 minutes

Grouping whole class

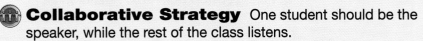 **Collaborative Strategy** One student should be the speaker, while the rest of the class listens.

2. Guide the Procedure

- Choose a day and location where there is little or no wind to minimize interference with the speaker's sounds. Instruct the speaker to speak in the same tone of voice and with the same volume for each trial.

 Have students record their data and answer questions on *Science Notebook* p. 333.

 You may wish to have students use the CD-ROM Spreadsheet to organize their data.

3. Assess Performance

Process Skills Checklist
- How well did students **collect** and **record data?**
- Were students able to **infer** the purpose of megaphones?

Analyze and Conclude
1. The student could be best heard when he/she used a megaphone because the megaphone directed the sound.
2. Megaphones are used in large open spaces to direct and amplify a speaker's voice toward the audience.
3. Both a megaphone and a band shell direct sound.

Activity
Muffling Sound

Have you ever been kept awake by the sound of a ticking clock or a dripping faucet? Can you control how far a sound carries?

Procedure

1. Place a small cardboard box on its side with the opening toward you. Place a ticking clock inside the box.

2. Walk away from the box in a straight line until you can no longer hear the clock ticking. **Measure** this distance with a meterstick. **Record** the distance in your *Science Notebook*.

3. With the alarm clock still in place, fill the box with one of the sound-absorbing materials. **Predict** how far you will be from the box when you will no longer be able to hear the clock ticking. Repeat step 2.

4. Repeat step 3, using a different material. **Predict** the sound-absorbing quality of each material. Continue until all the materials are used.

5. Make a list of all the materials, rating them from best to worst. (*Best* means "best at muffling sound.") **Compare** your results with those of other groups in your class.

Step 3

Analyze and Conclude

1. Do some materials muffle sound better than others? **Give evidence** to support your answer.

2. Which of the materials muffled sound best? What did the best mufflers have in common?

3. Would the addition of more of the same material muffle sound better? **Design an experiment** to find out.

4. Did all the students in your class have the same results with the materials they tested? Account for any differences in the results.

F77

Responding to Individual Needs

Auditory Activity In some occupations people wear special earmuffs to reduce sound. Using some of the materials they used in the activity, challenge students to design and construct noise-reducing earmuffs.

Activity   Muffling Sound

Preview *Students experiment with muffling sound with various kinds of sound-absorbing materials and should find that some materials have better sound-absorbing properties than others.*

Advance Preparation *See p. F74b.*

1. Get Ready

Time about 30 minutes

Grouping groups of 4–6

Collaborative Strategy Group members can take turns filling the box with the materials and measuring.

Safety Review safety precautions with students.

2. Guide the Procedure

- Caution students to be sure the clock stays upright and in the same place each time they wrap it.

- Have students record their data and answer questions on *Science Notebook* pp. 334–335.

- You may wish to have students use the CD-ROM Spreadsheet to organize their data.

3. Assess Performance

Process Skills Checklist
- Did students accurately **measure** and **record** distances to the ticking clock?
- Did students make reasonable **predictions?**
- Did students **compare** the sound-absorbing materials? Were they able to rate them?
- Were students able to **design an experiment** to test additional materials?

Analyze and Conclude
1. Yes, as evidenced by the differences in distance at which one must stand before no longer hearing the clock tick.
2. Plastic foam and cotton balls are among the best sound mufflers; cloth and shredded newspaper are among the poorest. The best mufflers seem to be soft, fluffy materials.
3. More material muffles sound better.
4. Variations in muffling ability may be due to the amount of material and tightness of packing.

Turn Up The Sound

Preview *Students focus on the volume, or intensity, of sound and the measurement of that intensity. Students also discover ways to reduce unwanted and harmful sound.*

1. Get Ready

Science Terms volume, intensity, decibel, noise pollution

Background

- Exposure to loud sounds can affect not only the ears but all parts of the body. One of the hazards of this exposure is that people tend to build up a tolerance to loud sound. As people develop this tolerance, they must continually increase the sound intensity in order for something to sound "normal." In this way, a person can become less aware of the damage being done to health.

- Continuous exposure to sounds above 85 decibels can result in hearing loss. Studies have shown that other effects of loud noise are increased irritability, lower productivity, and increased incidence of migraine headaches, fatigue, and allergic reactions.

Discussion Starter

- **What sounds bother you?** Encourage all responses. Some responses will focus on the loudness of a sound while others refer to the quality of the sound itself. Help students understand that different people have different likes and dislikes. What one student considers noise, another student might consider a pleasant sound.

- **Which of the sounds do you think could damage your hearing?** Allow students to speculate and to give reasons for their opinions.

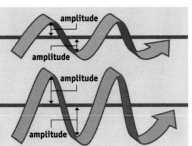

"Turn down that radio!" "Could you please turn up the TV a little?" What are you changing when you turn the radio "down" or the TV "up"? You are changing the volume, or loudness of the sound. **Volume** describes how loud—or soft—a sound is. It is related to the **intensity** of the sound, which is a measure of the energy of a sound wave. Recall from Chapter 3 that if you make a drawing of a sound wave, a loud sound would have a large amplitude. A soft sound would have a small amplitude.

Sound wave of a soft sound (*top*); sound wave of a loud sound (*bottom*)

Sounds vary in intensity, or volume. The intensity of sound is expressed in decibels (dB). ▼

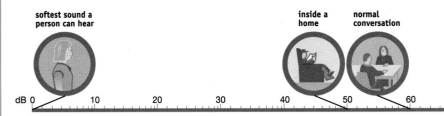

F78

Integrating the Curriculum

Science & Math

DECIBEL SCALE

What to Do Students can find relationships among the decibel scale, exponents, and the powers of 10. Remind students that $10^1 = 10$, $10^2 = 100$, and 10^2 is 10 times greater than 10^1. Ask students to make a chart or table that gives the level of representative sounds in powers of 10. (Hearing at 10^0, breathing at 10^1, whispers at 10^2, rustling newspaper at 10^3, and so on.)

What's the Result? How did you determine the power of ten at each level in the table? The number in the tens place of decibel value represents the exponent, or power of 10.

Measuring Volume

The unit used to measure sound intensity, or volume, is the **decibel** (des′ə bəl). A sound that most people can just barely hear has an intensity of 0 decibels, or 0 dB.

The table on this page lists various common sounds and their intensity, or volume, in decibels. The sound of normal breathing or rustling leaves, which has an intensity of 10 dB, is 10 times as loud as a sound that a person can just barely hear—0 dB. A 20-dB sound is 100 times as loud as a 0-dB sound and 10 times as loud as a 10-dB sound. Every increase of 10 decibels means the intensity of the sound has increased by a factor of 10.

Of course, whether a sound is loud enough to disturb you depends on other factors. The sound of a rustling newspaper is 10 times as loud as the sound of a whisper, but a whisper may disturb you if you're trying to study. The sound of street traffic is 1,000 times as loud as a rustling newspaper, but you may ignore it if you're playing ball on the

Source Sounds	Intensity (dB)
Barely audible	0
Breathing	10
Whispers	20
Rustling newspaper	30
Quiet conversation	40
Normal conversation	60
Street traffic	70
Rush hour traffic	90
Subway (near)	100
Thunder (near)	110
Loud rock music	120
Jet airplane (near)	140
Rocket engine (near)	180

playground. Also, devices such as megaphones, which direct sound toward you, can make sounds seem louder than they actually are.

A sound of 120 dB is loud enough to cause pain in the ears. Such sound is 1 billion times as loud as the 30-dB sound of a rustling newspaper. Where might you hear a sound this loud?

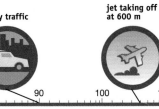

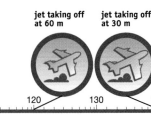

heavy traffic   jet taking off at 600 m   jet taking off at 60 m   jet taking off at 30 m

70 80 90 100 110 120 130 140

F79

Investigate Further

Science, Technology & Society

DECIBEL CHART

What to Do Students can expand upon the decibel chart in the text by making their own. They can make a bar graph, with a bar for every 10 decibels. Above or below each bar, they can draw or describe the source of a sound they think is appropriate. They could use the decibel chart in their text as a guide, but the sounds in their chart should be different from those in the text.

What's the Result? Choose an item from your chart that is above 80 decibels. What changes could you make in your life to avoid long exposure to that sound? Avoid turning up the volume to the maximum level on radios and television. (In most cases, it is not necessary to avoid loud sounds completely—just long, continuous exposure to them.)

Choose from the following strategies to facilitate discussion.

Connecting to the Activities

- *Muffling Sound, p. F77*
  In the activity, what characteristic of the sound did you change when you packed various materials around the ticking clock? Students changed the intensity of the sound reaching them. They did not, however, change the clock's volume; it was always ticking at the same volume.

What did the various materials do to the sound energy from the ticking clock? What evidence supports your answer? The materials absorbed much of the sound energy; the fact that the ticking could not be heard well at various distances supports this.

Making Inferences

When might a loud, unpleasant sound be desirable? An unpleasant sound might be useful as a warning—an approaching fire truck or other emergency vehicle, a smoke alarm, a carbon monoxide detector, or an alarm clock.

Responding to Individual Needs

Students Acquiring English Encourage students to describe the source of each sound illustrated in the decibel chart. They could describe the source in their native language as well as in English.

Making Judgments

Where would you place some everyday sounds you hear on the decibel chart? Encourage discussion of each suggestion to find the best place for it on the chart in terms of proposed volume.

Making Inferences

- **What loud sounds that you hear today were unknown 100 years ago?** Students will likely mention sounds from jet engines and other large machines, but they might also mention amplified music at concerts, loud radios and CD players, snow blowers, leaf blowers, power mowers, and hair dryers.

Thinking Critically

▪ **How do you add to the noise pollution of your community?** Students might mention the use of loud music or the use of outdoor machinery that is annoying to others.

▪ **How could you reduce noise pollution at home or in your community?** Responses might include reducing the volume of the TV and CD players, reducing the amount of time spent operating a hair dryer, and occasionally doing a chore manually instead of using a machine.

Making Comparisons

• **Where were you the last few times you heard sound reflected as an echo? What kind of materials reflected the sound and what did they have in common?** They were all hard substances such as rock walls in a canyon, or a brick or concrete wall of a gym, or the tiles surrounding a pool..

Identifying and Solving Problems

▪ **If a room in your house were producing annoying echoes, how would you try to fix it?** Add sound-absorbing materials such as throw rugs, carpeting, and cloth wall hangings.

SCIENCE IN LITERATURE

That's a Wrap: How Movies Are Made
by Ned Dowd

Students might enjoy working in small groups to write the script for a short movie scene, complete with sound effects. They can refer to the example in the book.

3. Assess Understanding

Groups of students can choose a sound they believe is annoying, disturbing, or harmful. Suggest that students work together to propose ways in which the sound can be changed or lessened so it is no longer annoying. Groups can present their ideas as posters and share them with the class. (For example, if students chose the noise from heavy traffic outside the school building, they might suggest adding sound-absorbing drapes to classroom windows.)

Noise Pollution

The growth of cities and technology has led to sounds and sound volumes that were unknown until recent centuries. Studies have shown that exposure to loud noise or loud music can damage a person's hearing. Besides causing damage to the ear itself, noise can cause stress-related disorders such as hives, ulcers, or high blood pressure. The occurrence of damaging sound in the environment even has a name—**noise pollution**!

An understanding of the properties of sound can help you reduce noise pollution. Like light, sound is absorbed by some materials and reflected by others. Materials that are hard, such as concrete or brick, reflect most of the sound that reaches them. Highway engineers

▲ In a recording studio a complex control panel allows the sound engineers to control sounds produced by the recording artists.

THAT'S A WRAP: HOW MOVIES ARE MADE
by Ned Dowd
Books for Young Readers, Simon & Schuster, 1991

You may say that you want to see a movie, but *seeing* is only half the experience. Try enjoying a movie with your hands over your ears! Movie makers know that the sound of a film is just as important as its images. That's why there are sound designers, boom operators, and sound mixers on movie crews. That's why the director yells, "Quiet on the set!"

Find out how a movie is made by reading *That's a Wrap: How Movies Are Made* by Ned Dowd. You'll learn how the stunts and special effects are recorded. From a whispered secret to an explosion, sounds make movies thrilling.

Investigate Further

Integrating the Sciences

LIFE SCIENCE

What to Do Tell students that many animals hear much better than humans do. Note that many animals' ears are different from those of humans. Some animals, such as owls, are quite good at locating the direction from which a sound is coming. Have pairs of students blindfold each other with scarves and test each others' hearing by making soft noises from different directions. Partners should point to the direction from which they think the sound is coming.
What's the Result? Discuss with students the result of their experiment. **How would the results differ if you had been listening to loud music?** Talk with students about how loud music can hinder someone's ability to hear for a while, even after the music stops playing.

take advantage of this property by building wooden or concrete barriers between highways and surrounding homes. These barriers help reduce noise by reflecting it.

Materials that are soft, such as cloth, plastic foam, and acoustical plaster, absorb much of the sound that reaches them. These materials are useful in reducing noise within buildings. In many buildings, ceilings and walls are built of such sound-absorbing materials. The hanging banners in school gymnasiums help absorb sound so that you can hear the gym teacher speaking. ■

A large cafeteria can be a very noisy place if it has no materials to absorb sound (*left*). A restaurant is often a quiet place because its chairs, floors, and walls have sound-absorbing materials (*right*).

=== INVESTIGATION 1 ===

1. Describe at least two specific ways that people can control sound.

2. What is a decibel? Draw and explain a scale that shows sounds around you expressed in decibels.

F81

Assessment

Portfolio

In My Opinion Encourage students to write a brief statement supporting or opposing an anti-noise ordinance that bans the playing of loud radios on streets, buses, and trains. If students oppose such ordinances, have them suggest alternatives to protect others from unwanted sounds.

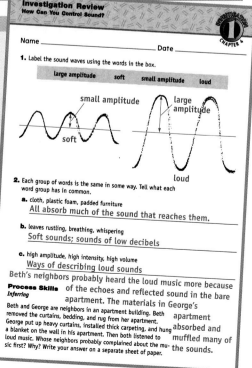

Investigation Review
How Can You Control Sound?

Name _____ Date _____

1. Label the sound waves using the words in the box.

| large amplitude | soft | small amplitude | loud |

small amplitude — large amplitude

soft

loud

2. Each group of words is the same in some way. Tell what each word group has in common.

a. cloth, plastic foam, padded furniture
All absorb much of the sound that reaches them.

b. leaves rustling, breathing, whispering
Soft sounds; sounds of low decibels

c. high amplitude, high intensity, high volume
Ways of describing loud sounds

Process Skills
Inferring
Beth and George are neighbors in an apartment building. Beth removed the curtains, bedding, and rug from her apartment. George put up heavy curtains, installed thick carpeting, and hung a blanket on the wall in his apartment. Then both listened to loud music. Whose neighbors probably complained about the music first? Why? Write your answer on a separate sheet of paper.

Beth's neighbors probably heard the loud music more because of the echoes and reflected sound in the bare apartment. The materials in George's apartment absorbed and muffled many of the sounds.

Close
the Investigation

Critical Thinking Skills
Applying, Synthesizing, Expressing Ideas

1. People can control sound by directing the sound as it leaves the source and by muffling or absorbing the sound after it leaves the source.

2. A decibel is a unit used to measure the intensity of sound. Students' scales should reasonably depict the relative loudness of common sounds.

Challenge Suggest that students contact your city or town clerk's office to find out if your community has any anti-noise ordinances. If it does, suggest that groups create bulletin board displays to tell others about the ordinances. Each display should show a noise that is discouraged by the ordinance. Have students discuss why some noises are prohibited only during the evening and night hours.

Following Up

Baseline Assessment Return to the class list of ways to amplify the sound of a dropped paper clip. Ask students if they are still satisfied with their original responses or if they now have other ideas on how to make the dropped clip heard. Let them revise the list accordingly.

Reteaching Collect several magazine photos depicting sounds. Discuss each sound in terms of its decibel level, whether or not it is a hazard to health, and, if so, what could reasonably be done to reduce the hazard.

 Use *Science Notebook* p. 336.

◀ **Investigation Review**
Use Investigation Review p. 149 in the *Assessment Guide*.

HOW DO PEOPLE HEAR?

Planner

Subconcept Sounds are transmitted through the structures of the ear to the auditory nerve, where nerve impulses are produced and transmitted to the brain; these impulses are interpreted by the brain as sound.

Objectives

- **Infer** which properties of sounds can be used to identify the sounds.
- **Identify** the parts of the human body involved in hearing.
- **Evaluate** why people's ability to hear varies.

Pacing 3–4 class periods

Science Terms auditory nerve, eustachian tube, semicircular canals, hearing aid

Activate Prior Knowledge

Baseline Assessment Ask students to draw their conception of the inside of the human ear. Save their drawings for use in Following Up.

Activity Identifying Sounds

Preview *Students examine their abilities to identify a variety of sounds and should find that some properties of sounds are helpful clues to their identification.*

1. Get Ready

Time about 30 minutes

Grouping groups of 4–6

Collaborative Strategy Students will need to take turns speaking. However, one student can record which speakers were identified and how often they were recognized.

INVESTIGATION ②

HOW DO PEOPLE HEAR?

Every day you are bombarded by sound. You may wake up to the jarring noise of an alarm clock. On the street, recyclers may be collecting your used glass. How can you tell one sound from another? This investigation explores hearing—and not hearing.

Activity
Identifying Sounds

MATERIALS
- blindfold
- assorted sound makers (bells, whistles, rattles)
- *Science Notebook*

How distinctive are sounds? Are there any two voices—or sounds—that are exactly alike? In this activity you'll test how well you can tell one sound from another.

Procedure

1. Blindfold one member of your group. Then have each student in your group, one by one, say a word or phrase. Have the blindfolded student identify each person who speaks. **Record** in your *Science Notebook* whether the blindfolded student could identify each person.

2. Repeat step 1. This time, have each student *whisper* the same word or phrase. **Record** whether each person was identified. **Discuss** your findings with your group.

3. Blindfold a different group member. Have each student, one by one, make a sound with a different sound maker.

4. **Record** whether the blindfolded student identified each sound maker. **Discuss** your findings as a group.

F82

Step 3

Responding to Individual Needs

Inclusion Activity As an alternative activity, you could play a variety of music, each with a distinct predominant instrument, such as percussion, brass, strings, or piano. Ask students to indicate when they can hear the predominant instrument and tell how the sounds of the instruments differ from one another. Ask them to identify the instrument being played.

Analyze and Conclude

1. In step 1, could the student correctly identify each person who spoke? What do you think allowed the blindfolded student to identify the speakers? If the student couldn't identify each person, give a reason why not.

2. In step 2, could the blindfolded student identify each student who spoke? Why might it have been difficult to identify the speakers?

3. Could the blindfolded student identify each sound maker? Which ones couldn't be easily identified?

4. In general, what properties of a sound can be used to identify it?

UNIT PROJECT LINK

Plan a soundtrack for the folk tale you have begun rehearsing. Include the instruments and other devices needed for the sound effects. Choose a narrator to tell the story. Decide how long the show will last. Then make an audiotape of the soundtrack, including the narration. Make sure the puppets' movements are synchronized with the soundtrack.

F83

Investigate Further

Unit Project Link

Encourage students to be creative when planning the soundtrack for their puppet show. Remind them that common objects can sometimes be used to create needed sounds. Explain that on old radio shows, coconut shells on a board were used to make the sound of galloping horses and a sheet of metal was shaken to create the sound of thunder. Suggest that students brainstorm ideas for creating the soundtrack and special effects. For help with sound effects, use Unit Project Master F3 (TRB p.101) Have them record their ideas on *Science Notebook* p. 339. When they are ready to perform their show, they might want to prepare a theater program. For help on this program, use Unit Project Master F8 (TRB p. 106)

Materials Hints Of the sound-makers used, try to get two that are similar in sound, such as two bells with different tones.

Safety Review safety precautions with students.

2. Guide the Procedure

- You might want to reserve the gym so that student groups can be more widely separated.
- To help eliminate distractions from neighboring groups, remind students that even when speaking to the blindfolded group member, they should speak quietly.
- Each speaker, in turn, should stand in the same location relative to the blindfolded listener.

 Have students record their data and answer questions on *Science Notebook* pp. 337–338.

 You may wish to have students use the CD-ROM Spreadsheet to organize their data.

3. Assess Performance

Process Skills Checklist

- How well did students **collect** and **record data** about voices and sounds that the blindfolded students identified?
- Did students listen carefully to a sound before **inferring** its identity?
- Were students able to **infer** what helped blindfolded students identify voices? Were they able to give reasons why a voice might not have been identified?
- Were students able to **communicate** what properties of a sound can be used to identify it?

Analyze and Conclude

1. Clues to the speaker's identity might include the pitch of the voice, the quality of the voice, and accents.

2. Students should report that, in general, it was much more difficult to identify the speakers who whispered because the distinguishing characteristics of the voices are missing.

3. Except for sound-makers with very similar pitch and tone, students should be able to accurately identify each one.

4. Possible responses might include using pitch, loudness, and sound quality (timbre).

American Sign Language

American Sign Language

Preview *Students focus on some ways in which hearing-impaired people communicate.*

1. Get Ready

Background

- American Sign Language (Ameslan or ASL) is largely the product of a collaboration that took place in the early nineteenth century. Thomas Hopkins Gallaudet, a Connecticut minister, and Laurent Clerc, a deaf sign-language teacher from Paris, France, developed ASL based on an existing French system. By 1964, Gallaudet College, a liberal arts college for the deaf, was established. Today, ASL is the fourth most commonly used language in the United States.

Discussion Starter

- **How can you communicate without speaking?** Let students demonstrate sign language they use.

2. Guide the Discussion

Choose from the following strategies to facilitate discussion.

Connecting to the Activities

- ***Identifying Sounds, p. F82***
  Without using words, how might you have identified the speaker? Point to the person or use a pre-arranged hand signal.

Responding to Individual Needs

Inclusion Activity Invite any students who use ASL to demonstrate the language and to teach the class how to say "hello" and simple phrases.

3. Assess Understanding

In groups, students can demonstrate examples of nonverbal communication in common use, such as waving the hand in greeting.

 "I even got to ride on an elephant!" Sara was excited as she told her parents about the trip to the zoo that day. She described the antics of the monkeys and the sheep, but she didn't say a word. How did Sara tell her story? She used American Sign Language—a method of communication that uses the hands, face, and body to express ideas.

People who can hear acquire language by listening to people around them and imitating what they hear. Deaf people need another way to learn language. They often use one of the many sign languages from around the world.

One form of sign language, American Manual Sign Language, uses hand gestures to spell out the letters of words. When using this sign language, a person must "sign" each letter of the word he or she wishes to express. The letters are put together to form words.

By contrast, American Sign Language, or ASL, uses signs to express single words or groups of words often used together. But ASL is not just a direct translation of English into signs. It is a language all its own, with unique expressions and ideas. Many of these expressions cannot be directly translated into the spoken word.

Many members of the deaf community prefer ASL over American Manual Sign Language because it offers more freedom of expression. ■

A girl signing "I sign in American Sign Language." ▼

I | sign | in | American Sign Language

Integrating the Curriculum

Science & Language Arts

What to Do As a class, create your own version of ASL for 10-20 words and ideas. Use stick figures or descriptions to "write" this alphabet on the chalkboard or chart paper. Then invite students to make a sentence using the sign language. Can the rest of the class correctly interpret the signs?

What's the Result? How difficult was it to create a language that didn't include sound? How effective were you at communicating with other students without sounds? Allow students to relate their difficulties and successes.

How the Ear Works

The Structure of the Ear

How do you hear sound? Sound waves are collected by the parts of the outer ear. Then the sound waves move to the middle ear, where they cause the eardrum to vibrate. The eardrum is connected to three tiny bones that transmit the force of sound vibrations from the eardrum. The last of the three bones pushes against a membrane that separates the middle ear from the inner ear.

In the inner ear, vibrations are transmitted to the cochlea. The cochlea contains fluid, which also vibrates. A membrane that runs along the entire length of the cochlea has about 30,000 tiny hair cells (not the same as the hairs on your head). When the fluid in the cochlea vibrates, some of these hairs move. Their movement causes nerve impulses to travel along the **auditory nerve** to the brain. The brain interprets the nerve impulses as sounds.

A Tunnel and Balance

The **eustachian tube** (yoo stā′kē ən toob) is a tunnel that connects the middle ear to the throat. It allows air to pass between the middle ear and the

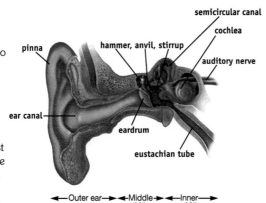

pinna
hammer, anvil, stirrup
semicircular canal
cochlea
auditory nerve
ear canal
eardrum
eustachian tube

←—Outer ear—→ ←Middle→ ←Inner→
ear   ear

throat, which helps keep air pressure within the ear the same as the outside air pressure. Have your ears ever hurt while you were flying in an airplane? The pain is caused when the air pressure inside your ear is different from the air pressure around you.

Your inner ear, especially the **semicircular canals**, helps you keep your balance. These canals are filled with fluid and contain hair cells that respond to movement. Nerve impulses from these cells give the brain the information needed to keep the body balanced. ∎

F85

Investigate Further

Integrating the Sciences

LIFE SCIENCE **What to Do** Students can research the different kinds of ears animals have and how they affect their sense of hearing. They might find out about the long ears of a jackrabbit, the large ears of an elephant, or the short ears of an Arctic fox. Students can also report on other structures that receive sound vibrations, including antennae on insects, and membranes on frogs.

What's the Result? Allow time for students to share information.

Multi-Age Classroom One group can research how different mammals hear, and other groups can research how insects, amphibians, or fish hear. Within each group students can divide up tasks such as writing and making up posters.

How the Ear Works

Preview *Students focus on the structure of the human ear and how sound is transmitted.*

1. Get Ready

Science Terms
auditory nerve, eustachian tube, semicircular canals

Background
- The three tiny bones in the middle ear that transmit and amplify vibrations from the eardrum are the maleus, incus, and stapes. They are commonly called the hammer, anvil, and stirrup because their shapes resemble those objects.

Discussion Starter
- **How do the outer parts of the ear help you to hear?** Some students may mention how the shape of the ear collects sound waves. The opening allows sound waves to enter the middle and inner ear.

2. Guide the Discussion

Use the following strategy to facilitate discussion.

Connecting to the Activities
- *Identifying Sounds, p. F82*
  Use what you now know about hearing to describe how you were able to hear sounds in the activity. The outer ear collected sound waves, which moved to the middle ear, where they caused bones to vibrate. Vibrations continued to the inner ear, where they were turned into nerve impulses, which traveled to the brain and were interpreted as sound.

3. Assess Understanding

Students can work in groups of four to make flow charts using arrows to show the path sound takes from its source to its interpretation by the brain.

Help for Hearing Loss

Preview *Students focus on the kinds of devices that can help people who have hearing loss.*

1. Get Ready

Science Term hearing aid

Background

• Electronic hearing aids are basically tiny telephones, consisting of a microphone, an amplifier, and a receiver. The first electronic hearing aid was made around 1900. Since then, hearing aids have become smaller, less expensive, and more convenient to wear. Some are even built into the frames of eyeglasses.

Discussion Starter

• **How would you feel about wearing a hearing aid if you needed one?** Allow students to discuss what they know about hearing aids from personal experience with a family member.

2. Guide the Discussion

Choose from the following strategies to facilitate discussion.

Connecting to the Activities

• *Directing Sound, p. F76*
How might the cone-shaped paper you used in the first activity be used as a simple hearing aid? It could be used to collect sound.

Responding to Individual Needs

Students Acquiring English On the chalkboard, have students trace the path of sound waves and electrical impulses to and from a hearing aid to show nonverbally how this instrument helps someone hear.

3. Assess Understanding

Students can work in groups to compare a hearing aid to other devices that amplify sound. Students should recognize that hearing aids increase the volume of the sound for the wearer.

Help for Hearing Loss

 About 10 percent of the population has some form of hearing loss, or deafness. There are several kinds of loss. Some people can't hear certain frequencies of sound; others hear all sounds but hear them more faintly than they are heard by people with normal hearing.

Hearing loss has many causes. A damaged eardrum can cause hearing loss, as can injury to the auditory nerve—the nerve leading from the ear to the brain. Damage to the auditory nerve cannot be corrected. But most deafness, including that due to nerve damage, can be helped through hearing aids and sometimes with surgery.

If your great-grandparents had hearing problems, they may have used an ear trumpet. This device, similar to a reverse megaphone, was used to funnel more sound into the ear.

Today, most hearing loss can be at least partially helped with a battery-powered hearing aid. A **hearing aid** receives sound waves and converts them into electrical impulses. The electrical signals are amplified, converted back to sound waves, and channeled to the eardrum through a plastic piece molded to fit inside the outer ear. The hearing aids are so tiny that it's difficult to tell if someone is wearing one.

Before hearing aids were invented, ear trumpets were used to funnel sound to the ear. ▷

F86

Investigate Further

Integrating the Sciences

LIFE SCIENCE

What to Do Tune in a radio to an all-news or talk station. Turn the volume to the lowest level at which you can still understand the speakers. Next, turn the bass to the maximum level and turn the treble to the minimum level. Explain to students that the sound they hear is a model of what some hearing-impaired people hear.
What's the Result? Which voices are more difficult to understand—high or low voices? Which sounds are harder to understand—vowels or consonants? How might you change how you speak to help a person with a hearing loss understand what you say? Students should conclude that they at least need to pronounce all vowel and consonant sounds very clearly.

Two kinds of electronic hearing aids are shown on this page. Both are comfortable and help with certain kinds of hearing loss. As you read on the opening page of this chapter, a new, tiny hearing aid is now available. This hearing aid is implanted deep in the ear canal. Because the device is placed very close to the eardrum, it prevents many of the problems of standard hearing aids. People who use this device find that they can understand normal conversation much more easily. The aid allows people to hear high-frequency sounds that are often distorted by other hearing aids.

Not all people with hearing loss can use this hearing aid. For example, some may have ear canals that are not the right shape to hold the hearing aid. Fortunately, engineers are always working on new ways to help hearing-impaired people. ■

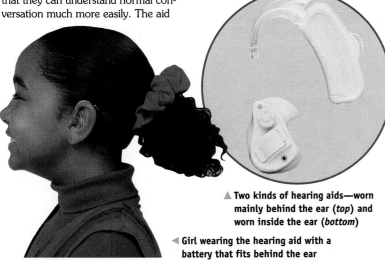

▲ Two kinds of hearing aids—worn mainly behind the ear (*top*) and worn inside the ear (*bottom*)

◀ Girl wearing the hearing aid with a battery that fits behind the ear

INVESTIGATION 2

1. Imagine that you are a sound wave traveling through a human ear. Describe your trip.

2. How is a hearing aid somewhat like a compact microphone and stereo set?

F87

Assessment

Portfolio
Make a Concept Map
Students can make three separate concept maps, one for each part of the ear. Then suggest that they use one or two words to link the maps together.

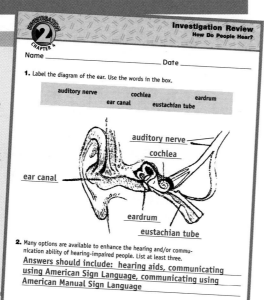

INVESTIGATION 2
Close the Investigation

Critical Thinking Skills
Synthesizing, Applying, Expressing Ideas

1. Possible response: I enter the outer ear and move through the ear canal, which is part of the middle ear. At the end of the ear canal, I strike the eardrum, which vibrates. Then I travel through three tiny bones—the hammer, anvil, and stirrup. I pass from the last bone to reach a membrane, and then enter the inner ear. Here I cause the fluid-filled cochlea and many tiny hair cells to vibrate. My vibrations are then changed to nerve impulses that travel by the auditory nerve to the brain.

2. A hearing aid receives sound waves as a microphone does. It changes them to electrical impulses that are amplified, converts them back to sound waves, and channels them to the eardrum as a stereo and its speakers do.

Challenge Suggest that students work in pairs to draw storyboards showing how loud or prolonged noises can damage the ear. Remind students that they should show what part of the ear is damaged.

Following Up
Baseline Assessment Return to the drawings students made of the ear. Let them use their new knowledge to make refinements to their drawings.

Reteaching Work with students to make a clay model of the ear. Use different colors of clay for the different parts. Let students shape the clay and suggest how the parts should connect and why they connect that way.

Use *Science Notebook* p. 340.

◀ **Investigation Review**
Use Investigation Review p. 150 in the *Assessment Guide*.

HOW IS SOUND TRANSMITTED AND RECORDED?

Planner

Subconcept Various electronic devices are used to amplify, record, and transmit sound.

Objectives
- **Investigate** ways in which sound can be amplified, recorded, and transmitted.
- **Compare** and **contrast** ways to record sound.

Pacing 2–3 class periods

Science Terms phonograph, audiocassettes, compact disc, information superhighway, Internet

Activate Prior Knowledge

Baseline Assessment Ask: **Which words do you associate with sound transmission and recording?** Record and save students' responses and save for use in Following Up.

INVESTIGATION ③ HOW IS SOUND TRANSMITTED AND RECORDED?

Within the last century, inventors achieved a long-time goal: to record great artists' performances so they could be heard by future generations. This investigation explores how sound is transmitted and recorded. It also explores some ideas for the future.

Activity

MATERIALS
- blank audiocassette
- bar magnet
- *Science Notebook*

Magnetic Sounds

You've probably purchased audiocassettes of your favorite recording artists. Perhaps you've taped your own voice. Do you have any idea how sounds are recorded? This activity will give you a hint about how it happens.

Procedure

Carefully **examine** the tape inside a blank audiocassette. In your *Science Notebook*, **record** your ideas on how sound is recorded on the tape. **Discuss** these ideas with your group. Then place a bar magnet close to the exposed part of the tape. **Observe** what happens and **record** your observations.

Analyze and Conclude

1. What happened when you brought the bar magnet close to the tape?

2. Based on your observations, what can you **infer** about the nature of the tape?

F88

Activity Magnetic Sounds

Preview *Students focus on learning about recording tape and should find that the tape is attracted to the magnet.*

1. Get Ready

Time about 10 minutes

Grouping groups of 4–6

  Collaborative Strategy One student might move the magnet closer and farther from the cassette tape, while another student records observations.

Safety Review safety precautions with students.

2. Guide the Procedure

- Encourage students to brainstorm as many ideas as possible on how sound is recorded on tape.

Have students record their observations and answer questions on *Science Notebook* p. 341.

You may wish to have students use the CD-ROM Spreadsheet to organize their data.

3. Assess Performance

Process Skills Checklist
- Did students make reasonable **inferences** as to how sound is recorded on tape?
- Did students **observe** and **record** data accurately?

Analyze and Conclude
1. The tape in the audiocassette was attracted by the magnet.
2. Because only magnetic objects are attracted to magnets, the audiocassette tape must be made with a magnetic metal or magnetized material.

Activity
Tape-Recording

You should keep your audiocassettes away from magnets. In this activity you will deliberately place a bar magnet near an audiocassette that contains a recording. What do you think will happen?

Step 1

Procedure

1. Tape-record the voices of the members of your group. Have each student say at least one sentence.

2. Rewind the tape and then play back the taped sentences.

3. In your *Science Notebook*, **record** how each student sounds. For example, **record** whether the taped students' voices sound the same as in normal conversation.

4. Remove the audiocassette from the tape recorder. While holding a bar magnet near the surface of the exposed tape, use a pencil to rewind the tape completely. **Predict** what you think will happen. **Discuss** your predictions with other members of your group.

5. Now play the tape. In your *Science Notebook*, **record** what you hear on the tape. Note whether there are any changes in the students' voices.

Analyze and Conclude

1. **Compare** how the students' voices sounded in step 2 and step 5. Account for any differences you heard.

2. If you heard any differences in the voices, **suggest a hypothesis** to explain what happened.

3. Write a statement about the effect of a bar magnet on tape-recorded sound. Why should you keep magnets away from audiocassette tapes?

F89

Responding to Individual Needs

Students Acquiring English Pair English-proficient students with students less proficient in English. Request that the proficient speakers aid their partners in preparing messages to be recorded. Then allow the less-proficient speakers time to practice their messages in English.

Activity
Tape-Recording

Preview *Students focus on the nature of tape-recording and should find that placing a magnet near a cassette recorder erases the recorded sounds.*

1. Get Ready

Time about 20 to 30 minutes

Grouping groups of 4–6

Multi-Age Strategy Students can work together to prepare their messages for taping. Encourage students to contribute as many ideas as they are capable of producing.

Safety Review safety precautions with students.

2. Guide the Procedure

- For best results, suggest that students speak slowly and distinctly when recording their messages.

Have students record their data and answer questions on *Science Notebook* pp. 342–343.

You may wish to have students use the CD-ROM Spreadsheet to organize their data.

3. Assess Performance

Process Skills Checklist
- Did students **make observations** comparing the sound of voices before and after taping?
- Did students **make predictions**, based on previous experience, that holding a magnet near a cassette tape would adversely affect the tape?
- Did students **record data** that accurately reflected their observations and predictions?

Analyze and Conclude

1. In step 2, recorded voices should sound much like the students' unrecorded voices. In step 5, the recorded voices should be erased or distorted if the magnet was not in complete contact with the exposed tape.

2. The voices sounded different because the magnet changed the magnetic tape. (Some students might say that the magnet changed the direction of some of the tiny magnetic particles on the magnetic tape.)

3. A bar magnet can erase or distort tape-recorded sound.

Recorded Sound

Preview *Students focus on ways in which sound can be recorded.*

1. Get Ready

Background

- Photographic processes can be used to record a soundtrack on movie film at the same time that pictures are filmed. Sound is changed by a microphone into electrical impulses. These impulses open and close a light valve, which allows varying amounts of light to fall on the film as the soundtrack. When the film is shown, a photoelectric cell reads the soundtrack and converts the light into electric current. When fed through amplifiers and loudspeakers, the current is increased and changed back into sound.

Discussion Starter

- **What do you think magnets, microphones, laser light, and your favorite rock group have in common?** Encourage students to speculate and to elaborate on their ideas. Suggest that they draw a concept web to represent their ideas.

Recorded Sound

Early Recordings

Thomas A. Edison had a knack for inventing devices that fascinated the public. In 1877 he invented a sound-recording device—the **phonograph** (fō′nə graf). To record sound, he used a thin metal disc that vibrated when sound waves struck it. A metal penlike device called a stylus was attached to the disc. The tip of the stylus touched a sheet of metal foil that was wrapped around a rotating cylinder.

When sounds made the disc vibrate, those vibrations were transferred to the stylus. As the stylus vibrated, the sound

cylinder

▲ An early phonograph

was recorded as a pattern of tiny hills and valleys in a spiral track on the cylinder.

By reversing the recording process, it was possible to hear the sounds on the

Thomas A. Edison and the phonograph he invented ▼

Investigate Further

 ### Science, Technology & Society

RECORDING **What to Do** Students can discuss how essential they feel sound recordings are to people. Remind them that the recording industry employs hundreds of thousands of people and takes in billions of dollars in sales. Suggest that students list all the jobs they can think of that rely on the recording industry and recording technology.

What's the Result? Encourage students to share their lists and discuss any additional benefits of this technology.

Multi-Age Classroom Students can work in pairs or small groups to compile their lists of jobs and benefits. Volunteers could take turns serving as the recorder.

cylinder. As the cylinder was turned, a stylus rose and fell over the hills and valleys in the recorded soundtrack. The vibrations produced sounds that traveled out through a megaphone attached to the stylus.

Edison's phonograph was a wonderful invention, but it did have some problems. The sound reproduction was poor, and the cylinders wore out after being played only a few times. Only one cylinder could be recorded at a time. A singer had to sing each time a recording was made on a cylinder.

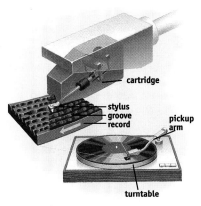

cartridge
stylus
groove
record
pickup
arm
turntable

▲ A long-playing (LP) record on a turntable

Invention of the Record

In 1888, Emile Berliner dramatically improved sound recording by inventing the disc record. Berliner produced a "master" copper plate that contained all the patterns of the recording. This copper plate could then be used to stamp out large numbers of copies on shellac resin discs. From then on, a singer had to sing a song only once—for the master disc—and then many copies could be made. The great opera singer Enrico Caruso made a recording that sold more than a million copies by 1900!

Inventions Improve Recordings

When plastics were developed, they were used to replace the shellac resin records. Plastic records were lighter and were less likely to break. But the greatest advantage of plastic records was that they could be made with narrower and more closely packed soundtracks. Only one song could fit on the old shellac resin records, but several songs could be recorded on one plastic record. Plastics led the way to long-playing (LP) records, which first appeared in 1948.

Sound in Stereo

Ten years later, stereophonic (stereo) records were introduced. Two separate microphones were used during the recording, and two separate soundtracks were cut in the recording disc. When a stereo record was played, each soundtrack was connected to a separate loudspeaker. The two speakers produced sound that was like a live performance. People quickly replaced their old one-speaker record players with new "stereos."

Sound on Tape

But then a new method for recording sound was developed—coating plastic tapes with a magnetic material such as iron oxide. Today, many people use

F91

Integrating the Curriculum

Science & Language Arts

COMMERCIALS **What to Do** Have students prepare a 2-3 minute commercial or public-service announcement for a sound-recording device. Remind them to include what the device does and how it works. They can perform their commercials as a play or make an audiotape of their work.

What's the Result? How effective do you think you were at educating or persuading your audience? Students should assess how effectively they presented their information.

Multi-Age Classroom Students can work in small groups to prepare their commercials or announcements. Allow groups to give presentations to the class and then to discuss audience reaction.

---

2. Guide the Discussion

Choose from the following strategies to facilitate discussion.

Making Comparisons

- On the chalkboard, list the major advances in recording mediums: cylinder, shellac resin disk, plastic record, magnetic tape, and CD. **What advantage does each advance have over the preceding one?** Answers might include more sound to each recording, lighter weight, more portable, and better sound quality. Suggest that students draw a diagram to represent each advantage.

Responding to Individual Needs

Gifted and Talented Activity Provide the following for students: a sewing needle, a small paper cup, an old record (one that is not valuable), and a phonograph turntable without a stylus, or a lazy Susan. Challenge students to devise a way of using the materials that allows them to listen to the record. (Placing the sewing needle through the bottom of the paper cup will allow the cup to act as an amplifier and the needle to act as a stylus. By gently holding the cup assembly against the turning record, students will be able to hear the recorded sound.)

Connecting to the Activities

- **Tape-Recording, p. F89**
  Radio stations use devices to erase sound tapes. What do you think these devices contain? Students should infer that the devices have a strong magnet that erases sound when it is passed in one direction, across the magnetic tape.

Making Inferences

 What materials and what technology needed to exist before magnetic tape recording could be invented? Students should recognize that materials such as microphones, magnetic oxide coatings, and electromagnets all needed to exist.

3. Assess Understanding

Students can work as a class to design and create a bulletin board illustrating the history of the development of sound-recording devices.

◄ An audiocassette, showing the magnetic tape on small reels

magnetic tape
record/playback head
erase head
magnetic tape
recorded iron oxide particles
erased iron oxide particles

audiocassettes—miniature versions of the older reel-to-reel tapes. When you record sound on tape, as you did on page F89, electric currents produced by sound waves entering a microphone are sent through the coil of an electromagnet (the recording head). The changing electric current in the coil causes changes in the magnetic field of the recording head. As the tape moves through the changing magnetic field of the head, a magnetic pattern is formed in the tiny crystals of iron oxide on the surface of the tape. The tape can then be passed through another head, called the playback head. This causes it to produce weak electrical signals that are then amplified. When these amplified electrical signals are fed to a loudspeaker, they reproduce the sounds that first entered the microphone.

By the mid-1980s audiocassettes were outselling records. This was due mainly to their convenience. Tapes could be played anywhere—even in a moving car.

Compact Discs (CDs)

Tapes store a magnetic "image" of sounds. Today, digital signals can also be used to store sound. In a digital recording, the electrical signal from the microphone is changed to a series of on-or-off electrical pulses that are recorded as strong or weak magnetic fields.

A **compact disc**, or CD, contains a digital recording. Along the very thin recording track of the disc, the "offs" are recorded as pits. The "ons" are recorded as the flat surface of the disc. As the disc spins on a CD player, the codes of offs and ons along the track are scanned by a laser beam and changed to electrical signals. These signals are then sent to the speakers. Today, CDs are fast replacing audiocassette tapes. What do you think might replace CDs? ■

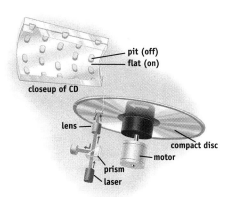

pit (off)
flat (on)
closeup of CD
lens
compact disc
motor
prism
laser

A compact disc (CD), showing an enlargement of "pits" (holes) and "flats" (flat surfaces) ▷

F92

Investigate Further

Cultural Connection

COMPARING MUSIC **What to Do** Provide students with records, cassette tapes, and CDs of a variety of music from different cultures (available at libraries). Students can listen to the recordings. For each cultural selection, encourage them to identify the instruments making the sounds. Have them list the instruments and describe the sounds they make.

What's the Result? Have students rate the quality of the sounds they heard with each type of recording device.

Delivering
Information

 STS
SCIENCE
TECHNOLOGY
& SOCIETY

Television provides the world with an amazing variety of entertainment. You can enjoy comedy, drama, music, and sports all on the same day in the comfort of your home. Satellites in orbit above Earth make it possible for people in nearly all parts of the world to view an Olympic event as it happens.

Through TV, you can see world leaders in action and observe the effects of wars and natural disasters. You can also see that even though people have different backgrounds and cultures, people all over the world have many of the same needs and interests.

The Information Superhighway
Your television will soon be part of the communication system of the future—the **information superhighway**. The telephone,

computer, and television will be combined to link people together in a way that was not possible before. Imagine being part of a worldwide network joining communication, entertainment, and information. Your telephone line will be your link to the information superhighway.

Small but powerful computers linked by telephone lines and television cable systems will take you to any stop you choose along the information superhighway. Even now, many personal-computer users browse through libraries and databases and communicate with

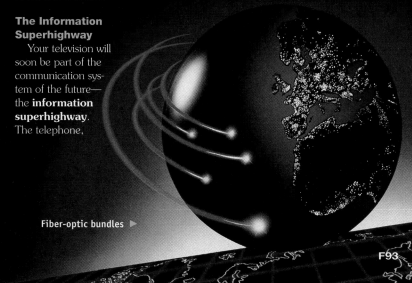

Fiber-optic bundles ▶

F93

Integrating the Curriculum

Science & Social Studies

 GLOBAL TV

What to Do Provide this information:

Country	TV sets per 1,000 people
United States	814
China	60
France	319
West Germany	404

Ask students what the data suggest about the potential success of the "information superhighway" in different countries. Ask them what other data they would need for a more complete picture.
What's the Result? **What conclusions can you draw from the data?** Among the countries listed, the United States would be most likely to be part of the information superhighway.

Delivering
Information

Preview *Students focus on the changes that television has made in people's lives and the changes the information superhighway might bring.*

1. Get Ready

Science Terms information superhighway, Internet

Background

• The Internet is an international web of interconnected computer networks. A person at a computer terminal can communicate by placing data in an Internet Protocol (IP) packet, an electronic envelope, and "addressing" the packet to a particular destination on the Internet. By 1994, the Internet had grown to an estimated 30,000 connected networks with about 25 million people accessing it.

Discussion Starter

• **How many hours do you watch TV each day? How would your life be different if you stopped watching it?** Let students speculate and describe what their lives might be like without television.

2. Guide the Discussion

Use the following strategy to facilitate discussion.

Connecting to the Activities

• ***Tape Recording, p. F89***
What other recording media use magnetic storage? Videotapes, computers

3. Assess Understanding

 Students working in small groups can make a booklet entitled "The Information Superhighway: Riding it Today and Tomorrow."

Close
the Investigation

Critical Thinking Skills
Expressing Ideas, Generating Ideas

1. Possible response: When Edison recorded sound, the vibrations of the sound were pressed into a wax cylinder. When a needle moved over the cylinder, it imitated the vibrations of the original sound and recorded them as hills and valleys on the cylinder.

2. Possible response: We would all have access to research information the moment we needed it.

Challenge Encourage students to describe what kind of sound recording or transmitting device they would like to invent. They should be sure to describe what it would do, who would be likely to use it, and how it is an improvement over current technology.

Following Up

Baseline Assessment Return to the list students made concerning sound transmission and recording at the start of the investigation. Ask students if they would like to add words to the list.

Reteaching Students can make a recording museum with models, pictures, or diagrams of early recording devices and examples of today's devices. Encourage students to write a few words about each device in the exhibit.

 Use *Science Notebook* p. 344.

Investigation Review ▶
Use p. 151 in the *Assessment Guide*.

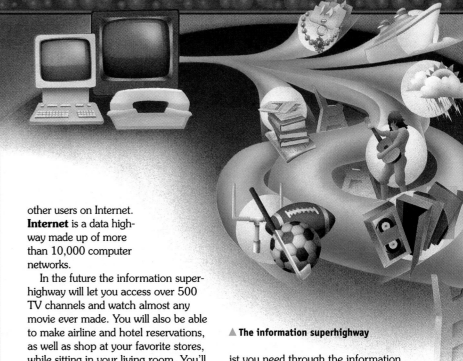

other users on Internet. **Internet** is a data highway made up of more than 10,000 computer networks.

In the future the information superhighway will let you access over 500 TV channels and watch almost any movie ever made. You will also be able to make airline and hotel reservations, as well as shop at your favorite stores, while sitting in your living room. You'll be able to buy whatever you wish by inserting a credit card into a slot beside your TV screen.

Your doctor will be able to provide you with better care because he or she will be able to reach the medical special-

▲ The information superhighway

ist you need through the information superhighway. The specialist will be able to view, examine, and talk with you and your family doctor.

What lies beyond the information superhighway? In another two or three decades you'll know! ■

INVESTIGATION 3

1. Choose a sound-recording system, either old or new, and describe how sound is recorded on this device.

2. Describe how you think your life may be changed if your home or school is linked to the information superhighway.

F94

Assessment

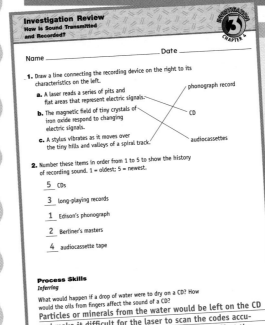

Investigation Review
How Is Sound Transmitted and Recorded?

Name _____ Date _____

1. Draw a line connecting the recording device on the right to its characteristics on the left.

a. A laser reads a series of pits and flat areas that represent electric signals.

b. The magnetic field of tiny crystals of iron oxide respond to changing electric signals.

c. A stylus vibrates as it moves over the tiny hills and valleys of a spiral track.

phonograph record

CD

audiocassettes

2. Number these items in order from 1 to 5 to show the history of recording sound. 1 = oldest; 5 = newest.

_5_ CDs

_3_ long-playing records

_1_ Edison's phonograph

_2_ Berliner's masters

_4_ audiocassette tape

Process Skills
Inferring

What would happen if a drop of water were to dry on a CD? How would the oils from fingers affect the sound of a CD?
Particles or minerals from the water would be left on the CD and make it difficult for the laser to scan the codes accurately. In the same way, oils from fingers could affect the way a laser scans the codes. Both situations could affect the sound quality.

Performance

Scene Small groups of students can write a scene, complete with sound effects and music, describing how the methods of recording sound have changed over time. They can make a videotape of their scene and play it back for their classmates.

REFLECT & EVALUATE

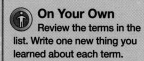 **WORD POWER**

audiocassette
auditory nerve
compact disc
decibel
eustachian tube
information superhighway
noise pollution
phonograph
semicircular canal

intensity
Internet
hearing aid
volume

 On Your Own
Review the terms in the list. Write one new thing you learned about each term.

With a Partner
Write each term in the list on one side of an index card and the definition on the other side. Use the cards to quiz your partner.

 BUILD YOUR PORTFOLIO

Design a poster to make people aware of the danger of loud noises. Show why loud noises are dangerous and suggest ways people can protect themselves.

Analyze Information

Look at the graph below. How does the sound shown at 50 dB compare with the sound at 60 dB? Suggest a sound that could be placed at 0 dB.

dB 0   10   20   30   40   50   60

Assess Performance

Some rooms in your home or school might be very noisy because they have few sound-proofing materials in them. Choose such a room and plan a way to reduce the noise level of the room.

Problem Solving

1. One thing actors must learn is to speak loudly enough to be heard by the audience. This skill is called "projecting the voice." Why do actors have to project more when an audience is present than at rehearsals?

2. One type of frequently used hearing aid was not worn in the ear. Instead, it was hooked over the ear and rested against the bone behind the ear. How, do you think, did this hearing aid help a person hear?

3. Devices such as LPs, cassette tapes, and CDs do not actually "store" sound itself. Explain what is meant by this statement.

F95

Chapter Test pp. 152–153 in the Assessment Guide

CHAPTER 4
Name _____ Date _____

Chapter Test
Hearing and Recording Sound

Analyzing Information Each item worth 14 points.
For items 1–3, circle the letter of the correct answer.

1. A stylus and cartridge are parts of which sound device?
(a.) phonograph   c. CD
b. audiocassette   d. hearing aid

2. Which of the following materials would be the best flooring to use to absorb sound?
a. concrete   (c.) carpeting
b. tile   d. wood

3. The sound having the highest decibel level is ___.
a. heavy traffic
b. whispering
c. thunder
(d.) nearby rocket engine

Problem Solving Each item worth 10 points.

4. The information superhighway provides people with many advantages. Describe three advantages of using the information superhighway and one disadvantage of using it.
Positive aspects might include availability of information through libraries and databases and communicating with other users. Disadvantages might include a decrease in the amount of time people communicate in person and the possibility of information being misused. Answers will vary.

Chapter Test
Hearing and Recording Sound
CHAPTER 4

Name _____ Date _____

5. Why does swallowing when you are in an airplane help to relieve the pressure in your ears?
Swallowing helps to equalize the air pressure inside your ear and the air pressure outside your body.

6. Explain how a hearing aid can help a person with a hearing loss.
A hearing aid receives sound waves, converts them to electrical signals, amplifies the signals, and converts them back to sound waves to help a person hear.

Word Power Each item worth 7 points.
the blanks using the words from the box.

compact disc   volume   decibels   auditory nerve

a compact disc, a laser reads pits and flat areas and produces a digital
the decibels of the sound waves produced from the coded signal is
d in volume. In your ear, vibrations caused by sound waves travel to
ditory nerve, and then into your brain. Then you hear your favorite song.

REFLECT & EVALUATE

Word Power

 On Your Own Have students use the Glossary to check definitions.

With a Partner Clues should reflect an understanding of the meaning of the terms.

Analyze Information

The 60 dB sound is ten times louder than the 50 dB sound. A very soft whisper might be placed at 0 dB.

Assess Performance

The students might suggest placing a rug on the floor or carpet the room. Adding heavy drapes or covering the walls and ceiling with acoustical tile also would help reduce the noise level.

Problem Solving

1. The audience and their clothing would absorb some of the sound made by actors' voices.

2. A behind-the-ear hearing aid vibrates the bones directly. The bones then vibrate the fluid in the cochlea. The vibrating fluid disturbs the hair-like nerves, and the nerves send electrical impulses to the brain. Finally, the brain perceives the impulses as sound.

3. The sound is actually converted into a changing electrical signal by a microphone, fed into a recording head, and converted into a series of patterns–grooves, pits and flats or magnetic particles oriented in one of two directions.

 Use *Science Notebook* pp. 345–346.

BUILD YOUR PORTFOLIO

Posters should show that loud sounds can contribute to hearing loss and stress-related disorders, such as hives, ulcers, or high blood pressure. Posters might include people wearing foam ear plugs or sound-blocking earmuffs. Other protections against noise pollution include sound barriers and sound-absorbing materials in homes, schools, and workplaces.

INVESTIGATE FURTHER!

UNIT PROJECT:
The Big Event

Students can begin their final preparations for the sound and light show using puppets by deciding on a guest list and then designing and making special invitations, perhaps in the shape of a puppet, spotlight, or musical instrument. On the day before the event, have students work in groups to prepare and decorate the classroom. For example, groups can set up the stage and lighting, make a welcoming banner, prepare a refreshments table, and design and make programs to distribute to the guests. For more information on the Big Event, see Wrapping Up the Project p. F1l. For assessment use Unit Project Scoring Rubric Master F9 (TRB p. 107).

 Have students use *Science Notebook* p. 347.

Experiment

Before students begin their projects, have them develop plans to organize their ideas. Allow time for students to display and share posters showing the results of their mixing different pigments.

Research

Before students begin work on their research, encourage them to develop outlines to organize their investigation and to assist in sharing what they learn with the class. Set aside an area of the classroom where students can display their work. You may wish to invite other classes to come in to see the displays and hear about what the students learned about light and sound.

Throughout this unit, you've investigated questions related to light and sound. How will you use what you've learned and share that information with others? Here are some ideas.

Hold a Big Event
to Share Your Unit Project

You and your class have been putting together a sound and light show using puppets as the characters. You've written and rehearsed the narration and worked on the special lighting effects. You've made models of musical instruments from different parts of the world and have rehearsed the songs played on the instruments. Now is the time to put the finishing touches on your show. Go over all the details until everything is perfect—the narration, the lighting, and the music. Then put on the show for another class or the entire school. You may even wish to invite your family and friends to enjoy the show!

Experiment

In this unit, you investigated the effects of mixing different colors of light. Create an experiment to discover if mixing different colors of paint pigments yields the same results as mixing different colors of light. Make a poster showing the results of your experiment.

Research

Choose a topic in this unit to investigate further at the library. You might want to learn more about musical instruments of different cultures. You might want to explore how the colors and sounds in fireworks are created. Or, you might want to find out what sound pollution is and why it can be dangerous. Find an interesting way to share what you learn.

F96

Home-School Connection

Closing Letter

Dear Family,

We hope you and your student have enjoyed learning about light and sound. If you would like to explore this topic further, here are some additional activities you can do together.

• Enjoy a concert or other musical experience. Listen to the tones and pitches of the music. Talk about which instruments sound high and which sound low.

• Arrange a family field trip to a store that sells musical instruments. Ask the clerk to demonstrate a few of the instruments. Note the different sounds each instrument makes and the way the sound is directed from the instrument.

• Explore reflections in mirrors. Talk about how a mirror shows reversed images. Try writing secret messages that can only be read when held up to a mirror.

• Read all about it! These books can help you learn more about light and sound.

101 Physics Tricks
by Terry Cash (Scholastic, 1990).
This book contains entertaining experiments that use everyday materials to explore a variety of physics topics including light and sound.

Color and Light
by Barbara Taylor (Sterling, 1991).
This book contains projects and activities for all ages showing how light makes color possible.

Sound and Music
by Barbara Taylor (Warwick Press, 1990).
This well illustrated book is about the basic principles of sound, with instructions for making various musical instruments.

The Closing Letter at the end of this unit suggests a variety of activities on musical instruments and mirrors that students and their families can do together as well as books they can read. Distribute the Closing Letter (TRB p. 32) to students at the end of this unit.

UNIT F — MATERIALS LIST

Following is a list of materials needed for activities in Unit F. Quantities are for a class of 30 students working in groups of 5. Quantities are also listed for those materials included in the Modular Deluxe Kit.

Materials	Class Quantity Needed	Modular Deluxe Kit Quantity	Activity Page
Consumable Materials			
cardboard, large pieces	6		F20
cardboard tubes	6 sets of 2	6 sets of 2	F36
cellophane, blue, red, green	1 roll, each color	1 sheet, each color	F44, F46
cups, paper	12	12	F61
cups, plastic	6	1 pkg (25)	F60
folders, manila	6		F30
modeling clay	1 lb.	4 colors, 1 lb	F36
newspaper	6 sheets		F30
paper, construction	1 large piece		F76
paper towels	1 roll		F21
paper, lens	6 sheets	1 pkg (50 sheets)	F30
pencils	12		F54, F61, F89
rubber bands, thin, medium, thick	18, 6 of each thickness	3 sizes, 12 of each	F44, F54, F65
string (twine) (assorted lengths)	1 roll	1 roll	F55, F61
tape, transparent	1 roll		F7, F36
vegetable oil (oil, corn)	36 oz	36 oz	F21
yarn, colored (10 cm-long pieces)	1 skein	1 skein	F55
Nonconsumable Materials			
clock, wind-up (must tick loudly)	1	1	F77
audiocassettes, blank (tape, cassette)	6	1	F88, F89
batteries, size D	18	18	F7
blindfolds	6		F82
bottles, small-necked plastic (identical)	18		F64
boxes, cardboard (small)	6	6	F65
boxes, shoe, cardboard, with cover	6	6	F77
cans, aluminum (empty)	15		F60
cups, plastic	15	25	F60
dowels, wooden (small—10 cm long)	6	6	F65
flashlights	18	6	F20, F30, F44
goggles	30	6	F14, F54, F55, F65
jars, unbreakable, 16 oz	6	6	F21
lenses, concave	6	6	F30
lenses, convex	6	6	F30
lenses, convex (A—15 cm focal length)	6	6	F36
lenses, convex (B—5 cm focal length)	6	6	F36
light bulb holders	6	1 pkg (6)	F7
light bulbs A (True Value Krypton Bulb, K-2)	6	6	F7
light bulbs B (Ray-O-Vac Krypton Bulb, K3-2)	6	6	F7
magnets, bar	6		F88, F89
materials, sound-absorbing (cotton balls, bubble wrap, plastic-foam peanuts)	variety	1/2 cu-ft plastic foam peanuts/ bubble wrap (2 sheets)	F77
metersticks (tape, metric)	6	6	F76, F77
mirrors, concave	6	6	F20
mirrors, convex	6	6	F20
mirrors, plane (mirrors, round)	6	6	F20

MATERIALS LIST *(Continued)*

Materials	Class Quantity Needed	Modular Deluxe Kit Quantity	Activity Page
objects, small, of different colors	assortment		F46
paper clips	12		F61
rulers	6	6	F30, F36, F54
scissors	6		F36
sound makers (bells, whistles, rattles, clickers)	variety	bells (6); clickers (6)	F82
springs, plastic coil (spring toy)	6	6	F14, F55
tape recorders	1		F89
wire, insulated copper	1 roll	1 roll (100 ft)	F7

**Additional kit options are available.
Contact your sales representative for details.**

THINK LIKE A SCIENTIST

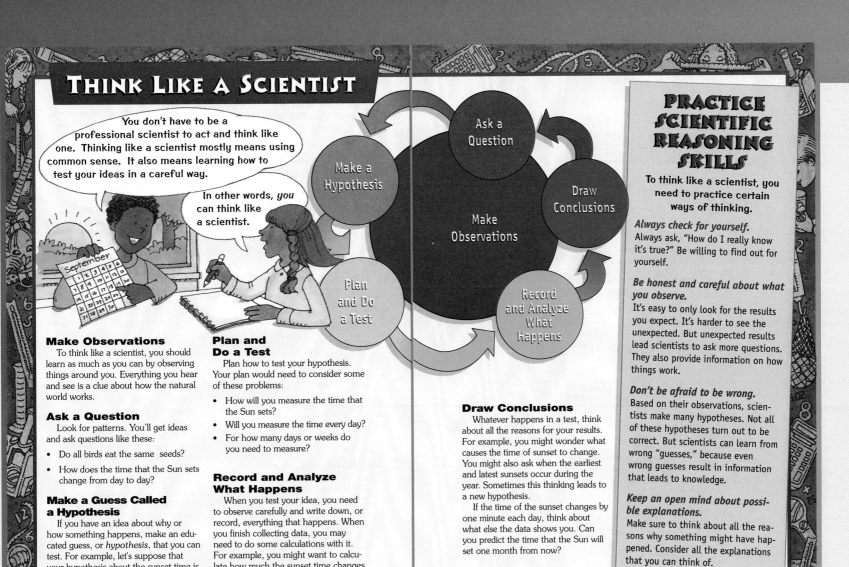

You don't have to be a professional scientist to act and think like one. Thinking like a scientist mostly means using common sense. It also means learning how to test your ideas in a careful way.

In other words, *you* can think like a scientist.

Make Observations

To think like a scientist, you should learn as much as you can by observing things around you. Everything you hear and see is a clue about how the natural world works.

Ask a Question

Look for patterns. You'll get ideas and ask questions like these:

- Do all birds eat the same seeds?
- How does the time that the Sun sets change from day to day?

Make a Guess Called a Hypothesis

If you have an idea about why or how something happens, make an educated guess, or *hypothesis*, that you can test. For example, let's suppose that your hypothesis about the sunset time is that it changes by one minute each day.

Plan and Do a Test

Plan how to test your hypothesis. Your plan would need to consider some of these problems:

- How will you measure the time that the Sun sets?
- Will you measure the time every day?
- For how many days or weeks do you need to measure?

Record and Analyze What Happens

When you test your idea, you need to observe carefully and write down, or record, everything that happens. When you finish collecting data, you may need to do some calculations with it. For example, you might want to calculate how much the sunset time changes in a week or a month.

Draw Conclusions

Whatever happens in a test, think about all the reasons for your results. For example, you might wonder what causes the time of sunset to change. You might also ask when the earliest and latest sunsets occur during the year. Sometimes this thinking leads to a new hypothesis.

If the time of the sunset changes by one minute each day, think about what else the data shows you. Can you predict the time that the Sun will set one month from now?

PRACTICE SCIENTIFIC REASONING SKILLS

To think like a scientist, you need to practice certain ways of thinking.

Always check for yourself.
Always ask, "How do I really know it's true?" Be willing to find out for yourself.

Be honest and careful about what you observe.
It's easy to only look for the results you expect. It's harder to see the unexpected. But unexpected results lead scientists to ask more questions. They also provide information on how things work.

Don't be afraid to be wrong.
Based on their observations, scientists make many hypotheses. Not all of these hypotheses turn out to be correct. But scientists can learn from wrong "guesses," because even wrong guesses result in information that leads to knowledge.

Keep an open mind about possible explanations.
Make sure to think about all the reasons why something might have happened. Consider all the explanations that you can think of.

H2

H3

WHAT CAUSES THE ROCK IN STATUES TO WEAR AWAY?

Here's an example of an everyday problem and how thinking like a scientist can help you explore it.

Make Observations
Make a Hypothesis

Before the class could begin setting up an experiment, there were some things they had to find out about the problem. First, they had to find out what the statue was made of. Ramon contacted City Hall and found out that the statue was made out of a stone called limestone.

Donelle told her classmates that she thought that the rain that fell on their town was sometimes acid. So Donelle and her classmates took samples of rainwater. They tested the rainwater with litmus paper and discovered that the rain was acidic.

The class thought about the new information they now had. It was time to use this information to formulate a hypothesis that they could test. Their hypothesis was "Acid rain eats away limestone."

Donelle and Ramon were walking through downtown when Ramon pointed to a statue, laughed, and said, "Look, that poor guy's nose has fallen off." Donelle laughed and as they both took a closer look at the statue, they could see that most of the statue's face was missing. Even the statue's body was pitted.

Donelle thought she knew why. She suspected that rain, snow, and ice were destroying the statue. "But it's stone," Ramon argued. "Stone doesn't dissolve in water. Does it?" "But don't we get acid rain here?" Donelle replied. "Maybe acid rain destroys stone."

The next day in school, Donelle described the "melting" statue to the

Make Observations
Ask a Question

class. Mr. Reynolds, their teacher, suggested that the class set up an experiment to find out what might be causing the damage to the statue. To begin, they came up with some questions that they wanted to answer.

What is destroying this statue?

Is rain destroying this statue?

Are cold winter temperatures destroying this statue?

The class decided that the first question was not specific enough. They

decided to test whether rain could be destroying the statue. Students were curious about whether pollution in the air, and thus in the rain, might be affecting the statue.

Scientific investigations usually begin with something that you have noticed or read about. As you think about what you already know, you'll discover some ideas that you're not sure about. This will help you to ask the question that you really want to answer.

When you use what you have observed to suggest a possible answer to your question, you are making a *hypothesis*. Be sure that your hypothesis is an idea that you can test somehow. If you can't think of an experiment or a model to test your hypothesis, try changing it. Sometimes it's better to make a simpler, clearer hypothesis that answers only part of your question.

H4

H5

Plan and Do a Test

Ramon, Donelle, and their classmates designed a way to test their hypothesis. First, Mr. Reynolds got some fairly equal-sized lumps of limestone for the class to use. Donelle set up three flat-bottomed beakers big enough to hold the chunks of limestone. Ramon created a table for recording information.

The students had discussed what kind of solutions they should use in each beaker. They decided to put rainwater they'd collected in one beaker. They decided to put a more acidic solution in the second beaker. Mr. Reynolds provided them with a solution of weak sulfuric acid. The students knew that the third beaker should contain only pure, distilled water.

The third beaker served as the students' control. The control part of an experiment is almost identical to the other parts of the experiment. It is different in just one way: it doesn't have the condition that is being tested. In this case, the class was testing the effects on limestone of water that is acidic. To make sure that their results only reflect the effects of acid, and not something else that might be in water, the students set up a control in which acid was missing.

After the three beakers were each filled with their specific liquid and labeled, the students found the mass of each chunk of limestone and then put one in each beaker.

The students placed the beakers on a lab table at the back of the classroom. A square piece of glass was placed over each beaker to keep out dirt and dust that might affect the results.

One way to try out your hypothesis is to use a test called an experiment. When you plan an experiment, be sure that it helps you to answer your question. But even when you plan, things can happen that make the experiment confusing or make it not work properly. If this happens, you can change the plan or the experiment, and try again.

Record and Analyze What Happened

After seven days, the mass of each limestone chunk was found again. The mass was recorded on the chart on the board. The chunk was replaced in the same beaker. This was repeated every seven days.

The students recorded the mass of the limestone chunks for fourteen weeks. At the end of the experiment, their chart looked like the one on the next page.

The students analyzed the data on their chart. Donelle noted that the more acidic the solution in the beaker, the more mass the limestone "lost." Ramon noted that the mass of the limestone in the beaker containing distilled water remained the same. The limestone in the rainwater beaker "lost" some mass, but not as much as the limestone chunk in the beaker containing sulfuric acid.

Mass of Limestone Each Week (in grams)														
Week	1	2	3	4	5	6	7	8	9	10	11	12	13	14
Rainwater	83	83	82	82	81	80	80	79	79	78	77	77	76	75
Sulfuric acid solution	76	74	71	69	68	65	63	60	59	55	53	50	48	45
Distilled water	79	79	79	79	79	79	79	79	79	79	79	79	79	79

When you do an experiment, you need to write down, or record, your observations. Some of your observations might be numbers of things that you counted or measured. Your recorded observations are called data. When you record your data, you need to organize it in a way that helps you to understand it. Graphs and tables are helpful ways to organize data. Then think about the information you have collected. Analyze what it tells you.

Draw Conclusions

Both Ramon and Donelle thought that it looked like their hypothesis was supported. Water containing an acid, or acid rain, did eat away limestone. But Ramon was still not completely satisfied. He wondered if acid rain affected all kinds of stone in the same way, or if it destroyed only limestone. Ramon posed his question to Mr. Reynolds and the other students. Then Patrick added, "And I wonder if cold weather makes the effects of acid rain even worse."

It was soon evident that though their experiment had showed that acid rain does affect limestone, a whole new set of questions occurred to them.

After you have analyzed your data, you should use what you have learned to draw a conclusion. A conclusion is a statement that sums up what you learned. The conclusion should be about the question you asked. Think about whether the information you have gathered supports your hypothesis or not. If it does, figure out how to test out your idea more thoroughly. Also think about new questions you can ask.

SAFETY

The best way to be safe in the classroom is to use common sense. Prepare yourself for each activity before you start it. Get help from your teacher when there is a problem. Most important of all, pay attention. Here are some other ways that you can stay safe.

Stay Safe From Stains

- Wear protective clothing or an old shirt when you work with messy materials.
- If anything spills, wipe it up or ask your teacher to help you clean it up.

Stay Safe From Flames

- Keep your clothes away from open flames. If you have long or baggy sleeves, roll them up.
- Don't let your hair get close to a flame. If you have long hair, tie it back.

Stay Safe During Cleanup

- Wash up after you finish working.
- Dispose of things in the way that your teacher tells you to.

Stay Safe From Injuries

- Protect your eyes by wearing safety goggles when you are told that you need them.
- Keep your hands dry around electricity. Water is a good conductor of electricity, so you can get a shock more easily if your hands are wet.
- Be careful with sharp objects. If you have to press on them, keep the sharp side away from you.
- Cover any cuts you have that are exposed. If you spill something on a cut, be sure to wash it off immediately.
- Don't eat or drink anything unless your teacher tells you that it's okay.

MOST IMPORTANTLY

If you ever hurt yourself or one of your group members gets hurt, tell your teacher right away.

DON'T MAKE A MESS If you spill something, clean it up right away. When finished with an activity, clean up your work area. Dispose of things in the way your teacher tells you to.

EYES Wear safety goggles when you are told to.

HAIR Keep it out of the way of a flame.

HANDS Keep your hands dry around electricity. Cover any cuts. Wear gloves when told to. Wash up after you finish.

MOUTH Don't eat or drink ANYTHING unless your teacher tells you it's okay.

CLOTHES Keep long sleeves rolled up. Protect yourself from stains. Stay away from open flames.

Using a Microscope

A microscope makes it possible to see very small things by magnifying them. Some microscopes have a set of lenses to magnify objects different amounts.

Examine Some Salt Grains

Handle a microscope carefully; it can break easily. Carry it firmly with both hands and avoid touching the lenses.

1. Turn the mirror toward a source of light. **NEVER** use the Sun as a light source.

2. Place a few grains of salt on the slide. Put the slide on the stage of the microscope.

3. While looking through the eyepiece, turn the adjustment knob on the back of the microscope to bring the salt grains into focus.

4. Raise the eyepiece tube to increase the magnification; lower it to decrease magnification.

Using a Calculator

After you've made measurements, a calculator can help you analyze your data. Some calculators have a memory key that allows you to save the result of one calculation while you do another.

Find an Average

The table shows the amount of rain that was collected using a rain gauge in each month of one year. You can use a calculator to help you find the average monthly rainfall.

1. Add the numbers. When you add a series of numbers, you don't need to press the equal sign until the last number is entered. Just press the plus sign after you enter each number (except the last one).

2. If you make a mistake while you are entering numbers, try to erase your mistake by pushing the clear entry (CE) key or the clear (C) key. Then you can continue entering the rest of the numbers you are adding. If you can't fix your mistake, you can push the (C) key once or twice until the screen shows 0. Then start over.

3. Your total should be 1,131. You can use the total to find the average. Just divide by the number of months in the year.

These keys run the calculator's memory functions.

This key erases the last entry.

Rainfall	
Month	Rain (mm)
Jan.	214
Feb.	138
Mar.	98
Apr.	157
May	84
June	41
July	5
Aug.	23
Sept.	48
Oct.	75
Nov.	140
Dec.	108

H10

H11

Using a Balance

A balance is used to measure mass. Mass is the amount of matter in an object. Place the object to be massed in the left pan. Place standard masses in the right pan.

Measure the Mass of an Orange

1. Check that the empty pans are balanced, or level with each other. The pointer at the base should be on the middle mark. If it needs to be adjusted, move the slider on the back of the balance a little to the left or right.

2. Place an orange on the left pan. Notice that the pointer moves and that the pans are no longer level with each other. Then add standard masses, one at a time, to the right pan. When the pointer is at the middle mark again, the pans are balanced. Each pan holds the same amount of mass.

3. Each standard mass is marked to show the number of grams it contains. Add the number of grams marked on the masses in the pan. The total is the mass in grams of the orange.

Using a Spring Scale

A spring scale is used to measure force. You can use a spring scale to find the weight of an object in newtons. You can also use the scale to measure other forces.

Measure the Weight of an Object

1. Place the object in a net bag, and hang it from the hook on the bottom of the spring scale. Or, if possible, hang the object directly from the hook.

2. Slowly lift the scale by the top hook. Be sure the object to be weighed continues to hang from the bottom hook.

3. Wait until the pointer on the face of the spring scale has stopped moving. Read the number next to the pointer to determine the weight of the object in newtons.

Measure Friction

1. Hook the object to the bottom of the spring scale. Use a rubber band to connect the spring scale and object if needed.

2. Gently pull the top hook of the scale parallel to the floor. When the object starts to move, read the number of newtons next to the pointer on the scale. This number is the force of friction between the floor and the object as you drag the object.

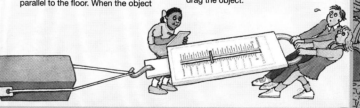

Using a Thermometer

A thermometer is used to measure temperature. When the liquid in the tube of a thermometer gets warmer, it expands and moves farther up the tube. Different units can be used to measure temperature, but scientists usually use the Celsius scale.

Measure the Temperature of a Cold Liquid

1. Half-fill a cup with chilled liquid.

2. Hold the thermometer so that the bulb is in the center of the liquid.

3. Wait until you see the liquid in the tube stop moving. Read the scale line that is closest to the top of the liquid in the tube.

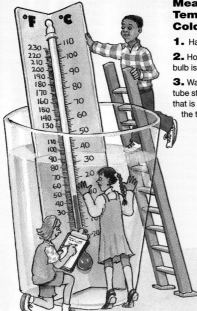

Measuring Volume

A graduated cylinder, a measuring cup, and a beaker are used to measure volume. Volume is the amount of space something takes up. Most of the containers that scientists use to measure volume have a scale marked in milliliters (mL).

Measure the Volume of Juice

1. Pour the juice into a measuring container.

2. Move your head so that your eyes are level with the top of the juice. Read the scale line that is closest to the surface of the juice. If the surface of the juice is curved up on the sides, look at the lowest point of the curve.

3. You can estimate the value between two lines on the scale to obtain a more accurate measurement.

▲ The bottom of the curve is at 50 mL.

This graduated cylinder has marks for every 1 mL.

This beaker has marks for each 25 mL. ▼

This measuring cup has marks for each 25 mL. ▼

Each container above has 50 mL of juice.

MEASUREMENTS

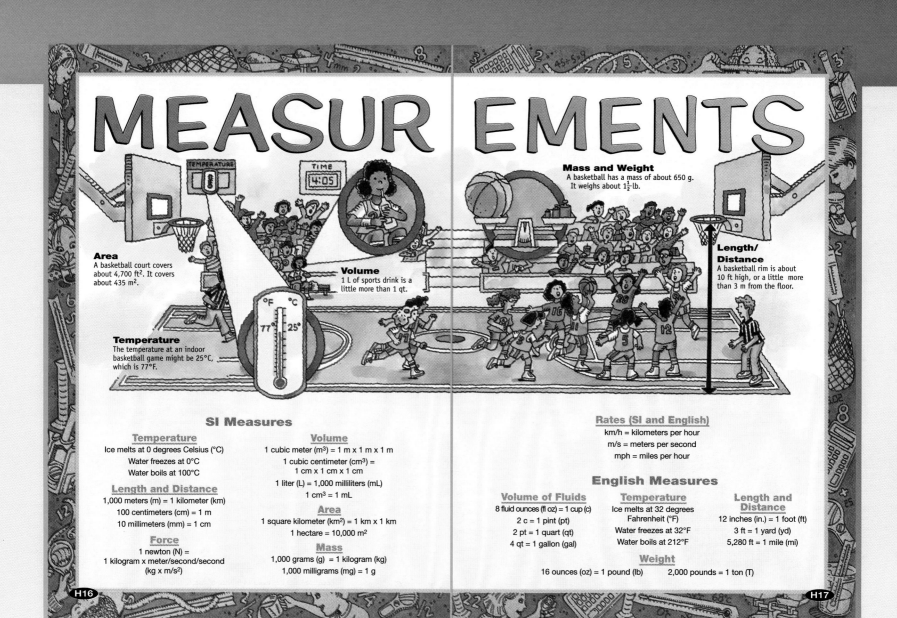

Area
A basketball court covers about 4,700 ft². It covers about 435 m².

Temperature
The temperature at an indoor basketball game might be 25°C, which is 77°F.

Volume
1 L of sports drink is a little more than 1 qt.

Mass and Weight
A basketball has a mass of about 650 g. It weighs about 1½-lb.

Length/ Distance
A basketball rim is about 10 ft high, or a little more than 3 m from the floor.

SI Measures

Temperature
Ice melts at 0 degrees Celsius (°C)

Water freezes at 0°C

Water boils at 100°C

Length and Distance
1,000 meters (m) = 1 kilometer (km)

100 centimeters (cm) = 1 m

10 millimeters (mm) = 1 cm

Force
1 newton (N) =

1 kilogram x meter/second/second (kg x m/s²)

Volume
1 cubic meter (m³) = 1 m x 1 m x 1 m

1 cubic centimeter (cm³) = 1 cm x 1 cm x 1 cm

1 liter (L) = 1,000 milliliters (mL)

1 cm³ = 1 mL

Area
1 square kilometer (km²) = 1 km x 1 km

1 hectare = 10,000 m²

Mass
1,000 grams (g) = 1 kilogram (kg)

1,000 milligrams (mg) = 1 g

Rates (SI and English)
km/h = kilometers per hour

m/s = meters per second

mph = miles per hour

English Measures

Volume of Fluids
8 fluid ounces (fl oz) = 1 cup (c)

2 c = 1 pint (pt)

2 pt = 1 quart (qt)

4 qt = 1 gallon (gal)

Temperature
Ice melts at 32 degrees Fahrenheit (°F)

Water freezes at 32°F

Water boils at 212°F

Length and Distance
12 inches (in.) = 1 foot (ft)

3 ft = 1 yard (yd)

5,280 ft = 1 mile (mi)

Weight
16 ounces (oz) = 1 pound (lb)   2,000 pounds = 1 ton (T)

Pronunciation Key

Symbol	Key Words	Symbol	Key Words
a	cat	g	get
ā	ape	h	help
ä	cot, car	j	jump
		k	kiss, call
e	ten, berry	l	leg
ē	me	m	meat
		n	nose
i	fit, here	p	put
ī	ice, fire	r	red
		s	see
ō	go	t	top
ô	fall, for	v	vat
oi	oil	w	wish
ᴏᴏ	look, pull	y	yard
o͞o	tool, rule	z	zebra
ou	out, crowd		
		ch	chin, arch
u	up	ŋ	ring, drink
ʉ	fur, shirt	sh	she, push
		th	thin, truth
ə	a in ago	*th*	then, father
	e in agent	zh	measure
	i in pencil		
	o in atom	
	u in circus	A heavy stress mark ′ is placed
		after a syllable that gets a heavy,
b	bed	or primary, stress, as in **picture**
d	dog	(pik′chər).
f	fall	

A

absolute age The actual age of an object. (E79) The *absolute age* of this statue is 3,500 years.

absolute magnitude The measure of a star's brightness, based on the amount of light it actually gives off. (B61) The Sun's *absolute magnitude* is less than that of many stars, but its apparent magnitude exceeds that of any other star.

adaptation (ad əp tā′shən) A structure or behavior that enables an organism to survive in its environment. (A70, A86) The thick fur of some animals is an *adaptation* to cold environments.

addiction (ə dik′shən) A condition in which a person has extreme difficulty in stopping the use of a drug. (G51) Sometimes it takes only a short time to develop an *addiction* to a drug.

alcohol (al′kə hôl) A drug that is found in some beverages, such as beer and wine. (G50) If a person drinks *alcohol* to excess, problems can occur.

alcoholism (al′kə hôl iz əm) A disease that results from the continual misuse of alcohol. (G60) Doctors continue to learn more about *alcoholism*.

amplitude (am′plə tood) A measure of the amount of energy in a sound wave. (F57) The *amplitude* of a loud sound is greater than the amplitude of a soft sound.

anticline (an′ti klīn) An upward fold of rock layers. (E84) Bending layers of rock formed an *anticline*.

eroded anticline

apparent magnitude The measure of a star's brightness as seen from Earth. (B61) A star's *apparent magnitude* depends on the amount of light it gives off and on its distance from Earth.

asexual reproduction (ā sek′sho͞o əl rē prə duk′shən) A process in which offspring are produced from one or more cells of a single parent. (A62) In *asexual reproduction*, the offspring is identical to the parent.

audiocassette (ô′dē ō kə set) A small container holding magnetic tape that is used for playing or recording sound. (F92) We inserted an *audiocassette* into the tape recorder.

auditory nerve (ô′də tôr ē nʉrv) A nerve in the ear that carries nerve impulses to the brain. (G39, F85) The *auditory nerve* contains sensory neurons.

axis The imaginary line on which an object rotates. (B13) Earth's *axis* runs between the North and South poles.

Big Bang Theory A hypothesis, supported by data, that describes how the universe began with a huge explosion. (B39) The *Big Bang Theory* holds that everything in the universe was once concentrated at one tiny point.

biodiversity (bī ō də vur′sə tē) The variety of organisms that live in Earth's many ecosystems; the variety of plants and animals that live within a particular ecosystem. (D58) The *biodiversity* of an ecosystem quickly changes after a natural disaster.

biome (bī′ōm) A major land ecosystem having a distinct combination of plants and animals. (D48) Some *biomes*, such as the tundra, do not easily support human populations.

biosphere (bī′ō sfir) A self-sustaining natural system of living things and their environment. (B87) For humans to survive in space, they must bring along a version of their *biosphere*.

black dwarf The cool, dark body that is the final stage in the life cycle of a low-mass star. (B66) When the Sun dies, it will become a *black dwarf*.

black hole An extremely dense, invisible object in space whose gravity is so great that not even light can escape it. (B67) Scientists think that the remains of a very massive star can collapse following a supernova explosion to form a *black hole*.

blood alcohol concentration A test that determines the level of alcohol in a person's blood. (G61) A police officer can easily find out if a driver is drunk by giving a *blood alcohol concentration* test.

bone The hard tissue that forms the skeleton. Also, one of the organs that makes up the skeleton. (G8) The human hand contains many small *bones*.

caffeine (ka fēn′) A drug that acts as a stimulant and is present in coffee, many teas, cocoa, and some soft drinks. (G50) Many people prefer to drink herbal teas that do not have *caffeine* in them.

carbon dioxide–oxygen cycle See oxygen–carbon dioxide cycle.

cardiac muscle (kär′dē ak mus′əl) Involuntary muscle tissue that makes up the heart. (G17) *Cardiac muscle* contracts rhythmically.

carnivore (kär′nə vôr) A consumer that eats only other animals. (D19, D30) Lions are *carnivores* that prey on zebras and other large plant eaters.

cartilage (kärt′əl ij) Tough, flexible tissue that is part of the skeleton. (G8) *Cartilage* helps protect bones as they move at joints.

cell The basic unit of structure of all living things. (A24) Even though plant *cells* can be different sizes, they still have many of the same structures.

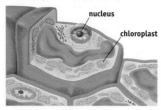

cell membrane A thin layer that surrounds all cells and allows water and dissolved materials to pass into and out of the cell. (A24) In plant cells, the *cell membrane* lies inside the cell wall.

cell respiration The process of using oxygen to release energy from food. (A35, A45, D34) Animals and plants release carbon dioxide as a waste product of *cell respiration*.

cell wall The tough outer covering of a plant cell that gives the cell its rigid shape. (A24) A *cell wall* is not found in animal cells.

cementation (sē men tā′shən) A process in which minerals, deposited as water evaporates, bind sediments into solid rock. (E44) Sandstone is a sedimentary rock formed by *cementation*.

cerebellum (ser ə bel′əm) The second largest part of the brain, coordinating the body's muscles. (G32) The *cerebellum* allows smooth movement.

cerebrum (sə rē′brəm) The largest part of the brain in which the processes of thinking, learning, and reasoning take place. (G31) The *cerebrum* is the part of the brain that allows people to understand and remember ideas.

chloroplast (klôr′ə plast) A structure in plant cells that captures light energy that is used in the food-making process. (A24, A33) *Chloroplasts* are located within cells in the leaves of a plant.

cleavage (klēv′ij) The tendency of some minerals to split along flat surfaces. (E15) Salt, or halite, shows *cleavage* in three planes.

clone (klōn) An exact copy of a parent organism produced by asexual reproduction. (A62) One way to *clone* a parent plant is to place a cutting from that plant in water.

coastal ocean A saltwater ecosystem that is relatively shallow and close to the shoreline and that supports an abundance of life. (D54) The *coastal ocean* is an ecosystem that lies beyond the shoreline.

comet (käm′it) A small object in space, made of ice, dust, gas, and rock, that orbits a star and that can form a gaseous tail. (B24) As a *comet* approaches the Sun, it begins to melt.

commensalism (kə men′səl iz əm) A close relationship between two kinds of organisms that benefits one of the organisms while neither benefiting nor hurting the other. (D21) The way that some insects use their resemblance to plants to hide from predators is an example of *commensalism*.

community (kə myōō′nə tē) All the organisms living together in a particular ecosystem. (D10) Raccoons, deer, and trees are part of a forest *community*.

compact disc (käm′pakt disk) A small disk on which sounds are digitally recorded and played back when read by a laser beam. (F92) This *compact disc*, or CD, contains one hour of music.

compound machine A machine that is made up of two or more simple machines. (C62) A pair of scissors is a *compound machine* because it contains two kinds of simple machines—a lever and a wedge.

compound microscope A viewing instrument that uses two lenses to magnify objects many times. (F41) The human hair appeared 1,000 times larger than actual size under the *compound microscope*.

compression (kəm presh′ən) A region in a sound wave where particles have been pushed together. (F57) The *compressions* produced by a vibrating tuning fork are areas of greater than normal air pressure.

concave lens (kän′kāv lenz) A lens that is thicker at the edges than it is in the middle and that causes light rays to spread apart. (F32) A *concave lens* is used to correct nearsightedness.

concave mirror A mirror that curves inward at the middle. (F23) A *concave mirror* is used in a reflecting telescope.

concrete (kän′krēt) A mixture of rock material and cement that is used as a building material. (E24) This sidewalk is made of *concrete*.

condensation (kän dən sā′shən) The process by which water vapor is changed to liquid water. (D36) *Condensation* can occur on a glass containing ice cubes.

conduction (kən duk′shən) The transfer of heat energy by direct contact between particles. (C13) Heat travels through a metal by *conduction*.

conifer (kän′ə fər) A tree or shrub that bears its seeds in cones. (A80) The cones of each species of *conifer* are distinct and different from each other.

constellation (kän stə lā′shən) A group of stars that form a fixed pattern in the night sky. (B10) The *constellation* Orion is best seen in the winter.

consumer (kən sōōm′ər) A living thing that obtains energy by eating other living things. (A36, D19) Meat eaters and plant eaters are *consumers*.

contact lens A thin lens worn over the cornea of the eye, usually to correct vision problems. (F35) Some people use *contact lenses* rather than eyeglasses to improve their vision.

convection (kən vek′shən) The transfer of heat energy through liquids and gases by moving particles. (C13) Heat is carried throughout water in a pot on the stove by *convection*.

convex lens (kän′veks lenz) A lens that is thicker in the middle than at the edges and that brings light rays together. (F32) A *convex lens* is used to correct farsightedness.

convex mirror A mirror that curves outward at the middle. (F23) The side-view mirror of a car is a *convex mirror*.

core The innermost layer of Earth, which consists of a molten outer part and a solid inner part. (E69) Temperatures inside the *core* of Earth are nearly as hot as those on the Sun's surface.

crest The highest point of a wave. (F57) The top of a water wave is its *crest*.

crust The outer layer of Earth. (E68) Earth's *crust* is a thin layer of rock.

cytoplasm (sīt′ō plaz əm) The jellylike substance that fills much of the cell. (A24) The nucleus, vacuoles, and many other cell structures float in the *cytoplasm*.

decibel (des′ə bəl) A unit used to measure the loudness or intensity of sound. (F79) Sounds that have an intensity greater than 120 *decibels* (db) can hurt your ears.

decomposer (dē kəm pōz′ər) A living thing that breaks down the remains of dead organisms. (A37, D19) *Decomposers*, such as bacteria, get their energy from the dead plants and animals they break down.

deciduous forest (dē sij′ōō əs fôr′ist) A biome that contains many trees and in which rainfall is moderate. (D51) *Deciduous forests* support a great variety of animal life.

deforestation (dē fôr is tā′shən) A mass clearing of a forest. (A93) *Deforestation* is a major concern of environmentalists.

desert A biome in which plant life is not abundant and rainfall is low. (D50) Because *deserts* are dry, desert plants have adaptations to conserve water.

dicot (dī′kät) A flowering plant that produces seeds with two seed leaves, or food-storing leaves. (A81) A trait of a *dicot* is that its leaves have netlike veins.

drug A substance, other than food, that can affect the function of body cells and tissues and that produces a change in the body. (G50) A person sometimes takes a pain-killing *drug* after suffering a back injury.

ecosystem (ek′ō sis təm) An area in which living and nonliving things interact. (D10) An oak tree and the organisms that inhabit it can be thought of as a small *ecosystem*.

effort force The force that must be applied to an object to move the object. (C30) The tow truck applied enough *effort force* to pull the car away.

electromagnetic radiation (ē lek trō-mag net′ik rā dē ā′shən) Wave energy given off by the Sun and some other objects. (F8) Visible light is a form of *electromagnetic radiation*.

electron microscope (ē lek′trän mī′krə skōp) A viewing instrument that magnifies objects thousands of times by using a beam of electrons instead of a beam of light. (F43) Doctors studied the virus through an *electron microscope*.

embryo (em′brē ō) An organism in its earliest stages of development; in most plants it is found inside a seed. (A61) When conditions for growth are suitable, the *embryo* inside the seed develops into a young plant.

endangered In danger of becoming extinct. (A92, D61) As the destruction of the Amazon rain forest continues, the number of *endangered* species increases.

energy The ability to do work or cause change. (C9, F8) *Energy* from the Sun warms the air.

erosion (ē rō′zhən) The wearing away and removing of rock and soil caused by such forces as wind and flowing water. (E84) The pounding waves caused *erosion* of the sandy shoreline.

eustachian tube (yo͞o stā′kē ən to͞ob) A tube that connects the throat and the middle ear. (F85) The *eustachian tube* equalizes the air pressure on both sides of the eardrum.

evaporation (ē vap ə rā′shən) The process by which liquid water changes to water vapor. (D36) One phase of the water cycle is the *evaporation* of water from lakes, rivers, and oceans.

extinct (ek stiŋkt′) No longer living as a species. (A92, D61) Traces of some *extinct* species can be found in fossils.

extraterrestrial (eks trə tə res′trē əl) A being from outer space; any object from beyond Earth. (B90) It would be extraordinary for scientists to discover that there is *extraterrestrial* life.

fault A break in rock along which rocks have moved. (E91) Forces within Earth's crust produce *faults*.

fern A nonseed plant that has roots, stems, and leaves and that is found mostly in moist, shady areas. (A79) On *ferns* that grow in tropical places, the fronds grow to a very tall size.

fertilization (furt ′l ə zā′shən) The process by which a male sex cell joins with a female sex cell. In flowering plants, fertilization takes place in the pistil. (A60) *Fertilization* occurs after a pollen tube reaches the ovary.

filter A device that lets certain colors of light pass through while absorbing others. (F48) The stage manager placed a red *filter* over the spotlight.

flower The reproductive structure of a flowering plant. (A16) Petals protect the reproductive parts of a *flower*.

flowering plant Living organisms that reproduce by seeds formed in flowers and that have roots, stems, and leaves. (A81) *Flowering plants* are the most common group of plants on Earth today.

focal point The point at which light rays passing through a lens come together. (F32) Rays of light meet at the *focal point*.

fold A bend in a layer of rock. (E83) Forces within Earth can cause a *fold* to form in rock layers.

food chain The path of energy transfer from one living organism to another in an ecosystem. (A36, D29) Energy moves from producers to consumers in a *food chain*.

food web The overlapping food chains that link producers, consumers, and decomposers in an ecosystem. (A37, D30) Some consumers in a *food web* eat both plants and animals.

force A pull or a push. (C28) When you open a door, you apply a *force*.

fossil (fäs′əl) The remains or traces of a living thing from the past, preserved in rock. (E46, E77) *Fossils* can include imprints of animal skeletons pressed into rock.

fracture (frak′chər) A break or crack in a bone. (G20) The skier suffered a leg *fracture* when he hit an icy patch.

free fall The motion of a freely falling object, such as a spacecraft in orbit around Earth. (B79) Astronauts experiencing *free fall* in space feel weightless.

frequency (frē′kwən sē) The number of waves (such as light or sound) produced in a unit of time, such as a second. (F18, F57) The *frequency* of light waves varies with the color of the light.

friction (frik′shən) Force produced by the rubbing of one thing against another; a force that acts to oppose motion. (C31) *Friction* prevents sneakers from slipping on a gym floor.

fruit The enlarged ovary of a flower that protects the developing seeds. (A61) Some *fruits*, such as peaches or mangoes, contain only one seed.

fulcrum (ful′krəm) The fixed point around which a lever pivots. (C50) If you use a lever to lift an object, the *fulcrum* is located between you and the object you are lifting.

galaxy (gal′ək sē) A vast group of billions of stars that are held together by gravity. (B70) The Milky Way is a typical spiral *galaxy*.

gas giant A large planet that is made up mostly of gaseous and liquid substances, with little or no solid surface. (B47) Jupiter is a *gas giant*.

geocentric model (jē ō sen′trik mäd′′l) A representation of the universe in which stars and planets revolve around Earth. (B37) Ptolemy proposed a *geocentric model* of the universe.

glucose (glōō′kōs) A sugar produced by plants that is the main source of energy for cells. (A33) *Glucose* is produced during photosynthesis.

grassland A biome containing many grasses but few trees and having low to moderate rainfall. (D50) Taller grasses occur in *grasslands* that have more abundant rainfall.

hardness A measure of how easily a mineral can be scratched. (E13) The *hardness* of diamond is greater than that of any other mineral.

hearing aid A small battery-powered electronic device that makes sounds louder. (F86) Most people who wear a *hearing aid* have improved hearing.

heliocentric model (hē lē ō sen′trik mäd′′l) A representation of the relationship between the Sun and planets in which the planets revolve around the Sun. (B37) Copernicus hypothesized a *heliocentric model* of the solar system.

herbivore (hʉr′bə vôr) A consumer that eats only plants or other producers. (D19, D30) Panda bears are *herbivores* that have a very limited diet because they only eat bamboo.

hertz (herts) A unit used to measure wave frequency. (F18, F68) If 100 waves are produced per second, the frequency of the wave is 100 *hertz*.

igneous rock (ig′nē əs räk) A type of rock that forms from melted rock that cools and hardens. (E40) *Igneous rock* forms from both magma and lava.

illegal drug A substance whose use is prohibited by law. (G50) One *illegal drug* in the United States is heroin.

inclined plane A simple machine with a sloping surface. It allows objects to be raised or lowered from one level to another without lifting them. (C43) A ramp is a kind of *inclined plane*.

index fossil (in′deks fäs′əl) A fossil used to determine the relative age of rock. (E78) The remains of a living thing that lived only at a certain time in the past makes a good *index fossil*.

information superhighway The futuristic concept of communications as an electronic highway system in which telephones, computers, and televisions are linked. (F93) The *information superhighway* will let students do library research from their homes.

intensity (in ten′sə tē) A measure of the amount of energy of sound. (F78) A sound that has high *intensity* is loud enough to be heard from a distance.

Internet (in′tər net) A system of interconnected computer networks. (F94) Telephone lines link computer users with the *Internet*.

joint The place where two bones meet. (G8) Your elbow *joint* enables you to bend your arm.

joule (jōōl) The basic unit of energy and of work. (C19) Scientists measure amounts of energy in *joules*.

kinetic energy The energy that something has because of its motion. (C20) As a boulder rolls down a steep hill, it gains *kinetic energy*.

lake A freshwater ecosystem characterized by still, or standing water. (D53) *Lakes* support fish, birds, algae, and other forms of life.

lava (lä′və) Melted rock material that reaches Earth's surface before it cools and hardens. (E41) A volcano carries *lava* to Earth's surface.

leaf A plant part in which photosynthesis takes place. (A14) In a plant such as cabbage, it is the *leaf* that people eat.

lens A piece of glass or other transparent material with at least one curved surface that brings together or spreads apart light rays passing through it. (F32) The *lens* in a camera focuses an image on the film.

lever (lev′ər) A simple machine made up of a bar that pivots around a fixed point (a fulcrum). (C50) A *lever* can help lift a heavy object with less effort.

ligament (lig′ə mənt) A band of strong tissue that connects bones and holds them in place. (G8) A *ligament* holds bones together at a joint.

light-year A unit of measurement representing the distance that light travels in one year. (B61) Scientists use the unit called a *light-year* when measuring the distances to stars.

luster (lus′tər) The way that the surface of a mineral looks when it reflects light. (E13) Silver and gold have a shiny, metallic *luster*.

machine A device that makes work easier by reducing the amount of force needed to do a job. (C43) A *machine* can make it easier to move, lift, carry, or cut something.

magma (mag′mə) Melted rock material that forms deep within Earth. (E40) Some igneous rocks, such as granite, form from *magma*.

mantle A thick layer of rock between the crust and the core of Earth. (E69) The top of the *mantle* is solid rock but below that is a section of rock that can flow.

mechanical advantage (mə kan′i-kəl ad vant′ij) The number of times that a machine multiplies the effort force applied to it. (C44) To find the *mechanical advantage* of an inclined plane, divide the length of its sloping surface by its height.

medulla (mi dul′ə) The part of the brain that controls the involuntary functions of the body, such as heart rate and breathing. (G32) The *medulla* is located in the brain stem and controls many things you do without thinking.

metamorphic rock (met ə môr′fik räk) A type of rock that forms from existing rocks because of changes caused by heat, pressure, or chemicals. (E47) Slate is a *metamorphic rock* that forms from the sedimentary rock shale.

meteor (mēt′ē ər) A piece of rock or metal from space that enters Earth's atmosphere. (B25) A *meteor* appears as a streak of light, which is why it is also called a shooting star.

meteorite (mēt′ē ər īt) The remaining material of a meteor that has landed on the ground. (B25) In 1902, scientists were able to examine the largest *meteorite* ever known to land in the United States.

Milky Way Galaxy A gigantic cluster of billions of stars that is home to our solar system. (B70) The Sun is located in one of the arms of the *Milky Way Galaxy*.

mineral A solid element or compound found in nature and having a definite chemical composition and crystal structure. (E12) Quartz is a *mineral*.

model Something used or made to represent an object or an idea. (E68) The plastic *model* was a miniature copy of the actual airplane.

monocot (män′ō kät) A flowering plant that produces seeds with a single seed leaf, or food-storing leaf. (A81) About one third of all flowering plants are *monocots*.

moon A natural object that revolves around a planet. (B44) The planet Mars has two known *moons*.

moss A small nonseed plant that lacks roots, stems, and leaves and grows mostly in moist areas in woods or near stream banks. (A78) The leaflike part of a *moss* only grows a few centimeters above ground.

motor neuron (mōt′ər nōō′rän) A nerve cell that carries impulses from the brain and spinal cord to muscles and glands in the body. (G28) When people exercise, *motor neurons* carry impulses from the spinal cord to different muscles in the body.

mutualism (myōō′chōō əl iz əm) A close relationship between two or more organisms in which all organisms benefit. (D22) Bees carrying pollen from flower to flower as they obtain nectar is an example of *mutualism*.

narcotic (när kät′ik) A habit-forming drug that depresses the function of the nervous system. (G55) Morphine is a *narcotic* drug that is often given to cancer patients.

nebula (neb′yə lə) A huge cloud of gas and dust found in space. (B64) A *nebula* can form when a supernova explodes.

nerve impulse (nurv im′puls) A message carried through the body by neurons. (G28) *Nerve impulses* pass from one neuron to another as they move through the body.

neuron (nōō′rän) A nerve cell. (G28) The brain is connected to all parts of the body by *neurons*.

neutron star (nōō′trän stär) The remains of a massive star that has exploded in a supernova. (B67) A typical *neutron star* is less than 20 km in diameter.

newton A unit used to measure force. (C29) About 300 *newtons* of force was applied in moving the rock.

nicotine (nik′ə tēn) A drug found in the tobacco plant. (G50) People become addicted to cigarettes because of the *nicotine* in the tobacco.

nitrogen cycle The cycle through which nitrogen gas is changed into compounds that can be used by living things and then is returned to the atmosphere. (D42) The *nitrogen cycle* is of great importance to all life forms because nitrogen is needed to make protein.

noise pollution The occurrence of loud or unpleasant sound in the environment. (F80) The sounds of city traffic are a form of *noise pollution*.

nonseed plant A plant that reproduces without forming seeds. (A78) Mosses are *nonseed plants*.

nucleus (nōō′klē əs) The cell structure that controls all of a cell's activities. (A24) The *nucleus* was clearly visible after it was stained.

octave (äk′tiv) The series of eight notes that makes up a musical scale. (F69) The music student practiced playing *octaves* on the piano.

omnivore (äm′ni vôr) A consumer that eats both plants and animals. (D19, D30) Because they eat both meats and vegetables, many humans are *omnivores*.

opaque (ō pāk′) Not letting light through. (F47) The *opaque* curtains kept out the sunlight.

open ocean A large saltwater ecosystem containing both floating and free-swimming organisms. (D55) The *open ocean* covers much of Earth's surface.

optic nerve A bundle of neurons that carries impulses from the *eye* to the brain. (G39) If there is damage to the *optic nerve*, messages from the *eye* cannot be received by the brain.

ore (ôr) A mineral or rock that contains enough of a metal to making mining the metal profitable. (E27) Hematite is an *ore* mined for its iron content.

overtone A fainter, higher tone that harmonizes with the main tone produced by a musical instrument or the human voice. (F58) The blending of *overtones* gives the flute its unique sound.

oxygen–carbon dioxide cycle A natural cycle in which plants and other producers use carbon dioxide and produce oxygen, and living things use oxygen and produce carbon dioxide. (B86, D34) The *oxygen–carbon dioxide cycle* must be duplicated in space if humans wish to make long voyages to other planets.

parasitism (par′ə sīt iz əm) A relationship between two organisms in which one organism lives on or in the other, feeds upon it, and usually harms it. (D21) The way in which fleas live off dogs is an example of *parasitism*.

phloem cell (flō′əm sel) A plant cell that, when linked with other similar cells, forms a system of tubes for carrying nutrients from the leaves down through the stem and root. (A11) The *phloem cells* form a major transport system in plants.

phonograph (fō′nə graf) A device that reproduces sounds recorded on a disk. (F90) We played old records on the *phonograph*.

photosynthesis (fōt ō sin′thə sis) The process by which producers, such as plants, make their own food by using energy from the Sun. (A33) *Photosynthesis* takes place primarily in the leaves of plants.

pistil (pis′til) The female reproductive structure of a flower. (A16) A *pistil* consists of three main parts—the stigma, the style, and the ovary.

pitch The highness or lowness of a sound. (F68) A tuba produces sounds with a low *pitch*.

plane mirror A mirror that has a flat surface. (F22) The mirror over the bathroom sink is a *plane mirror*.

planet A large body in space that orbits a star and does not produce light on its own. (B17) Earth is one of nine known *planets* that revolve around the Sun.

plant kingdom A major group of living things that are multicellular and that carry out photosynthesis. (A78) Living organisms in the *plant kingdom* make their own food.

pollination (päl ə nā′shən) The transfer of pollen from the male part of one flower to the female part of another flower. (A60) Some *pollination* is done by insects.

population (päp yōō lā′shən) A group of the same kind of organisms that live in an area. (D10) There is a huge *population* of frogs in that marsh.

potential energy The energy that an object has because of its position or structure; stored energy. (C18) A coiled spring has *potential energy*.

precipitation (prē sip ə tā'shən) The process by which water from clouds falls back to the Earth. (D36) *Precipitation* falls to the Earth in the form of rain or snow.

producer (prō dōōs'ər) An organism that makes its own food through photosynthesis. (A36, D18) Plants and algae are examples of *producers*.

protein (prō'tēn) Organic compounds that form the structure and control the processes that take place in living things. (D41) *Proteins* provide the body with materials that help cells grow and repair themselves.

protostar (prōt'ō stär) A concentration of matter found in space that is the beginning of a star. (B64) When the temperature inside a *protostar* becomes high enough, nuclear reactions begin and it turns into a star.

pulley (pōōl'ē) A simple machine made up of a wheel around which a rope or chain is passed. (C53) A *pulley* helps lift objects that would be too heavy to lift directly.

---

quarry (kwôr'ē) A mine, usually near or at Earth's surface, from which rock is removed. (E52) Granite, sandstone, limestone, slate, and marble are some rocks that come from a *quarry*.

---

radiation (rā dē ā'shən) The transfer of energy by waves. (C11) Energy given off by the Sun travels as *radiation* through space.

radio telescope A gigantic antenna designed to receive radio signals from space. (B92) *Radio telescopes* are important tools for studying distant stars and galaxies.

rarefaction (rer ə fak'shən) A region in a sound wave where there are fewer particles than normal. (F57) The *rarefactions* that a vibrating violin string produces are areas of lower than normal air pressure.

receptor (ri sep'tər) A sensory neuron that receives stimuli from the environment. (G37) Sensory *receptors* in the skin make it possible for people to feel heat, cold, pressure, touch, and pain.

red giant A very large old reddish star that has greatly expanded and cooled as its fuel has begun to run out. (B65) As the Sun reaches old age, it will turn into a *red giant*.

reflecting telescope An instrument for viewing distant objects that uses a curved mirror at the back of its tube to gather light and produce an image. (B22, F39) This observatory uses a *reflecting telescope* to observe faraway galaxies.

reflection (ri flek'shən) The bouncing of light or sound off a surface. (F22) The *reflection* of sunlight off the snow made us squint.

reflex (rē'fleks) A simple behavior pattern involving an automatic response to a stimulus. (G42) The girl's automatic *reflex* quickly got her foot out of the hot water.

refracting telescope An instrument for viewing distant objects that uses two lenses to gather light and produce an image. (B21) The *refracting telescope* gave us a closer look at the Moon.

refraction (ri frak'shən) The bending of light as it passes from one material into another. (F24) Light traveling from air into water will undergo *refraction*.

relative age The age of an object as compared to other objects. (E78) The order of layers of rock shows the *relative ages* of the layers.

resistance force A force that resists, or opposes, motion. (C30) Friction is a *resistance force*.

retina (ret''n ə) The light-sensitive area at the back of the eye on which an image is formed. (F32) The *retina* contains two kinds of cells.

revolution (rev ə lōō'shən) The movement of an object around another object or point. (B14) It takes about 365 days for Earth to make one *revolution* around the Sun.

river A freshwater ecosystem characterized by running water. (D52) Salmon are able to swim against the current in a *river*.

rock The solid material composed of minerals that forms Earth's crust. Also, the material, sometimes molten, that forms Earth's inner layers. (E40) *Rocks* are weathered by wind and rain.

rock cycle The continuous series of changes that rocks undergo. (E60) In the *rock cycle*, changes are brought about by factors such as weathering, melting, cooling, or pressure.

root The underground part of a plant that anchors the plant and absorbs water and nutrients. (A10) Carrots and turnips have only one large single *root*.

rotation (rō tā'shən) The spinning motion of an object on its axis. (B14) It takes about 24 hours for Earth to make one complete *rotation*.

S
---

sapling (sap'liŋ) A young tree. (A67) The year after a tree seed germinates, the young plant is called a *sapling*.

satellite (sat'l īt) A natural or human-built object that revolves around another object in space. (B44) The Moon is a natural *satellite* of Earth.

sediment (sed'ə mənt) Bits of weathered rocks and minerals and pieces of dead plants or animals. (E43) Over time, *sediments* can form sedimentary rocks, such as sandstone and limestone.

sedimentary rock (sed ə men'tər ē räk) A type of rock that forms when sediments harden. (E43) Most *sedimentary rocks* form in layers.

seed coat A tough, protective covering on a seed, enclosing the embryo and its food supply. (A 61) When the leaves on a young plant start to grow and open up, the *seed coat* falls off.

seed dispersal The scattering of seeds away from the parent plant. (A88) The wind is one way in which *seed dispersal* is carried out.

seed leaf A first leaf found inside a seed, providing food for the tiny developing plant. (A66) A monocot seed contains one *seed leaf*.

seedling (sēd'liŋ) A young growing plant after it first sprouts and develops new leaves. (A66) In spring the forest floor is covered with green *seedlings*.

seed plant A plant that reproduces by forming seeds. (A78) Corn and wheat are *seed plants*.

semicircular canal Any of several curved tubelike structures of the inner ear that help the body to maintain balance. (F85) The *semicircular canals* respond to movements of the head.

sensory neuron (sen'sər ē nōō'rän) A nerve cell that carries impulses from the senses to the brain and spinal cord. (G28) *Sensory neurons* carry impulses from your eyes to your brain.

sexual reproduction The production of offspring that occurs when a male sex cell joins a female sex cell. (A59) The *sexual reproduction* of flowers is greatly aided by insects.

shoreline The ecosystem where land and ocean meet. (D54) The *shoreline* varies in width around the world.

simple microscope A microscope that uses a single lens to magnify objects. (F41) A magnifying glass is a *simple microscope*.

skeletal muscle Voluntary muscle tissue; also, one of the muscles that moves bones. (G17) Tendons attach *skeletal muscles* to bones.

skeletal system The system of bones and tissues that supports and protects the body. (G8) The human *skeletal system* contains 206 bones.

smelting (smelt'iŋ) The process of melting ore to remove the metal from it. (E28) Workers obtain iron by *smelting* iron ore in a blast furnace.

smooth muscle Involuntary muscle tissue that lines the inside of blood vessels, intestines, and other organs. (G17) *Smooth muscles* move food through the digestive system.

solar system The Sun and the planets and other objects that orbit the Sun. Also, any star and the objects that revolve around it. (B34) Our *solar system* consists of the Sun, nine known planets, and many smaller objects.

sound A form of energy that travels through matter as waves. (F56) The *sound* made the floor vibrate.

sound synthesizer (sound sin'thə-sī zər) An electronic device that can produce a wide variety of sounds. (F71) The composer used a *sound synthesizer* to create a new musical composition.

sprain An injury in which the ligament at a joint is torn or twisted. (G19) An ankle *sprain* can take weeks to heal.

stamen (stā'mən) The male reproductive structure of a flower. (A16) Pollen is produced in the *stamens*.

star A huge object in space, made up of hot gases, that shines by its own light. (B17) Many *stars* are believed to have systems of planets.

starch (stärch) A substance found in plants that is a storage form of glucose. (A35) Potatoes contain a lot of *starch*.

stem The part of a plant that supports the leaves and flowers and carries water to these parts of the plant. (A12) The trunk of a tree is a *stem*.

steroid (stir'oid) A drug that helps to build up muscle tissue and strength. (G55) Some athletes have used *steroids*.

stimulant (stim'yōō lənt) A drug that increases the activity of the nervous system. (G55) Many people drink coffee because it acts as a *stimulant*.

stimulus (stim'yōō ləs) An event or environmental condition that triggers a nerve impulse, thus causing an organism to respond. (G28) The *stimulus* of a loud sound can make a person jump.

stoma (stō'mə; *pl.* stō ma'tə) One of many small openings, or pores, usually on the underside of a leaf, through which gases enter and leave a plant. (A46) The *stomata* on a water lily are on the top of the leaf.

strain An injury in which a muscle or tendon is torn slightly or stretched too far. (G20) Lifting the heavy couch gave me a back *strain*.

streak (strēk) The colored powder made by rubbing a mineral against a ceramic surface. (E15) Although pyrite is yellow, it produces a black *streak*.

substance abuse (sub'stəns ə-byōōs') The improper use, or abuse, of alcohol or drugs. (G50) *Substance abuse* can damage a person's health.

supernova (sōō'pər nō və) An exploding star. (B66) When a red giant star uses up all its fuel, it collapses and explodes in a *supernova*.

syncline (sin'klīn) A downward fold of rock layers. (E84) Forces in Earth pushing on rock formed a *syncline*.

taiga (tī′gə) A biome that contains many coniferous trees and in which rainfall is moderate. (D51) The *taiga* is south of the tundra.

taste bud A receptor on the surface of the tongue that responds to different substances and makes it possible to taste. (G38) There are only four basic types of *taste buds.*

tendon (ten′dən) A strong cord of tissue that joins a muscle to a bone. (G17) *Tendons* pull on bones like strings pull on the limbs of a puppet.

terrestrial planet (tə res′trē əl plan′it) An object in space that resembles Earth in size, in density, and in its mainly rocky composition. (B44) Mars is a *terrestrial planet.*

timbre (tam′bər) The quality of sound that sets one voice or musical instrument apart from another. (F58) The same note played on a violin and on a trumpet differ in *timbre.*

translucent (trans loo′sənt) Letting light through but scattering it; objects cannot be clearly seen through translucent material. (F48) The *translucent* glass dimmed the room.

transparent (trans per′ənt) Letting light through; objects can be clearly seen through transparent material. (F47) Window glass is usually *transparent* so that people can see through it.

transpiration (tran spə rā′shən) A process in which a plant releases moisture through its stomata. (A46) *Transpiration* adds water to the air.

tropical rain forest A biome distinguished by lush vegetation, abundant rainfall, and plentiful sunlight. (D50) The *tropical rain forest* supports the greatest variety of life of any biome.

tropism (trō′piz əm) A growth response of a plant to conditions in the environment, such as light or water. (A50) Growing toward a light source is an example of a plant *tropism.*

trough (trôf) The long narrow hollow between two waves. (F57) A *trough* occurs between two wave crests.

tundra (tun′drə) A biome characterized by cold temperatures and low precipitation. (D51) The *tundra* blooms in summer.

universe (yoon′ə vurs) The sum of everything that exists. (B70) Our solar system is part of the *universe.*

vacuole (vak′yoo ōl) A cell part that stores water and nutrients. (A24) Some plant cells have large *vacuoles.*

vacuum (vak′yoo əm) A space that is empty of any matter. (F17) Light waves can travel through a *vacuum.*

vibration A back-and-forth movement of matter. (F56) It is the *vibration* of the guitar strings that produces sound.

visible light A form of electromagnetic energy that can be seen. (F8) The eye responds to *visible light.*

volume The loudness or softness of a sound. (F78) Please turn up the *volume* on the radio.

water cycle A continuous process in which water moves between the atmosphere and Earth's surface, including its use by living things. (B87, D36) The *water cycle* is powered by energy from the Sun.

wave A disturbance that carries energy and that travels away from its starting point. (F17) The experiment measured how quickly light *waves* travel.

wavelength The distance between one crest of a wave and the next crest. (F17, F57) Red light has a longer *wavelength* than does blue light.

weathering The breaking up of rocks into sediments by such forces as wind, rain, and sunlight. (E62) Through *weathering*, igneous rock can be broken down into sediments.

wetland Any one of three ecosystems—marsh, swamp, or bog—where land and fresh water meet. (D53) *Wetlands* help purify water.

wheel and axle A simple machine made of two wheels of different sizes that pivot around the same point. (C58) A doorknob, along with its shaft, is an example of a *wheel and axle.*

white dwarf A very small, dying star that gives off very little light. (B65) When the Sun's fuel runs out, it will collapse into a *white dwarf.*

work The movement of a force through a distance. (C28) *Work* is done in lifting an object.

xylem cell (zī′ləm sel) A plant cell that, when joined with other similar cells, forms a transport system throughout a plant. (A11) The wood of a tree is formed mainly of *xylem cells.*

INDEX

*Activity
Blue entries indicate Teaching Guide material.

*Activity
Blue entries indicate Teaching Guide material.

*Activity

Blue entries indicate Teaching Guide material.